OXFORD REVISION GU

GCSE

MATHEMATICS
through diagrams

Andrew Edmondson

Oxford University Press

Oxford University Press,
Great Clarendon Street, Oxford OX2 6DP

Oxford New York
Athens Auckland Bangkok Bogota Bombay
Buenos Aires Calcutta Cape Town Dar es Salaam Delhi
Florence Hong Kong Istanbul Karachi
Kuala Lumpur Madras Madrid Melbourne
Mexico City Nairobi Paris Singapore
Taipei Tokyo Toronto Warsaw

and associated companies in
Berlin Ibadan

Oxford is a trade mark of Oxford University Press

First published 1998

0 19 914708 6 (Student's edition)
0 19 914709 4 (Bookshop edition)

Acknowledgement
Oxford University Press is grateful to London Examinations, a division of Edexcel Foundation, for the permission to reproduce questions from specimen examination papers.

Ideal for revision, *Oxford Revision Guide: GCSE Mathematics* includes

- all the topics required for **intermediate** and **higher** levels of all syllabuses
- hundreds of worked examples
- specimen exam questions and solutions with full cross-referencing to where concepts are explained.

Typesetting, design and illustration by Andrew Edmondson
Cartoons by Hardlines, Charlbury, Oxford
Printed in Great Britain

CONTENTS

NOTE Higher level material is indicated by **H**

Syllabuses

Foundation, higher and intermediate – three levels of examination

The scale of grades at GCSE is A*, A, B, C, D, E, F and G. It would be impossible to grade pupils from A* to G based on the same examination, as pupils expecting an A would find all the questions too easy, or pupils expecting an F would find them too hard. To overcome this problem, there are three **tiers** or levels of exam called **Foundation, Intermediate** and **Higher**. Pupils entered for the Foundation tier can achieve grades G to D; those entered for the Intermediate tier can achieve grades E to B; those entered for the Higher tier can achieve grades C to A*.

Examining groups and syllabuses – which one are you studying?

There are several examining groups or boards that set syllabuses and examinations, which are listed below with their abbreviations. Make sure you know which group and syllabus you are studying for. You can obtain a copy of the syllabus, sample examination papers and other useful publications from your examining group; these will give you a good idea of what to expect when your examination comes. Full details of how to contact the examining groups are given on page 9.

EDEXCEL: London Examinations

IGCSE: University of Cambridge Local Examinations Syndicate

MEG: Midland Examining Group

NEAB: Northern Examinations and Assessment Board

NICCEA: Northern Ireland Council for the Curriculum, Examinations and Assessment

SEG: Southern Examining Group

WJEC: Welsh Joint Education Committee

The IGCSE is an international GCSE. One of the two available syllabuses is entirely assessed by two end of year examinations, there being no coursework, terminal task or aural test.

Assessment – how they award your grade

Your GCSE grade can be based on several kinds of assessment: written **examinations**, **coursework**, **terminal tasks** and **aural tests**.

There is one set of examinations for the Foundation tier, another set for the Intermediate tier and another for the Higher tier; so you will sit one of these. You normally have to take two examination papers but see Modular Syllabuses below. Most of these examinations can be retaken in November.

Investigative work is assessed either by coursework completed during the course or by terminal tasks taken under examination conditions. Coursework and terminal tasks are explained in more detail on pages 6 and 7.

Some syllabuses require you take an aural test in which you answer questions read out by your teacher. See page 7 for more details.

In general, the examinations account for 80% of the final grade and the coursework/terminal tasks for 20% (if there is an aural test, it accounts for 5% or 10%). The details of the assessment structure for each examining group and syllabus are given in the table on the opposite page. Find your own syllabus on the table and make sure you know what you are expecting. Percentages indicate the contribution of each component to the final grade.

Modular Syllabuses

The SEG and MEG both offer modular syllabuses in which several shorter written examinations can be taken during the course.

The MEG modular syllabus is mainly designed for students taking their mathematics course over 2 years. In March of their first year, students take a module test; this is a practice test and gives the student and teacher feedback. In November and April of their second year, students take two further module tests; the better mark obtained counts towards their final grade. If a student is on a 1 year course, he or she will take the November and April module tests, but only the mark obtained from the last test will count towards his or her final grade. A longer final examination is taken in May or June. Coursework is completed during the course. An advantage of this syllabus is that most module tests can be taken at two levels (stages); students can decide which stage to take, depending on their past performance and the grade they are aiming for.

MEG also offers the MEI modular syllabus, designed for post-16 students. Students take three written papers. The first paper may be taken in January or June of the first or second year of the course. The other two papers are taken in June of the final year. One syllabus has a mixture of coursework and terminal tasks. The other allows intermediate level students to take terminal tasks only. An advantage of this flexible syllabus is that successful completion of the first written paper at the foundation or intermediate level provides credit towards a student's GNVQ.

The SEG modular syllabus is also designed for post-16 students, including adults returning to education after a break. Students take three module examinations, an aural test and submit coursework. The three module examinations can be taken all at once or spread over 2 years, offering great flexibility.

Examinations can be taken in the Winter, Spring and Summer, as shown.

	Modules
Winter	1, 2, 3
Spring	1, 2
Summer	1, 2, 3

Assessment structure

Examination board and syllabus	Written papers	Aural test	Coursework/terminal tasks
EDEXCEL			
Syllabus A (1385)	2 papers (40% each)	No	Coursework (20%). Minimum of 2 extended tasks selected from a bank of tasks supplied by EDEXCEL and marked by the teacher
Syllabus B (1386)	2 papers (40% each)	No	Terminal tasks (20%). 1 short and 1 long task in a single examination
IGCSE			
Syllabus 0580	1 paper with short questions (35%) and 1 paper with longer questions (65%)	No	No coursework or terminal task
Syllabus 0581	1 paper with short questions (30%) and 1 paper with longer questions (50%)	No	Coursework (20%). 1 or 2 tasks set and marked by the teacher
MEG			
Syllabus A (1662)	2 papers (40% each)	No	Coursework (20%). 2 tasks set and marked by MEG. Written up in 3 hours of classwork
Syllabus B (1664)	2 papers (37.5% each)	Yes (5%)	Coursework (20%). A range of tasks set and marked by the teacher
Syllabus C (1666)	Two year course: 3 module tests (30%) and 1 terminal paper (50%) One year course: 2 module tests (30%) and 1 terminal paper (50%)	No	Coursework (20%). As above
Syllabus D (1668)	1 paper with short questions (40%) and 1 paper with longer questions (40%)	No	1 piece of coursework (10%) set and marked by the teacher and 3 terminal tasks (10%) in a single examination
Syllabus E (1668)	1 paper with short questions (40%) and 1 paper with longer questions (40%)	No	As above for foundation and higher levels. Intermediate level students do 3 terminal tasks in a single examination
NEAB			
Syllabus A (1131)	2 papers (40% each)	No	Coursework (20%). A minimum of 2 tasks set and marked by the teacher
Syllabus B (1132)	2 papers (40% each)	No	Terminal tasks (20%). 2 tasks in a single examination
NICCEA			
Syllabus A	2 papers (35% each)	Yes (10%)	Coursework (20%). 2 extended tasks set and marked by the teacher: one practical, the other a mathematical investigation
Syllabus B	2 papers (35% each)	Yes (10%)	Terminal task (20%). 1 task set and marked by the teacher
SEG			
Syllabus 2500T	2 papers (37.5% each)	Yes (5%)	Coursework (20%). Two tasks set and marked by the teacher
Syllabus 2500X	2 papers (37.5% each)	Yes (5%)	Coursework (20%). Choice of 2 tasks from a set of 4 supplied and marked by SEG
Modular (2520T)	2 module tests (18.75% each) and 1 terminal module test (37.5%)	Yes (5%)	Coursework (20%). Choice of 1 task from 2 tasks supplied and marked by SEG, plus 1 task set and marked by the teacher
Modular (2520X)	2 module tests (18.75% each) and 1 terminal module test (37.5%)	Yes (5%)	Coursework (20%). Choice of 2 tasks from a set of 4 supplied and marked by SEG
WJEC			
Syllabus A	2 papers (40% each)	No	Coursework (20%). A range of tasks set and marked by teacher
Syllabus B	2 papers (40% each)	No	Terminal tasks (20%). 2 tasks in a single examination

Coursework

Practical work, including investigations, will be marked by your teacher throughout the course and will count 20% towards your final grade. There are three separate skill areas in which you will be awarded a mark:

- Making and monitoring decisions to solve problems.
- Communicating mathematically.
- Developing skills of mathematical reasoning.

These three areas are explained in more detail below. You will be awarded a mark out of 8 in each area. You will have opportunities throughout the course to practise and improve your skills. Your teacher will tell you which tasks are to be assessed. Your best mark in each of the three areas will normally be used, though the marks must come from at least two different pieces of coursework.

Some syllabuses require just two extended tasks. Extended tasks are longer, involve a wide range of skills and are open ended. At least one of these must be of a practical nature, e.g. performing an experiment, a statistical investigation, designing a children's playground. You may also be given a mathematical investigation in which you investigate a purely mathematical problem or puzzle. This may also be an extended task, allowing you to pursue further lines of enquiry.

You can order a coursework guide from your examination board; the addresses are given on page 9. This contains good and bad examples of students' coursework with comments and assessment by the examiners.

Your teacher may use tasks provided by the examination board or devise his or her own tasks. It is important that the tasks you are given allow you to achieve maximum marks; for example, an intermediate task may not be suitable for a higher level student.

You will probably spend 2 to 5 weeks of classroom and homework time completing your tasks. A large part of your coursework will be done in the classroom, especially writing your report. Your teacher will be available to help you and monitor your progress; but if you need a lot of help your marks will be reduced accordingly. Your teacher has to authenticate your work and will take steps to make sure that it is your own.

If you are resitting your GCSE, you will probably be able to carry forward your best coursework marks from last year.

Making and monitoring decisions to solve problems

First read the problem carefully and think about what you are trying to find out. Then write a short plan, which could include some of the following:

- Title and description of the task.
- Materials and equipment required, e.g. stopwatch, cardboard, scissors.
- Sources of information, e.g. magazines, textbooks
- Your intended approach, e.g. 'first, I will draw 3 intersecting lines; then I will count the number of intersections, inner regions and outer regions; then I will repeat this for 4 lines, 5 lines etc.; I will record my results in a table and look for patterns and relationships; etc.'.
- The mathematical topics you expect to use, e.g. calculating areas, percentages, drawing graphs.
- Your predicted results, e.g. 'I expect to find that men prefer listening to jazz'.

Record all your results carefully and clearly, either in a list or in a table with precise headings. Remember to include units. Look over your working regularly, checking for inaccuracies and errors. Repeat an experiment to obtain a second set of readings.

Communicating mathematically

You should write up your investigation clearly and neatly in the form of a report. Here is a skeleton report:

- Title of task. Include a description of the project.
- Your plan.
- Results. Use a table if necessary.
- Comments. Make comments on any patterns you noticed, ideas you had, predictions of what you thought would happen next.
- Illustrations. Use appropriate diagrams to illustrate your results, e.g. bar charts, graphs, designs.
- Conclusions. Make your conclusions about the results. This means describing what your results actually show, not what you expected them to show! Generalise your conclusion. Use algebra where possible.
- Extension. Suggest ways in which the task may be extended and/or improved. Carry out the extension if time allows.
- Final summary. Summarise the entire task and findings in a single paragraph.

Your report should be self-contained and clear enough for the average person to understand; give it to a friend or member of your family to read.

Make sure you describe any problems you encountered and how you overcame them.

Your teacher may ask you questions about your task and will record your ability to discuss it mathematically.

Developing skills of mathematical reasoning

You are expected to apply mathematical reasoning during your task in addition to the more mechanical aspects of collecting information, making tables, drawing diagrams, performing calculations etc.

At the planning stage and whilst you are carrying out your task, write down and then test any predictions, hypotheses or ideas that you have. Look for possible patterns, rules and relationships and try to express them in words and algebra. If your prediction turns out to be wrong, try and find another explanation for the results and test it further. Use logical reasoning to explain your results.

Here are a few more tips to bear in mind:

- Choose a task that interests you and stick to it.
- Make sure your task contains enough mathematics.
- Rely on your teacher for guidance; he or she may be the one who is assessing your work.
- Explain everything you have done, including your diagrams, measurements, tables, calculations, graphs etc.
- Be original.
- Double check your results for accuracy.
- Don't leave your coursework to the last minute. It counts up to 20% of your marks! Put the coursework deadlines in your diary.
- Don't copy other people's work. Don't copy from books without acknowledging it in your report (even then, don't copy much). This is called plagiarism.

Terminal tasks

Terminal tasks are mini-coursework tasks taken under examination conditions at the end of your course and are an alternative to ordinary coursework. They require many of the skills needed for coursework. Your teacher will have practice tasks that can be worked on in the classroom and at home and which can be used for mock tests. You can order more terminal tasks from your examination board; the addresses are given on page 9.

Aural test

A few syllabuses require you to take an aural test. This will take place about a month before your final examinations during a normal lesson. Your teacher will read out each question twice. You then write your working and answer on the answer paper provided. You will only be allowed to use a pen: no calculator, ruler etc.

You should have lots of practice throughout your course so that you can develop the necessary skills and build confidence. Your teacher will have a supply of past papers. You can order more test papers from your examination board so that someone can test you at home; the addresses are given on page 9.

Here are a few tips on taking aural tests:

- Arrive for the test with time to spare so that you can relax.
- Listen carefully. Let your teacher know if you have a hearing difficulty well in advance of the test date.
- Write down any values or important words during the first reading of a question. Fill in any gaps at the second reading.
- Work out all but the simplest of calculations on paper rather than in your head. Use your pen!
- Check that your answers make sense.
- As soon as a new question begins, stop working on the previous question. You need to hear each question both times and cannot afford to miss any information.
- Look ahead to the next question if you finish a question early.
- Turn the page in good time for the next question.

Tips on how to study

Think about how you are going to study. Work out a routine and stick to it. Here are a few tips:

- Get organised from the beginning. Buy all the equipment you need at the beginning of your course: textbooks, scientific calculator, ringbinder folder and paper, pens, pencils, eraser, highlighter pens, ruler, protractor, compasses, graph paper etc. Keep these items in your school/college bag. Read the instructions that come with your calculator. Organise your folder.
- Take notes from the board. When you get home read through them again and rewrite them neatly. Make a shorter summary or start an alphabetical 'results' notebook if you have a bad memory; writing helps your memory. Learn formulas by repeating them for a few days and giving yourself short memory tests; this saves you time looking up formulas in the examination.
- Work through your homework while the lesson is fresh in your mind, the same day if possible. Read through the relevant topics in this book for more information and worked examples.
- Take regular breaks when working at home. Don't spend a long time stuck on a question; make a note of it with your highlighter pen and ask your teacher for help.
- Get into the habit of presenting your work clearly and logically. When writing your answer to a question, use your notes as a guide or find a similar worked example in this book.
- Keep a diary to record test dates, deadlines for homework and coursework, term times etc.

Success in examinations

If you have worked hard during your course and put in a lot of effort, there are some steps you can take to ensure that your examination result reflects this.

Be prepared

If the thought of an examination fills you with dread, then you are probably not fully prepared. Of course everybody will be a bit nervous about an important examination, but there is no reason why you should fall apart and fail to do yourself justice if you know what to expect before you go in. The best preparation is working through past examination papers and looking at your syllabus to avoid any nasty surprises. A positive attitude will help you - try to look on the examination as an opportunity to show the examiner all the things you have learnt during your course.

Make sure you have everything ready the night before: pens, pencils, ruler, protractor, compasses, calculator etc. Ask your teacher if tracing paper will be provided; if not, take your own.

Plan your time

Work out how much time you should spend on each question, based on how many marks it has. There are about 100 marks available in most final examinations. If the examination lasts 2 hours, you can spend just over one minute per mark. Also, the space available for your answer gives you a rough idea how much working is necessary; however, if there is a large space, you don't have to fill it.

If you get stuck on one part of a question, don't abandon the whole question; you may be able to do some of the remaining parts, even if this means making up an answer to the part you could not do.

Don't spend ages racking your brains to think of the answer to one part of a question - go on and start the next question instead. You will probably get more marks for attempting *all* the questions than for finishing a few questions completely. If you have time left at the end, you can go back and think about the more difficult parts when you will be feeling more relaxed. You can also use this time to check your working.

Read carefully

Read each question more than once to make sure it really does say what you think it says. Follow the instructions to the letter, as marks can only be awarded for precise answers to the question asked, not for any other information about the subject.

Present your work clearly

Remember that the examiner will have a large pile of papers to mark in a short space of time. Struggling to read your writing or follow an illogical argument will not help, so write as clearly as you possibly can in the time available and think through what you are going to write before you start. The examiner is *trying* to award you marks - make it easy to find them.

Show all of your working. Get into the habit of writing out your working for every question you answer. Then, if your answer is wrong, you could still get most of the available marks.

Use a few words to help the examiner understand what you are doing. For example, when calculating the total area of a shape, instead of just writing the calculation $5\times7 + 3\times4 = 47\text{ cm}^2$ you could write:
Total area $= 5\times7 + 3\times4 = 47\text{ cm}^2$

Accuracy

Look at the question to see if a particular degree of accuracy is required. If not, you are expected to give your answers to a reasonable degree of accuracy. You will lose marks if you are consistently inaccurate.

Work to a greater degree of accuracy than required for the final answer. For example, if a question asks for an answer correct to 3 significant figures, write down your working calculations correct to 4 significant figures, then round your final answer to 3 significant figures.

Use a calculator for all but the simplest of calculations.

When measuring lengths, you are expected to work to the nearest 1 mm. When measuring angles, you are expected to work to the nearest 1° or 2°. Always use your protractor to draw right angles. Using a sharp pencil for drawing.

Plot the points of graphs as accurately as you can; use crosses (not dots) to mark them. If graph paper makes you dizzy, use a ruler to help you line up the points and also to read off values.

Stay calm

If you find a question you have no idea about, do not panic! Breathe slowly and deeply and have another look. It's likely that if you stay calm and think clearly, it will start to make more sense, or at least you may be able to answer part of it. If not, then don't agonise about it but concentrate first on the questions you *can* answer.

How to revise

You will probably have found by talking to other pupils that everybody has a different way of revising. It's important to make sure that your method is an effective one.

Working through past examination papers

The best way to revise mathematics is to work through past examination papers. Work through as many as time allows so that you feel comfortable when presented with your final examination papers.

Throughout the last year of your course you should become familiar with the examination papers you are going to take. Ask your teacher for some past examination papers. Order more papers from your examination board; the addresses are given on this page. You should have at least 5 of each examination paper plus the specimen papers for the year of your examination.

It's a good idea to practise more examination questions in any areas of the syllabus that you are unsure of. Ask your teacher for practice questions or find some in your textbook.

When working through past examination papers:

- Look at the marks available and work out roughly how much time you should aim to spend. Practise more questions you are taking too long over.
- Get used to writing your working in the space provided.
- If you get stuck, find a similar worked example in this book. If you still cannot solve the problem, make a note of it and ask your teacher. Don't waste your time agonising over a question: it makes you unnecessarily anxious and leaves you with a false impression of how well you are doing.
- Use some of your later papers as mock examinations. Work through some or all of a paper under timed conditions, without taking a break.
- Try working with a friend. You may be able to help each other when you get stuck.

Make a revision timetable

Plan your revision period; don't leave revising until the last minute. A blank revision timetable is provided overleaf. You should have a bunch of past examination papers and examination questions to work through. Put these in order and arrange them on your timetable. Allocate say 4 hours to work through a 2 hour paper; you can always modify this estimate once you get started.

You could also put those topics you are unsure of on the timetable; use your syllabus to help you. Make sure you cover all of these by the end of your revision period.

Once you have made the timetable, though, make sure you really do start revising - don't kid yourself that planning your revision is all you need to do!

Find a suitable place to revise

You need somewhere quiet where you will not be interrupted. Some people can concentrate with music playing, but if you can't, then turn it off. If you find it difficult to work at home, then try going to a library or some other quiet place.

Take regular breaks

Your concentration will start to wander and you will be less effective if you work solidly for hours without a break. Divide up your study periods into chunks of about 40 minutes, and then go and make a drink, or have a brief walk, or do something completely different for about 10 minutes. Then you can go back for the next session feeling refreshed, and sometimes you will find that you understand things more clearly after a break.

Of course, don't do this during a mock examination.

Don't panic at the last minute

If you have stuck to your revision timetable, you should feel as relaxed and confident as you can about the examination. There is then no point in panicking and trying to learn it all again the night before. Just have a quick look through some of the past examination papers you worked through, and then relax. If you are nervous and feel convinced you have forgotten everything, then take some exercise or do something else to clear your thoughts and stop worrying. You will probably find that when you come back and have another look, you have remembered far more than you thought.

Exam Organisation Addresses

EDEXCEL (formerly **ULEAC**)
Stewart House, 32 Russell Square, LONDON, WC1B 5DN.
Tel: 0171 331 4000 Fax: 0171 331 4044

Midland Examining Group (MEG) and International General Certificate of Education (IGCSE)
Head Office, Syndicate Buildings, 1 Hills Road, CAMBRIDGE, CB1 2EU.
Tel: 01223 553311 Fax: 01223 460278

Northern Examinations and Assessment Board (NEAB)
12 Harter Street, Manchester, M1 6HL.
Tel: 0161 953 1170 Fax: 0161 953 1177

Northern Ireland Council for the Curriculum Examinations and Assessment (NICCEA)
Beechill House, 42 Beechill Road, BELFAST, BT8 4RS.
Tel: 01232 704666 Fax: 01232 799913

Southern Examining Group (SEG)
Associated Examining Board, Stag Hill House, GUILDFORD, Surrey, GU2 5XJ.
Tel: 01483 506506 Fax: 01483 300152

Welsh Joint Committee (WJEC)
Welsh Joint Education Committee, 245 Western Avenue, CARDIFF, CF5 2YX
Tel: 01222 265000 Fax: 01222 575994

Revision timetable

Date							
Day	**Monday**	**Tuesday**	**Wednesday**	**Thursday**	**Friday**	**Saturday**	**Sunday**
Topic/Exam paper							
Time/Comments							
Date							
Day	**Monday**	**Tuesday**	**Wednesday**	**Thursday**	**Friday**	**Saturday**	**Sunday**
Topic/Exam paper							
Time/Comments							
Date							
Day	**Monday**	**Tuesday**	**Wednesday**	**Thursday**	**Friday**	**Saturday**	**Sunday**
Topic/Exam paper							
Time/Comments							
Date							
Day	**Monday**	**Tuesday**	**Wednesday**	**Thursday**	**Friday**	**Saturday**	**Sunday**
Topic/Exam paper							
Time/Comments							
Date							
Day	**Monday**	**Tuesday**	**Wednesday**	**Thursday**	**Friday**	**Saturday**	**Sunday**
Topic/Exam paper							
Time/Comments							

Whole Numbers

1. Basic Arithmetic

Make sure you can answer these questions *without* using a calculator.

1. *There are 857 boys and 946 girls in a school. How many children are there altogether?* $857 + 946$
2. *The battle of Waterloo took place in 1815. The battle of Hastings took place in 1066. How many years apart are these events?* $1815 - 1066$
3. *Boxes contain 17 tiles each. How many tiles are there in 12 boxes?* 17×12
4. *Lollipops cost 13p each. How many can be bought for 234p?* $13 \overline{)234}$

2. Sum, Difference, Product, Quotient

The **sum** of 6 and 2 is written 6+2 or 2+6. Both calculations give the same answer, 8.

The **difference** of 2 and 6 is written 6−2 or 2−6. The **positive difference** is 6−2 = 4. The **negative difference** is 2−6 = -4.

The **product** of 2 and 6 is written 2×6 or 6×2. Both calculations give the same answer, 12.

The **quotient** of 2 and 6 is written 6÷2 or 2÷6. These calculations give different answers.

NOTE Another way of writing 6÷2 is $\frac{6}{2}$.

3. Brackets

A bracket contains a *single* number. For example, the bracket (6+2) contains the single number 8.

When a bracket is multiplied by a number, the × sign is usually omitted. For example:

3×(4+1) is usually written 3(4+1)

(2+3)×(5−2) is usually written (2+3)(5−2)

4. BoDMAS

Always use the following order of working when performing a calculation.

① Work out **B**rackets
② **D**ivide and **M**ultiply
③ **A**dd and **S**ubtract

Remember this using the word BoDMAS

Examples

3(4+1) = 3×(4+1) = 3×(5) = 3×5 = 15
brackets first........... drop brackets......then multiply

4+3×2 = 4+6 = 10
multiply first.........then add

3+4(3−1)+6÷3−5 = 3+4×2+6÷3−5 = 3+8+2−5 = 8
brackets first....................................multiply and divide..............add and subtract

4×3×2 = 12×2 = 24
4×3×2 = 4×6 = 24
Multiply any two numbers first; you will always get the same answer

12÷2÷3 = 6÷3 = 2
6÷3×4 = 2×4 = 8
Work from left to right with combinations of × and ÷ signs

5. Natural Numbers

Whole positive numbers are sometimes called **natural** numbers:

1, 2, 3, 4, 5, 6, ...

6. Multiplying and Dividing by Zero

Multiplying numbers by 0 always gives 0.

For example, 5×0 = 0, 0×5 = 0, 3×5×0 = 0

Dividing 0 by any number (other than 0) always gives 0.

For example, 0÷5 = 0 or $\frac{0}{5} = 0$

Dividing by 0 is impossible.

For example, 5÷0 or $\frac{5}{0}$ is impossible

7. Powers

4^3 is shorthand for 4×4×4 and is called the **3rd power** of 4. It is commonly called the **cube** of 4. We also say that 4 has been **raised to the 3rd power**. So, $4^3 = 4\times4\times4 = 64$.

NOTE 4^3 does ***not*** mean the same as 4×3. Here is the difference:
$4^3 = 4\times4\times4$ whereas $4\times3 = 4+4+4$

Similarly, 4^2 is shorthand for 4×4 and is called the **2nd power** of 4, or more commonly the **square** of 4 (or 4 squared). So, $4^2 = 4\times4 = 16$.

4^1 is another way of writing 4

Question *Calculate the value of* 2^4+3^2.

$2^4+3^2 = 2\times2\times2\times2 + 3\times3 = 16+9 = 25$

Base → 4^3 ← Index (plural: indices)

8. Power of a Bracket

$(\ )^2$ means $(\ )\times(\ )$ $(\ )^3$ means $(\ )\times(\ )\times(\ )$

So, $(5+3)^2 = (5+3)\times(5+3) = 8\times8 = 64$

And $(6-1)^3 = (6-1)\times(6-1)\times(6-1) = 5\times5\times5 = 125$

Also $(5\times3)^2 = (5\times3)\times(5\times3) = 15\times15 = 225$.

You get the same answer by squaring each number in the bracket and multiplying the results together:

$(5\times3)^2 = 5^2\times3^2 = 5\times5 \times 3\times3 = 25\times9 = 225$

So we have the result: $(5\times3)^2 = 5^2\times3^2$

Similarly: $(6\div3)^2 = 6^2\div3^2 = \left(\frac{6}{3}\right)^2$

NOTE $(5+3)^2$ is ***not*** equal to 5^2+3^2 . Here's why:
$(5+3)^2 = 8^2 = 64$ whereas $5^2+3^2 = 25+9 = 34$

Whole Numbers (Contd)

9. Roots

The opposite process of calculating the power of a number is finding its **root**.

The 3rd power (cube) of 2 is written 2^3 and is equal to 8. The **3rd root (cube root)** of 8 is written $\sqrt[3]{8}$ and equals 2.

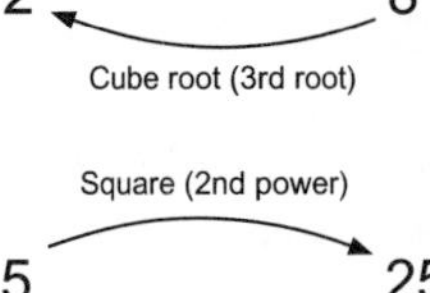

The 2nd power (square) of 5 is written 5^2 and equals 25. The **2nd root (square root) of 25** is written $\sqrt[2]{25}$, or simply $\sqrt{25}$, and is equal to 5.

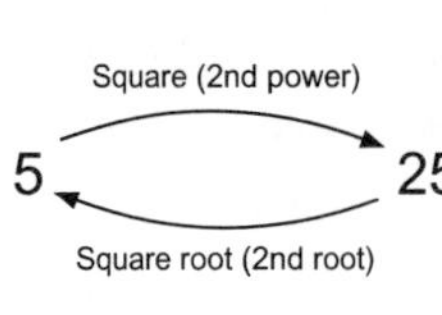

Question *Calculate $\sqrt[4]{16}$ without using a calculator.*

$\sqrt[4]{16}$ is the 4th root of 16.

The answer must be 2, because:

4th power, 2 → 16; 4th root, 16 → 2

4th power of 2 = $2^4 = 2\times2\times2\times2 = 16$

So, $\sqrt[4]{16} = 2$ because $2\times2\times2\times2 = 16$

NOTE $\sqrt[4]{16}$ does ***not*** mean $16\div4$ (see above).
$\sqrt{16+9}$ is ***not*** equal to $\sqrt{16}+\sqrt{9} = 4+3 = 7$.
$\sqrt{16+9} = \sqrt{25} = 5$ is correct.

10. Powers and Roots

Powers and roots cancel each other out.

For example:

$$6 \xrightarrow{\text{Square}} 6^2 = 36 \xrightarrow{\text{Square root}} \sqrt{36} = 6$$

Another way of writing this is $\sqrt{6^2} = 6$

Similarly, $(\sqrt{6})^2 = 6$ or $\sqrt{6}\times\sqrt{6} = 6$

11. Multiples

$1\times3 = 3$ $2\times3 = 6$ $3\times3 = 9$ $4\times3 = 12$ $5\times3 = 15$ $6\times3 = 18$ $7\times3 = 21$ $8\times3 = 24$ $9\times3 = 27$	These numbers are called **multiples** of 3.
$1\times4 = 4$ $2\times4 = 8$ $3\times4 = 12$ $4\times4 = 16$ $5\times4 = 20$ $6\times4 = 24$ $7\times4 = 28$ $8\times4 = 32$ $9\times4 = 36$	These numbers are called **multiples** of 4.

Some of the multiples of 3 and 4 are the same They are called **common multiples**.

3, 6, 9, 12, 15, 18, 21, 24, 27, ... Multiples of 3
4, 8, 12, 16, 20, 24, 28, 32, 36, ... Multiples of 4

12 and 24 are common multiples of 3 and 4.

12 is the **lowest common multiple (LCM)** of 3 and 4. It is the smallest number that both 3 and 4 divide into exactly.

12. Factors

The **factors** of 12 are those numbers that divide exactly into 12: 1, 2, 3, 4, 6, 12
(Don't forget to include 1 and 12.)

The factors of 18 are: 1, 2, 3, 6, 9, 18

Some of the factors of 12 and 18 are the same; they are called **common factors**.

1, 2, 3, 4, 6, 12 Factors of 12
1, 2, 3, 6, 9, 18 Factors of 18

The common factors of 12 and 18 are 1, 2, 3, and 6.

The **highest common factor (HCF)** of 12 and 18 is 6.

13. Prime Numbers

A **prime number** is a number that can be divided exactly only by itself and 1. For example, 11 is prime. Here are the first few prime numbers:

2, 3, 5, 7, 11, 13, 17, 19, 23, 29

1 is not considered to be a prime number.

14. Prime Factors

The factors of 12 are: 1, 2, 3, 4, 6, 12

Of these, 2 and 3 are prime numbers and so are called **prime factors**.

Question *What are the prime factors of 2^5?*

$2^5 = 2\times2\times2\times2\times2 = 32$

The factors of 32 are: 1, 2, 4, 8, 16, 32

So, 2 is the only prime factor of 2^5.

15. Product of Prime Factors

Any number can be written as a product of its prime factors, i.e. can be broken down into its prime factors.

Question *Express 36 as the product of its prime factors*

① Write down the first few prime numbers:
2, 3, 5, 7, 11, 13, ...

② Divide 36 by the first prime number, 2, as many times as possible (see opposite).

③ Then divide by the next prime number, 3, as many times as possible, and so on until you get to 1.

2)36
2)18
3)9
3)3
1 stop

④ Write down the product of all the prime numbers you divided by:
$36 = 2\times2\times3\times3$

⑤ Write any repeated prime numbers as powers (i.e. using index form):
$36 = 2^2\times3^2$

This is called **expressing a number as a product of primes using index form**.

Number Patterns (Sequences)

1. Number Patterns (Sequences)

A **number pattern** or **sequence** is an ordered list of numbers connected by a rule.

The numbers in the pattern below start with 3 and are connected by the rule 'add 2', i.e. adding 2 to one number gives the next number.

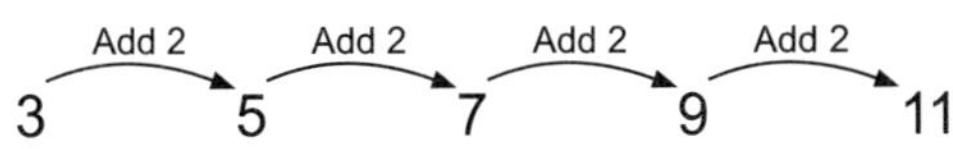

Some rules involve several steps. For example, starting with 1 and using the rule 'double then add 3' gives the number pattern:

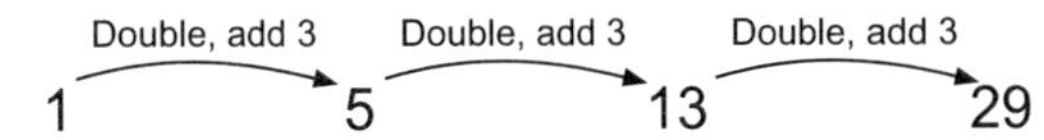

Some rules involve several previous numbers in the pattern. For example, starting with the numbers 2, 3 and using the rule 'add the two previous numbers' gives the number pattern:

Add   Add

2   3   5   8   13

Add   Add

Some number patterns involve negative numbers. For example, starting with 6 and using the rule 'subtract 2' gives the number pattern:

6, 4, 2, 0, −2, −4, ...

Other sequences involve fractions. For example, starting with $\frac{1}{2}$ and using the rule "increase the numerator by 1, increase the denominator by 1" gives the number pattern below:

$\frac{1}{2}$ $\frac{2}{3}$ $\frac{3}{4}$ $\frac{4}{5}$ $\frac{5}{6}$ ....

Number patterns often arise in coursework investigations. For example, the numbers of matches in these triangles form a number pattern:

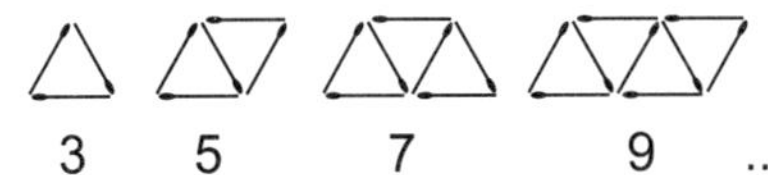

Number of matchsticks   3   5   7   9   .....

2. Number Patterns You Should Know

Even numbers	2, 4, 6, 8, 10, ...
Odd numbers	1, 3, 5, 7, 9, 11, ...
Prime numbers	2, 3, 5, 7, 11, 13, 15, 17, 19, 23, ...
Natural numbers	1, 2, 3, 4, 5, 6, 7, 8, 9, ...
Square numbers	$1^2, 2^2, 3^2, 4^2, 5^2, 6^2$, ... ↓ 1, 4, 9, 16, 25, 36, ...
Cube numbers	$1^3, 2^3, 3^3, 4^3, 5^3$, ... ↓ 1, 8, 27, 64, 125, ...
Powers of 2	$2^0, 2^1, 2^2, 2^3, 2^4, 2^5, 2^6$, ... ↓ 1, 2, 4, 8, 16, 32, 64, ...

3. Finding the Rule for a Number Pattern

Follow these steps to find the rule for your number pattern.

① **Is the pattern one you know?**

9, 16, 25, 36, ... Square numbers, starting with 3^2

② **Is the pattern a modification of one you know?**

2, 5, 10, 17, 26, ... Square numbers + 1

③ **Try adding consecutive numbers:**

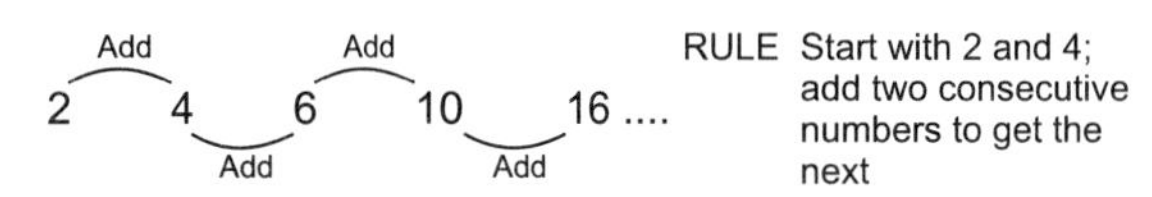

RULE Start with 2 and 4; add two consecutive numbers to get the next

④ **Look at the differences between consecutive numbers:**

7   10   13   16   19 ....

3   3   3   3

Same difference

RULE Start with 7; add 3

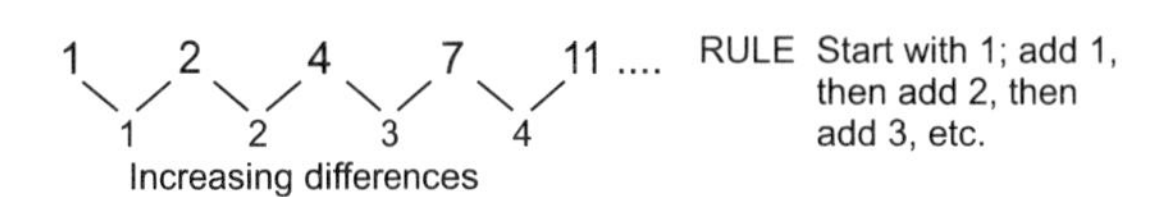

RULE Start with 1; add 1, then add 2, then add 3, etc.

⑤ **Try multiplying consecutive numbers:**

RULE Start with 1 and 2; multiply two consecutive numbers to get the next

⑥ **Try dividing consecutive numbers:**

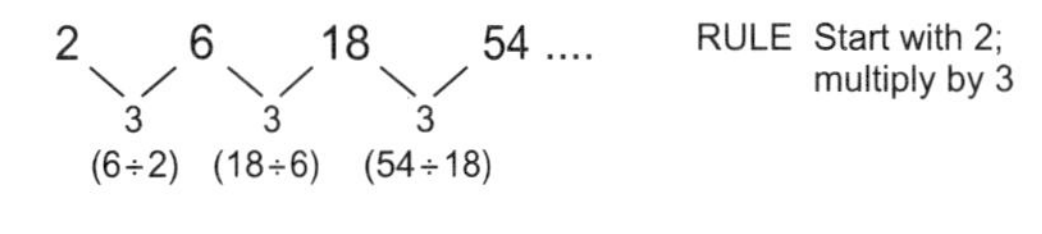

RULE Start with 2; multiply by 3

48   24   12   6 ....

2   2   2

(48÷24) (24÷12) (12÷6)

RULE Start with 48; divide by 2

If none of these steps worked, try the methods in Box 4

4. Terms of a Sequence

Each number in a sequence (number pattern) is called a **term** and occupies a certain **position** in the sequence.

Position	1st,	2nd,	3rd,	4th,	5th, ...
Term	3,	6,	9,	12,	15, ...

You can often find the value of a term by knowing its position. In the above sequence, each term can be found by multiplying its position by 3:

Position	1	2	3	4	5 ....
	×3	×3	×3	×3	×3
Term	3	6	9	12	15 ....

So we can now also find the 20th and 100th terms:

20th term = 20×3 = 60   100th term = 100×3 = 300

more

Number Patterns (Contd)

4. Terms of a Sequence (Contd)

Question *Find the 7th, 20th and 100th terms of the sequence: 3, 7, 11, 15, 19, 23, ...*

First, write down the positions of the terms:

Position 1, 2, 3, 4, 5, 6, ...
Term 3, 7, 11, 15, 19, 23, ...

Then find the rule connecting each term and its position number:

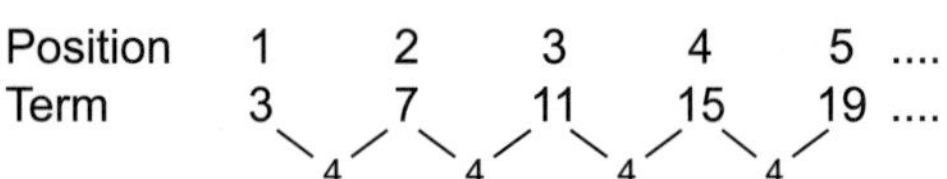

A difference of 4 means that the rule involves multiplying the position number by 4:

Position	1,	2,	3,	4,	5,	6,	....
4× Position	4,	8,	12,	16,	20,	24,	....
Term	3,	7,	11,	15,	19,	23,	....

You can see that each term is calculated by multiplying each position by 4 and then subtracting 1.

So, 7th term $= 4\times7-1 = 28-1 = 27$

20th term $= 4\times20-1 = 80-1 = 79$

100th term $= 4\times100-1 = 400-1 = 399$

Question *As part of his coursework, Philip drew the following sequence of patterns:*

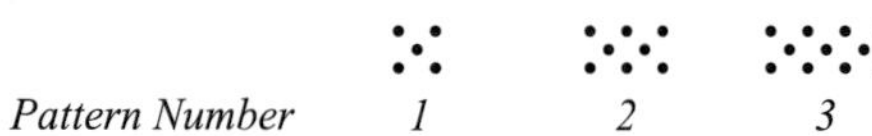

Pattern Number 1 2 3

(a) Complete the table below.

Pattern number	*1*	*2*	*3*	*4*	*5*
Number of dots	*5*	*8*	*11*	*14*	

(b) What is the number of the pattern with 137 dots?

(a) The number of dots can be found using the rule 'multiply the pattern number by 3 and add 2'.

Number of dots in pattern 5 is: $3\times5+2 = 17$

(b) *Reverse the rule* to find the number of the pattern with 137 dots, i.e. 'subtract 2, then divide by 3':

$137-2 = 135$ then $135\div3 = 45$

So, the 45th pattern has 137 dots.

Question *Find the next term in the sequence below.*

Position 1st, 2nd, 3rd, 4th, 5th, ...
Term 2, 5, 10, 17, 26, ...

One of the terms of this sequence is 226. What is the position of this term?

Try squaring the position numbers.

Position number	1,	2,	3,	4,	5,	....
Square of position number	1,	4,	9,	16,	25,	....
Term	2,	5,	10,	17,	26,	....

You can see that each term is found using the rule 'square the position number and add 1'.

So, the next term = 6th term $= 6^2+1 = 36+1 = 37$

To find the position number of the term 226, *reverse the rule,* i.e. 'subtract 1 and then square root'.

Subtract 1 $226-1 = 225$
Square root $\sqrt{225} = 15$

So, the term 226 has position number 15.

5. Describing Sequences Using Algebra

Sequences can be briefly described using algebra.

n represents the position of any term
u_1 represents the 1st term
u_2 represents the 2nd term, etc.
u_n represents the nth term (the **general term**)

For the sequence 3, 6, 9, 12, 15, ... we have:

Position 1, 2, 3, 4, 5, 6, ..., n, ...
Term 3, 6, 9, 12, 15, 18, ..., nth term, ...
u_1, u_2, u_3, u_4, u_5, u_6, ..., u_n, ...

Each term in this sequence is found using the rule 'multiply the position number by 3'. So,

1st term $= u_1 = 3\times1 = 3$
2nd term $= u_2 = 3\times2 = 6$
3rd term $= u_3 = 3\times3 = 9$, etc.
nth term $= u_n = 3\times n = 3n$

Question *Write down the first three terms of the sequence where $u_n = n^2+1$.*

1st term $= u_1 = 1^2+1 = 1+1 = 2$
2nd term $= u_2 = 2^2+1 = 4+1 = 5$
3rd term $= u_3 = 3^2+1 = 9+1 = 10$

Question *Write down the nth term, u_n, for the sequence 1, 3, 5, 7, 9, ...*

First, write down the positions of the terms:

Position 1, 2, 3, 4, 5, 6, ..., n, ...
Term 1, 3, 5, 7, 9, 11, ..., u_n, ...

Find the rule connecting the terms and their positions.

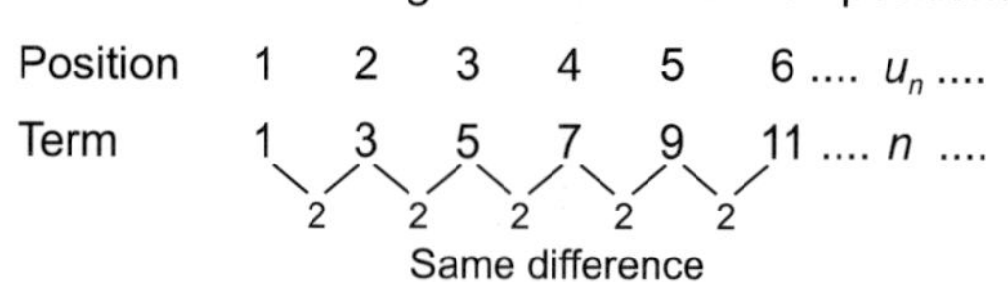

A difference of 2 means that the rule involves multiplying the position number by 2. Each term is found using the rule 'multiply the position number by 2, then subtract 1':

Term = 2×(Position number)−1

So, u_n = nth term $= 2\times n-1 = 2n-1$

Question *For the sequence 2, 6, 12, 20, 30, ...*
(a) Find the next term.
(b) Write down an expression for u_n.
(c) Find the value of n when $u_n = 4970$.

(a) Write down the positions of the terms:

Position 1 2 3 4 5 6 7 ....
Term 2 6 12 20 30 ? ....

Each term is found by multiplying its position number by the next position number:

	Multiply	Multiply	Multiply		Multiply	
Position	1	2	3	4	n	$n+1$ ....
Term	2	6	12	20	u_n	u_{n+1} ....

So, the next term is $6\times7 = 42$

(b) The position of u_n is n and the next position is $n+1$.
So, $u_n = n\times(n+1) = n(n+1)$

(c) We must find n such that $n(n+1) = 4970$. Since $n+1$ is close to n, then $n(n+1)$ is close to $n\times n$ or n^2. So, $n^2 \approx 4970$, giving $n \approx \sqrt{4970} = 70.5$.
Try $n = 70$: $n(n+1) = 70\times71 = 4970$. Correct

Negative Numbers

1. Positive and Negative Numbers

Positive and negative numbers can be represented as points on a straight line called the **number line**.

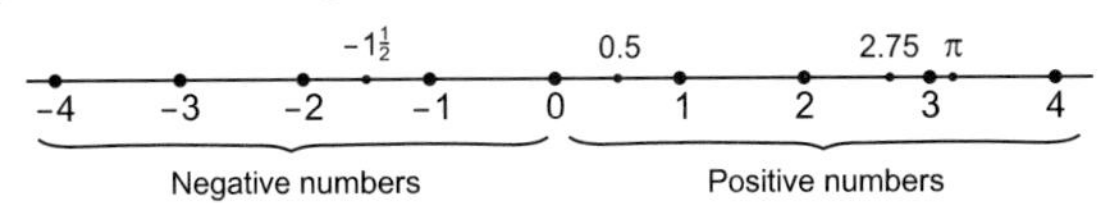

There are several ways of writing positive and negative numbers. For example,

2 can be written +2, (+2) or $^+2$

–2 can be written (–2) or $^-2$ and is called *negative 2*

NOTE $^+2$ and $^-2$ are called **directed numbers**

2. Integers

Whole numbers are sometimes called **integers**. They include the positive and negative numbers and zero.

.... –3, –2, –1, 0, 1, 2, 3, ...

3. Plus and Minus

Minus is the name of the sign –

Plus is the name of the sign +

So, 3+4–2 expressed in words is 'three plus four minus 2'

4. The Sign –

In calculations, the sign – can mean subtract or take away, or it can mean negative. For example,

5–2 means '5 subtract 2' or '5 take away 2'

–2+5 means 'negative 2 add 5' (the negative number –2 added to 5)

5. Distance Between Numbers

The distance between two numbers on the number line is always positive. For example, the distance between the numbers –2 and 3 is 5, as shown on the number line below.

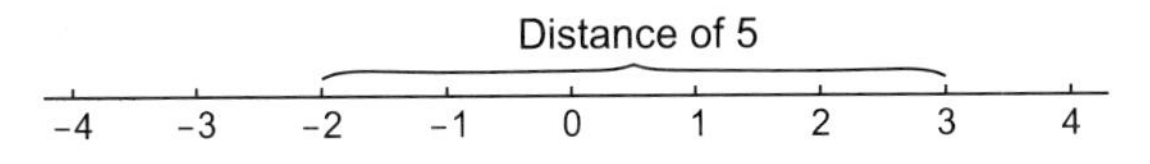

Question *The temperature in a thawing freezer increased from –15 °C to –3 °C. What was the rise in temperature?*

The diagram shows that the temperature rose by 12 °C (the distance between –15 and –3 is 12).

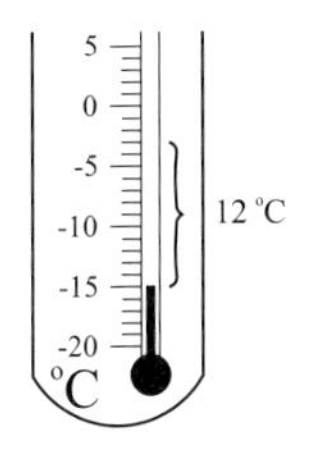

6. Adding and Subtracting

Use the number line to add/subtract two numbers.

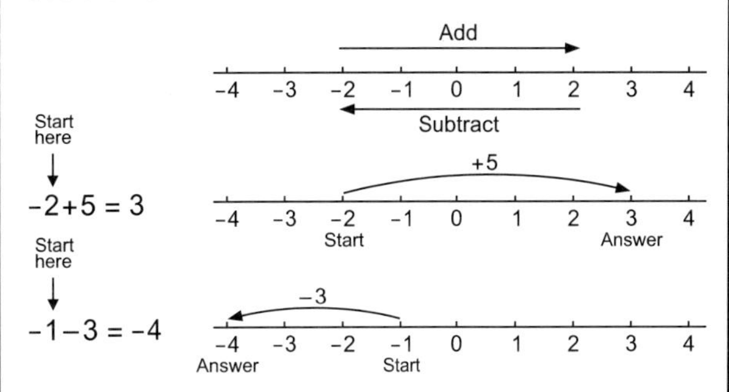

Sometimes you will see two + or – signs next to each other, e.g. 2+–3. Use the rules on the right to replace them with a single sign.

++	gives	+
––	gives	+
+–	gives	–
–+	gives	–

Examples

2+–3 = 2–3 = –1

–(–5)–2 = ––5–2 = +5–2 = 3

7. Rearranging Numbers

–2+5 and +5–2 both give the same answer of 3.

So, –2+5 can be rearranged to give +5–2. Notice how **the signs stay with the numbers**.

Similarly, –2+5–1+4 = +5+4–2–1 = 9–3 = 6

8. Adding/Subtracting Several Numbers

When adding/subtracting more than two numbers, first combine the + numbers into a single number and then the – numbers into a single number:

–3+2+4–1–6+3+5

= +2+4+3+5–3–1–6 Rearrange numbers first

= +14–10 Combine numbers

= 4

9. Multiplying and Dividing

Use these rules for multiplying numbers.

+×+ = +	–×– = +
+×– = –	–×+ = –

Examples

–2×–5 = +10 = 10 $(-3)^2 = (-3)\times(-3) = +9 = 9$

–2+–3×4 = –2+–12 = –2–12 = –14 or alternatively

–2+–3×4 = –2–3×4 = –2–12 = –14

Use the same rules for dividing numbers. For example:

–6÷–2 = +3 = 3 or equivalently $\frac{-6}{-2} = +3 = 3$

$\frac{-8}{2} = \frac{-8}{+2} = -4$ and $\frac{8}{-2} = \frac{+8}{-2} = -4$ and $-\frac{8}{2} = -4$

The last example shows that $\frac{-8}{2} = \frac{8}{-2} = -\frac{8}{2} = -4$

Fractions

1. Making Fractions

Question *A whole pie is divided into 4 equal parts. Brian eats 3 parts. What fraction of the pie does he eat?*

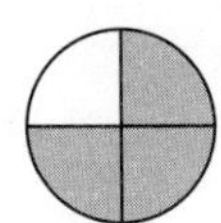

Brian eats 3 parts **out of** 4 parts = 3 parts **out of** 4 parts = $\frac{3}{4}$

So, he eats $\frac{3}{4}$ (three quarters) of the pie.

2. The Divide Sign ÷

The divide sign looks like a fraction, with dots instead of numbers. The divide sign can be used as an alternative way of writing a fraction. For example:

$\frac{3}{4}$ can be written as $3 \div 4$

3. Mixed Numbers and Improper (Top Heavy) Fractions

4 quarters of a pie + 4 quarters of a pie + 3 quarters of a pie = 11 quarters = $\frac{11}{4}$ ← **Improper fraction** (top heavy fraction)

1 whole pie + 1 whole pie + $\frac{3}{4}$ of a pie = $2 + \frac{3}{4}$ = $2\frac{3}{4}$ ← **Mixed number**

So, $2\frac{3}{4} = \frac{11}{4}$

π is a special number approximately equal to $3\frac{1}{7}$.

π is often written as an improper fraction, i.e. $\frac{22}{7}$.

Question *Convert $2\frac{3}{4}$ to an improper fraction.*

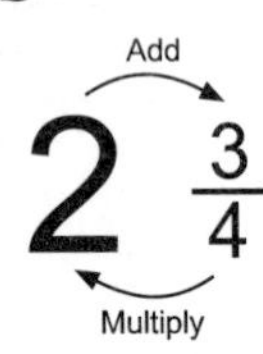

$4 \times 2 + 3 = 8 + 3 = 11$

So, $2\frac{3}{4} = \frac{11}{4}$

Denominators must be the same

Question *Convert $\frac{11}{4}$ to a mixed number.*

Divide 4 into 11

(4)) 11 = (2) rem (3)

So, $\frac{11}{4} = 2\frac{3}{4}$

Circled numbers make the mixed number

4. Whole Numbers Written as Fractions

When working with fractions it is helpful to write a whole number as a fraction. For example:

$\frac{4}{1} = 4 \div 1 = 4$.

So we can write the whole number 4 as the fraction $\frac{4}{1}$

5. Rational Numbers

Fractions are **rational numbers**, which also include all positive and negative whole numbers, zero and all finite decimals. For example:

$-2\frac{3}{4}$, $-1\frac{1}{3}$, $-\frac{3}{4}$, 0, $\frac{1}{2}$, $\frac{2}{3}$, $\frac{3}{4}$, 2.34, $3\frac{1}{2}$, $\frac{19}{5}$

NOTE $2.34 = \frac{234}{100}$

6. Equivalent Fractions

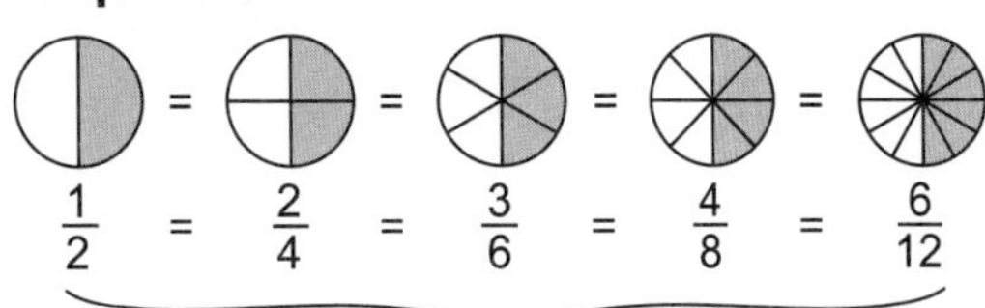

$\frac{1}{2} = \frac{2}{4} = \frac{3}{6} = \frac{4}{8} = \frac{6}{12}$

Equivalent fractions

Multiplying both the top and bottom of a fraction by the *same* number gives an **equivalent fraction**.

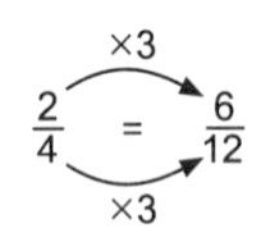

$\frac{2}{4} \xrightarrow{\times 3} \frac{6}{12}$

Question *Fill in the missing numbers.*

$\frac{3}{5} = \frac{\quad}{10} = \frac{\quad}{20} = \frac{300}{\quad}$

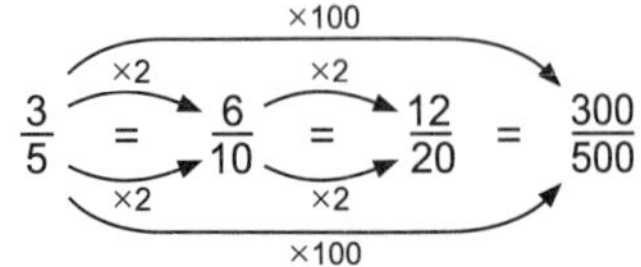

$\frac{3}{5} = \frac{6}{10} = \frac{12}{20} = \frac{300}{500}$

7. Cancelling

Dividing both the top and bottom of a fraction by the *same* number also gives an equivalent fraction. This is called **cancelling**.

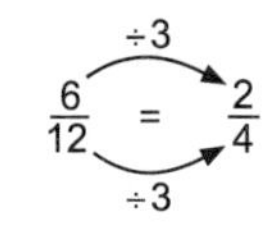

$\frac{6}{12} \xrightarrow{\div 3} \frac{2}{4}$

Question *Reduce the fraction $\frac{30}{48}$ to its lowest terms.*

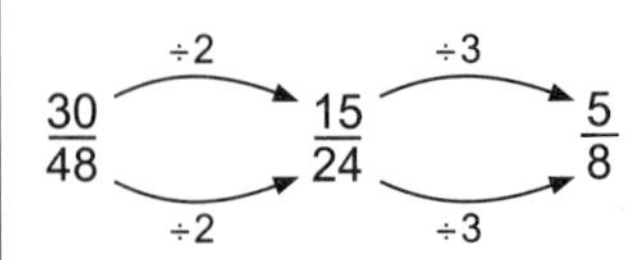

$\frac{30}{48} \xrightarrow{\div 2} \frac{15}{24} \xrightarrow{\div 3} \frac{5}{8}$

Since 5 and 8 cannot be further divided, the fraction has been **reduced to its lowest terms**.

A quicker way of writing this is to cross out the cancelled numbers and write in the new numbers.

$\frac{\not{30}\ \not{15}\ 5}{\not{48}\ \not{24}\ 8} = \frac{5}{8}$

8. Adding and Subtracting Fractions

$\frac{1}{5} + \frac{2}{5} = \frac{3}{5}$

When fractions have the *same* denominator, simply add/subtract their numerators.

The above addition can also be written:

$$\frac{1}{5} + \frac{2}{5} = \frac{1+2}{5} = \frac{3}{5}$$

When fractions have *different* denominators, change them to equivalent fractions with the *same* denominator.

Question *Express $\frac{4}{5} - \frac{2}{3}$ as a single fraction.*

First, change the denominators 5 and 3 into the same number.

The smallest number that both 5 and 3 divide into exactly is 15 (their lowest common multiple; see Box 11, p12).

Next, change $\frac{4}{5}$ and $\frac{2}{3}$ into equivalent fractions with 15 as denominator:

$\frac{4}{5} \xrightarrow{\times 3} \frac{12}{15}$ and $\frac{2}{3} \xrightarrow{\times 5} \frac{10}{15}$

So, $\frac{4}{5} - \frac{2}{3} = \frac{12}{15} - \frac{10}{15} = \frac{12-10}{15} = \frac{2}{15}$

Question *Jane spends $\frac{1}{4}$ of her pocket money on a magazine, $\frac{1}{3}$ on sweets and $\frac{1}{6}$ on make-up.*
(a) What fraction of her pocket money does she spend?
(b) What fraction of her pocket money is left?
(c) If 80p is left, how much pocket money does she get?

(a) Total spent $= \frac{1}{4} + \frac{1}{3} + \frac{1}{6}$

$= \frac{3}{12} + \frac{4}{12} + \frac{2}{12}$ LCM of 4, 3 & 6 is 12

$= \frac{\cancel{9}^3}{\cancel{12}_4}$ Cancel to lowest terms

$= \frac{3}{4}$

(b) Jane's whole pocket money is represented by 1.
So, remaining pocket money $= 1 - \frac{3}{4} = \frac{1}{4}$

(c) If $\frac{1}{4}$ of Jane's pocket money is 80p then her whole pocket money $= 4 \times 80\text{p}$

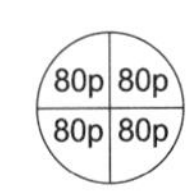

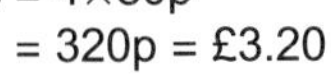
$= 320\text{p} = £3.20$

11. Sequences of Fractions

$\frac{1}{2}$ — $\frac{1}{2}$

$\frac{1}{2} + \frac{1}{4} = \frac{2}{4} + \frac{1}{4} = \frac{3}{4}$ — $\frac{3}{4}$

$\frac{1}{2} + \frac{1}{4} + \frac{1}{8} = \frac{4}{8} + \frac{2}{8} + \frac{1}{8} = \frac{7}{8}$ — $\frac{7}{8}$

$\frac{1}{2} + \frac{1}{4} + \frac{1}{8} + \frac{1}{16} = \frac{8}{16} + \frac{4}{16} + \frac{2}{16} + \frac{1}{16} = \frac{15}{16}$ — $\frac{15}{16}$

Notice that each numerator is 1 less than the denominator.

What is the next fraction?

9. Multiplying Fractions

Cancel numerators and denominators if possible. Then multiply numerators together and denominators together.

Examples

$\frac{4}{3} \times \frac{5}{6} = \frac{\cancel{4}^2}{3} \times \frac{5}{\cancel{6}_3} = \frac{2}{3} \times \frac{5}{3} = \frac{2 \times 5}{3 \times 3} = \frac{10}{9} = 1\frac{1}{9}$

$2\frac{3}{4} \times 1\frac{1}{5} = \frac{11}{4} \times \frac{6}{5}$ Change to improper fractions

$= \frac{11}{\cancel{4}_2} \times \frac{\cancel{6}^3}{5}$ Cancel numerators and denominators

$= \frac{11 \times 3}{2 \times 5}$ Multiply numerators and denominators

$= \frac{33}{10} = 3\frac{3}{10}$ Change to a mixed number

Question *Calculate $\frac{3}{5}$ of 170 m.*

$\frac{3}{5}$ of 170 $= \frac{3}{5} \times 170$ **of** means $\times$

$= 3 \div 5 \times 170 = 102$ m

Question *Ahmed runs $\frac{2}{3}$ of a kilometre every day. How far does he run in 5 days?*

$5 \times \frac{2}{3} = \frac{5}{1} \times \frac{2}{3} = \frac{10}{3} = 3\frac{1}{3}$ km NOTE Change 5 into $\frac{5}{1}$

10. Dividing Fractions

Change $\div$ to $\times$ and turn the second fraction upside down.

Example

$\frac{7}{2} \div \frac{3}{4} = \frac{7}{2} \times \frac{4}{3}$ Now multiply as usual

$= \frac{7}{\cancel{2}_1} \times \frac{\cancel{4}^2}{3} = \frac{7 \times 2}{1 \times 3} = \frac{14}{3} = 4\frac{2}{3}$

Question *A dog eats $\frac{2}{3}$ of a tin of food each day. How long will 8 tins last?*

Method 1 Each tin contains 3 thirds.
So, 8 tins contain $8 \times 3 = 24$ thirds.
Each day the dog eats 2 thirds.
So, 8 tins will last $24 \div 2 = 12$ days.

Method 2 Calculate how many $\frac{2}{3}$ there are in 8

$8 \div \frac{2}{3} = \frac{8}{1} \div \frac{2}{3} = \frac{8}{1} \times \frac{3}{2} = \frac{8 \times 3}{1 \times 2} = \frac{24}{2} = 12$

12. BoDMAS and Fractions

Question *Simplify $2\frac{1}{4} + 1\frac{1}{4} \times 1\frac{2}{5}$.*

$2\frac{1}{4} + 1\frac{1}{4} \times 1\frac{2}{5} = \frac{9}{4} + \frac{5}{4} \times \frac{7}{5}$ Change to improper fractions

$= \frac{9}{4} + \frac{\cancel{5}^1}{4} \times \frac{7}{\cancel{5}_1}$ Cancel before multiplying

$= \frac{9}{4} + \frac{1 \times 7}{4 \times 1}$ BoDMAS: multiply first

$= \frac{9}{4} + \frac{7}{4}$

$= \frac{16}{4}$

$= 4$

Decimals

1. Decimal System

The decimal system is based on columns. Each column is worth ten times the column to its right.

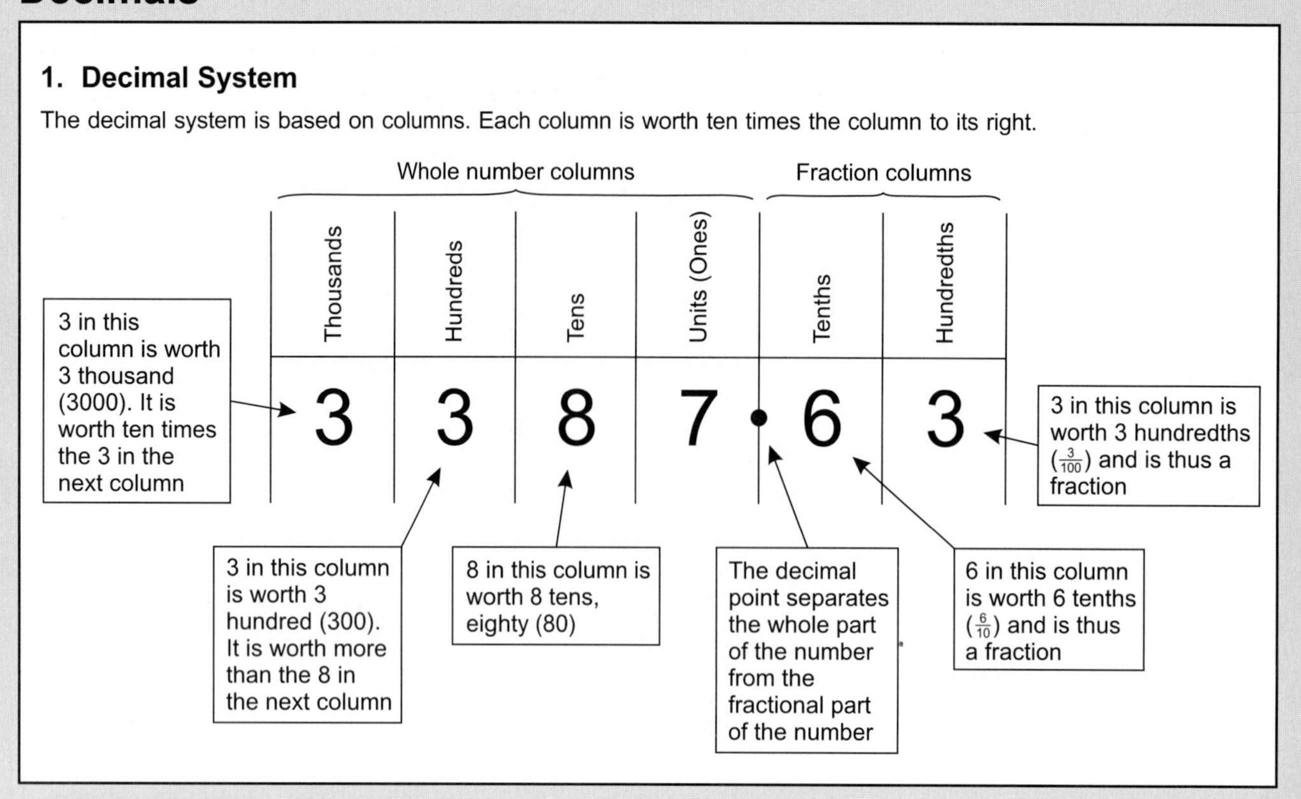

2. Digits

The numbers 0, 1, 2, 3, 4, 5, 6, 7, 8, 9 are called **digits**.

3. Reading and Writing Decimals

Question *Write in words the number 692 023 907.*

Long numbers are written in groups of three digits, starting from the decimal point. This helps us to read the number

Millions	Thousands	
6 9 2	0 2 3	9 0 7
Six hundred and ninety two (million)	Twenty three (thousand)	Nine hundred and seven

So, 692 023 907 in words is six hundred and ninety two million, twenty three thousand, nine hundred and seven.

4. Decimal Places

The number of digits after the decimal point is called the number of **decimal places (dp)**. Here are some examples:

15.634	0.002	4.00
3 decimal places	3 decimal places	2 decimal places

5. Arranging Decimals in Order of Size

Question *Arrange these decimals in order of size, from smallest to largest:*

0.0101 0.0099 0.0109 0.1 0.011

Write down the numbers in a column, keeping the decimal points in line.

0.0101
0.0099
0.0109
0.1
0.011

Fill in any spaces in the columns with zeros (see the bold zeros).

0.0101
0.0099
0.0109
0.1**000**
0.011**0**

Imagine the decimal points are missing and ignore any initial zeros (see the bold numbers). Now the numbers can easily be compared.

0.0**101**
Smallest 0.00**99**
0.0**109**
Largest 0.**1000**
0.0**110**

We can now write the numbers from smallest to largest (this is called **ranking** the numbers).

0.0099 0.0101 0.0109 0.0110 0.1000

6. Adding and Subtracting Decimals

Keep the decimal points in line with each other, then add/subtract as for whole numbers.

Examples

$$\begin{array}{r} 2.3 \\ +4.5 \\ \hline 6.8 \end{array} \qquad \begin{array}{r} 8.3 \\ -3.2 \\ \hline 5.1 \end{array} \qquad \begin{array}{r} 13.04 \\ +\ 0.592 \\ \hline 13.632 \end{array} \qquad \begin{array}{r} 0.532 \\ -0.096 \\ \hline 0.436 \end{array}$$

Question *Ms Parker spent £2.38 on stamps, £3.94 on birthday cards and 65p on a pen. How much did she spend altogether?*

First, change 65p to £0.65 then add up the numbers.

So, Ms Parker spent £6.97 altogether.

$$\begin{array}{r} 2.38 \\ 3.94 \\ +0.65 \\ \hline 6.97 \end{array}$$

7. Multiplying and Dividing by 10

Multiplying by 10 moves the decimal point one place to the right.

$$10 \times 3.6894 = 36.894$$

Similarly

$$100 \times 3.6894 = 368.94$$

and

$$1000 \times 3.6894 = 3689.4$$

Dividing by 10 moves the decimal point one place to the left.

$$4567.8 \div 10 = 456.78$$

Similarly

$$4567.8 \div 100 = 45.678$$

and

$$4567.8 \div 1000 = 4.5678$$

8. Multiplying Decimals

You should know how to multiply simple numbers involving decimals *without* using a calculator.

Question *Calculate the value of 0.2×0.03 without using a calculator.*

① Count the total number of decimal places of the numbers being multiplied:

$$0.2 \qquad 0.03$$

Total of 3 decimal places

more

8. Multiplying Decimals (Contd)

② Write the numbers without their decimal points:

02×003 or simply 2×3

③ Multiply these numbers together:

$2\times3 = 6$ which can be written 6.

④ Move the decimal point of your answer to the left and insert 0s to make a number with the decimal places found in step 1:

.006.

So, $0.2\times0.03 = 0.006$

Question *A plastic moulding weighs 0.03 g. What is the weight of 50 mouldings?*

Calculate 50×0.03 using the above method. There is a total of 2 decimal places in 50 and 0.03

$50\times003 = 50\times3 = 150 = 1.50.$

So, $50\times0.03 = 1.50$ g or simply 1.5 g

Question *Salmon costs £5.63 per kg. What is the cost of 0.6 kg correct to the nearest p?*

Calculate 0.6×5.63 using the above method. There are a total of 3 decimal places in 0.6 and 5.63:

$06\times563 = 6\times563 = 3378 = 3.378.$

So, $0.6\times5.63 = 3.378$

The cost of the salmon is £3.378 ≈ £3.38

9. Dividing Decimals

You should know how to divide simple numbers involving decimals *without* using a calculator.

Question *A roll of tape, 3.36 m long, is cut into 7 equal pieces. What is the length of each piece?*

Length of each piece = 3.36 m ÷ 7

Divide as with whole numbers. Write the decimal point of the answer above the decimal point of the number being divided,

$$\begin{array}{r} 0.48 \\ 7\overline{)3.36} \\ 2\,8\downarrow \\ \underline{56} \end{array}$$

The length of each piece of tape is 0.48 m,

Question *The thickness of a business card is 0.4 mm. A pile of cards is 50 mm high. How many cards are in the pile?*

Number of cards in pile = 50÷0.4

When dividing by a decimal use the following method:

① Move the decimal points of *both* numbers the same number of decimal places to the right until the number doing the dividing (the **divisor**) becomes a whole number.

0.4 becomes 4. or simply 4

50 = 50.0 and so becomes 500. or simply 500

② Divide as usual using these numbers.

$$\begin{array}{r} 125 \\ 4\overline{)500} \end{array}$$

So, 50÷0.4 = 125

There are 125 business cards in the pile.

Decimals (Contd)

10. Changing Decimals to Fractions

Question *Express 0.125 as a fraction in its lowest terms.*

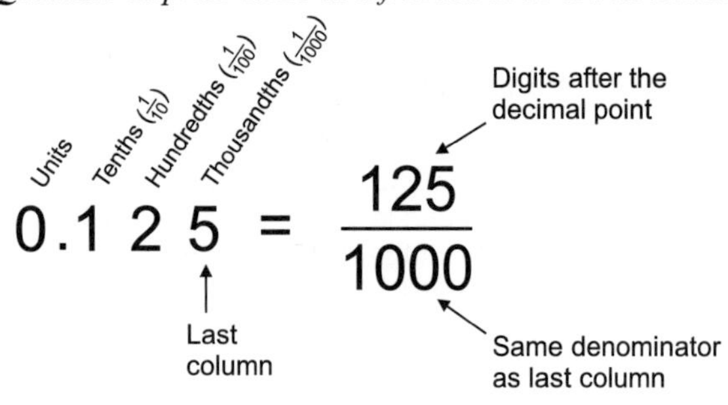

Question *Express 7.08 as a mixed fraction.*

Separate the whole part, 7, from the fraction part, 0.08, i.e. $7.08 = 7 + 0.08$.

Now, $0.08 = \frac{8}{100} = \frac{2}{25}$

So, $7.08 = 7 + 0.08 = 7 + \frac{2}{25} = 7\frac{2}{25}$

11. Changing Fractions to Decimals

Another way of writing the fraction $\frac{3}{5}$ is $3 \div 5$. So we can use a calculator to convert $\frac{3}{5}$ to a decimal:

$\frac{3}{5} = 3 \div 5 = 0.6$

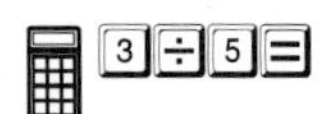

Question *Express $2\frac{5}{8}$ as a decimal.*

Now, $2\frac{5}{8}$ can be written $2 + \frac{5}{8}$

And $\frac{5}{8} = 5 \div 8 = 0.625$

So, $2\frac{5}{8} = 2 + \frac{5}{8} = 2 + 0.625 = 2.625$

Question *Write down the numbers below in increasing order of size*

$\frac{3}{4}$ 0.7 $\frac{13}{20}$

Convert the fractions to decimals:

$\frac{3}{4} = 3 \div 4 = 0.75$ and $\frac{13}{20} = 13 \div 20 = 0.65$

Now compare the decimals (see Box 5, p18):

Largest 0.75
0.70
Smallest 0.65

Write down the original numbers in order of size:

$\frac{13}{20}$ 0.7 $\frac{3}{4}$

12. Recurring Decimals

Often a calculation results in a never-ending decimal. For example:

$\frac{4}{7} = 4 \div 7 = 0.571\,428\ ....$

Sometimes, the digits after the decimal point form a pattern. For example:

$\frac{123}{999} = 123 \div 999 = 0.123\,123\ ....$ (Try this yourself)

This is called a **recurring decimal**, and written briefly as $0.\dot{1}2\dot{3}$ (the recurring pattern is between the dots).

more

12. Recurring Decimals (Contd)

Here are two more examples:

$\frac{1}{3} = 1 \div 3 = 0.333\,333\ ... = 0.\dot{3}$ Only one dot needed

$\frac{467}{180} = 467 \div 180 = 2.594\,444\ ... = 2.59\dot{4}$

Question *Express the recurring decimal 0.345 345 345 ... as a fraction.*

$0.345\,345\,345\ ... = 0.\dot{3}4\dot{5} = \frac{345}{999}$ ← Write down a 9 for each digit in the recurring pattern.

Question *Express the recurring decimal 0.071 717 1... as a fraction. Hence, express 0.271 717 1... as a fraction.*

Write down a 9 for each digit of the recurring pattern, followed by any 0s after the decimal point.

$0.071\,717\,171\ ... = 0.0\dot{7}\dot{1} = \frac{71}{990}$

Now, $0.271\,717\ ... = 0.2 + 0.071\,717\ ...$

$= \frac{2}{10} + \frac{71}{990} = \frac{198}{990} + \frac{71}{990} = \frac{269}{990}$

13. Rational and Irrational Numbers

H

A **rational number** is a number that can be written as a common fraction (Box 5, p16). Rationals include all whole numbers (integers). Here are some examples:

2 (because it can be written $\frac{2}{1}$ or $\frac{6}{3}$ for example)

$-2\ (= -\frac{2}{1})$ $0\ (= \frac{0}{1})$ $\frac{4}{7}$ $-\frac{2}{3}$ $3\frac{1}{7}$ $-1\frac{2}{5}$

$2.75\ (= 2\frac{3}{4})$ $0.\dot{1}2\dot{3}\ (= \frac{123}{999})$

An **irrational number** *cannot* be written as a fraction. Here are some examples:

$\sqrt{5}$ $\sqrt{\frac{1}{5}}$ $\sqrt{\frac{9}{5}}$ $\sqrt[3]{7}$	Roots that cannot be calculated exactly
$5+\sqrt{2}$ $4\times\sqrt{5}$	Numbers involving these roots
π 2π $\pi+2$	Numbers involving π
sin 20° tan 30°	Many trigonometric values cannot be calculated exactly

Some numbers look like irrational numbers but are not. For example, $\sqrt{9}$ is the rational number 3.

Question *Find an irrational number between 3 and 4.*

Square 3 to get $3^2 = 9$
Add 1 to get $9+1 = 10$
Square root the answer $= \sqrt{10}$.
Check: $\sqrt{10} = 3.16....$

Question *n is a positive integer such that $\sqrt{n} \approx 15.4$, correct to 1 decimal place. Find the value of n and explain why $\sqrt{n}$ is irrational.*

$\sqrt{n} \approx 15.4$. So, $n \approx 15.4^2 = 237.16$ (see Box 5, p39)

So, $n = 237$ (n is given as a positive whole number).

Check: $\sqrt{237} = 15.394.... \approx 15.4$ (1 dp)

Since $\sqrt{237}$ does not work out exactly, it is irrational.

Accuracy and Approximation

1. Rounding Off Numbers

Rounding off a number means replacing it by a simpler but less accurate number. For example, instead of saying that there were 283 fans at a concert, it is simpler to say there were about 300.

We always round off to a certain **degree of accuracy**. In the above example, 283 was rounded off *correct to the nearest 100 people*. We chose 300 instead of 200 because 283 is closer to 300 than 200. So, 283 was **rounded up** to 300.

Similarly, if 283 were rounded off to the nearest 10, it would be **rounded down** to 280, because 283 is closer to 280 than 290.

Using this rule, 285 would be rounded *up* to 290.

Less than 5, round *down*.
5 or more, round *up*.

So, 12.65 g $\approx$ 12.7 g (correct to the nearest $\frac{1}{10}$ g)
and 12.64 g $\approx$ 12.6 g (correct to the nearest $\frac{1}{10}$ g)

Question *A small cake weighs 33 g. What is this weight correct to the nearest 5 g?*

33 g is closer to 35 g than 30 g.
So, 33 g is approximately 35 g, to the nearest 5 g.

We write 33 g $\approx$ 35 g

$\simeq$ and $\approx$ both mean **approximately equal to**

Question *The diameter of Jupiter is 142 800 km. Write this distance correct to the nearest 1000 km.*

142 800 km is closer to 143 000 km than 142 000 km. So, 142 800 km $\approx$ 143 000 km, to the nearest 1000 km.

2. Significant Figures

In Box 1, we replaced the number 283 with the simpler number 300. The reason that 300 is simpler than 283 is because it only has one **significant figure (sf)**, 3: the other figures (digits) are 0

$$285 \approx 300$$

(285: 3 significant figures; 300: 1 significant figure)

We say that 283 is approximately equal to 300, **correct to 1 significant figure**, and write:
285 $\approx$ 300 (1 sf)

Here are more examples of significant figures:

58 000 (2 sf) 5.7 (2 sf) 0.0009 (1 sf) 508 000 (3 sf (0 is a significant figure because it is in between non-zero digits))

Significant figures can be used to approximate both large and small numbers.

Question *The distance from the Earth to the Moon is 384 400 km. Express this distance correct to 1 significant figure.*

Replace the unwanted significant figures by 0:

384 400 $\approx$ 400 000 km (correct to 1 sf)
(384 400: 4 sf; 400 000: 1 sf)

3. Decimal Places

Decimal places (dp) can be used to approximate *small* numbers.

For example, the number below has 6 decimal places (6 digits after the decimal point).

$$5.483\ 268$$

(6 decimal places)

This number can be simplified (approximated) by using fewer decimal places:

5.483 268 (6 dp)
$\approx$ 5.48 (2 dp)

Similarly 0.057
$\approx$ 0.06 (2 dp) — Round the number *up* because 7 is greater than 5 (see Box 1)

and 4.239
$\approx$ 4.2 (1 dp) — Round the number *down* because 3 is less than 5

and 0.0499
$\approx$ 0.0 (1 dp) — This shows that an answer of 0.0 does not mean the same as 0

4. Accuracy

You are expected to express your answers to a reasonable degree of accuracy. For example, if you are calculating the area of a circular lawn and your calculator gives you the answer 1325.694 31 m^2, a reasonable degree of accuracy would be correct to the nearest 10 m^2, giving an answer of 1330 m^2.

Question *What would be a reasonable degree of accuracy when describing (a) the weight of a person; (b) the thickness of a pencil; (c) the number of people attending a first-division football match.*

(a) Correct to the nearest kg.
(b) Correct to the nearest mm.
(c) Correct to the nearest 1000 people.

Always check the question to see if a certain degree of accuracy is required, e.g. to the nearest 10 m^2.

5. Estimation

The result of a calculation can be estimated by replacing the numbers involved by simpler, approximate numbers. For example:

$59\times3.2 \approx 60\times3 = 180$ 59 replaced by 60, 3.2 by 3

There are often several ways of estimating a calculation. For example:

$$\frac{40.21+19.75}{0.3\times12} \approx \frac{40+20}{0.25\times12} = \frac{60}{\frac{1}{4}\text{ of }12} = \frac{60}{3} = 20$$

$$\frac{40.21+19.75}{0.3\times12} \approx \frac{40+20}{0.\dot{3}\times12} = \frac{60}{\frac{1}{3}\text{ of }12} = \frac{60}{4} = 15$$

The second estimate is more accurate because 0.3 is closer to $\frac{1}{3}$ than to $\frac{1}{4}$.

Make sure your estimate is accurate enough:
$0.6\times21 \approx 1\times20 = 20$ Poor
$0.6\times21 \approx 0.5\times20 = 10$ Good

Accuracy and Approximation (Contd)

6. Error

Kulvinder measured the height of her friend Paula to be 140 cm. Paula's true height was 136 cm. So, Kulvinder made an **error** of 140 − 136 = 4 cm.

All of the lengths below are approximately 140 cm, correct to the nearest 10 cm (see Box 1).

135 cm 136 cm 137 cm 138 cm 139 cm 140 cm
141 cm 142 cm 143 cm 144 cm 144.9 cm 144.99 cm

So, if a person was measured to be 140 cm tall correct to the nearest 10 cm, the *true* height could be anywhere between 135 cm and 145 cm (the **lower** and **upper bounds**).

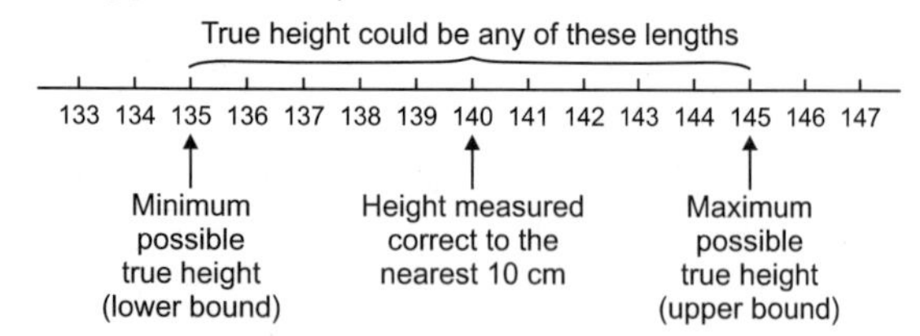

This can be written briefly as:

135 cm ⩽ True height < 145 cm

NOTE Strictly speaking, the true height cannot be 145 cm (hence the < sign), because a height of 145 cm would be rounded *up* to 150 cm.

The greatest error would occur if the person's true height were 135 cm. So, the greatest possible error is 140 − 135 = 5 cm, half the degree of accuracy, 10 cm.

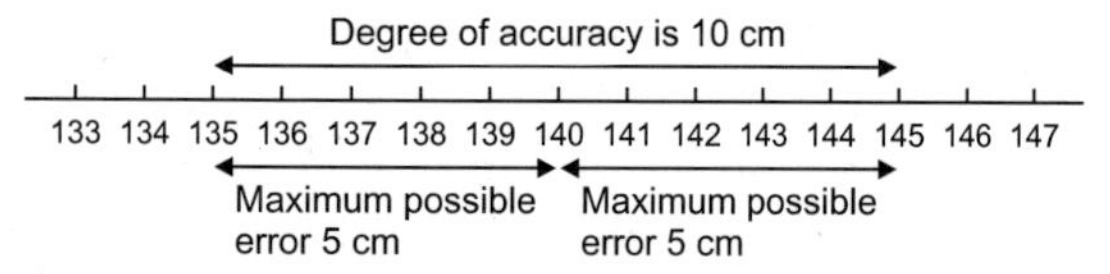

The maximum possible error of a measurement is half its degree of accuracy.

Question *The weight of a packet of tea is accurate to the nearest 5 g. What is the minimum possible weight of a 185 g packet?*

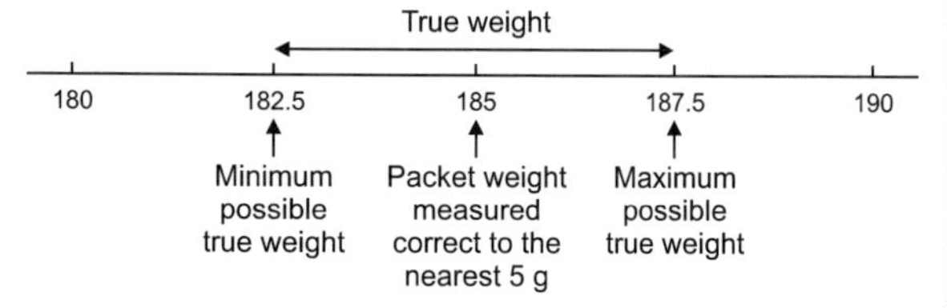

The diagram shows that the minimum possible true weight of the packet of tea is 182.5 g

Question *A machine is set to produce metal bolts of length 18 mm. The greatest possible error made by the machine is 0.2 mm. What are the upper and lower bounds of the length of bolt produced by the machine?*

The machine could produce a bolt whose length was up to 0.2 mm larger or smaller than the set value of 18 mm. So, the maximum possible length of a bolt is 18 + 0.2 = 18.2 mm and the minimum possible length is 18 − 0.2 = 17.8 mm

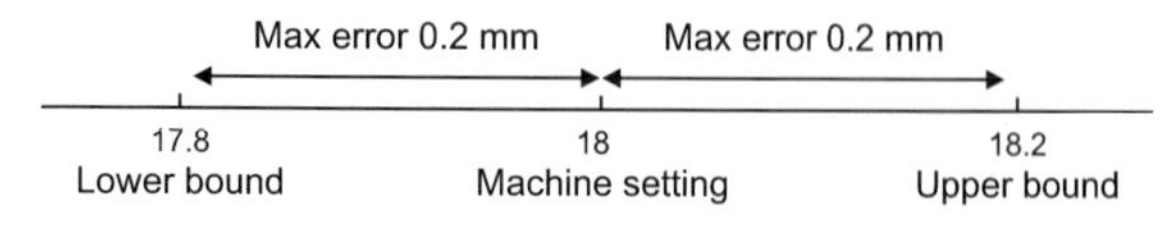

7. Upper and Lower Bounds

H

When we use approximate numbers in a calculation, we obtain an approximate result. The true result lies somewhere between the lower and upper bounds of the calculated value. We can find these lower and upper bounds when we know the degrees of accuracy of the numbers used in the calculation.

Calculations Involving Addition and Subtraction

Question *The length and width of the rectangle are correct to the nearest tenth of a centimetre. Calculate the upper and lower bounds for the perimeter of the rectangle.*

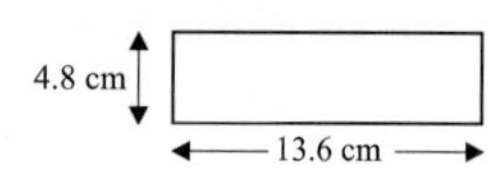

First, calculate the lower and upper bounds of the length and width (see Box 6)

13.55 cm ⩽ Length < 13.65 cm
4.75 cm ⩽ Width < 4.85 cm

Using the upper bounds will give the greatest possible perimeter, i.e. the upper bound of the perimeter:

Upper bound = 13.65 + 13.65 + 4.85 + 4.85 = 37 cm

Using the lower bounds will give the smallest possible perimeter, i.e. the lower bound of the perimeter:

Lower bound = 13.55 + 13.55 + 4.75 + 4.75 = 36.6 cm

Write the lower and upper bounds of the perimeter as follows:

36.6 cm ⩽ Perimeter < 37 cm

Question *A heap of sand has a volume of 1.75 m^3, correct to 2 decimal places. John removes some sand and estimates its volume to be 0.4 m^3, correct to 1 decimal place. What is the upper bound of the volume of sand remaining?*

Firstly, calculate the lower and upper bounds of the heap of sand and the amount removed:

1.745 m^3 ⩽ Heap < 1.755 m^3
0.35 m^3 ⩽ Removed sand < 0.45 m^3

Greatest amount of sand remaining (upper bound) is

(Upper bound of heap) − (Lower bound of removed sand)

= 1.755 − 0.35
= 1.405 m^3

Calculations Involving Multiplication

Question *The diameter of a circle is 4.73 m, measured correct to 2 dp Calculate the upper and lower bounds of (a) the diameter, (b) the radius.*

(a)

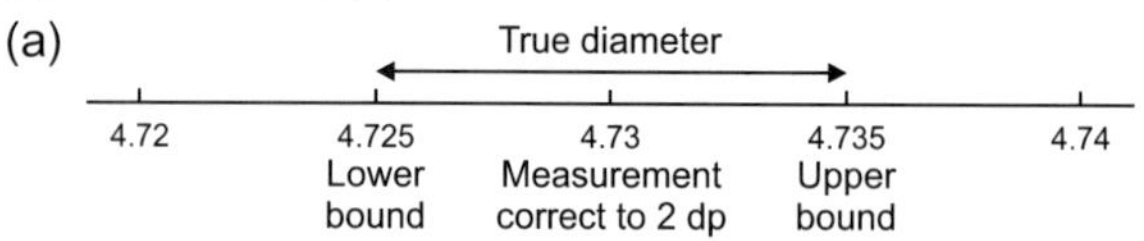

The diagram shows that the true value of the diameter lies somewhere between 4.725 m and 4.735 m. So we can write:

4.725 m ⩽ Diameter < 4.735 m

(b) The radius is half the diameter and so its lower and upper bounds can be found by halving the bounds of the diameter:

4.725 ÷ 2 = 2.3625 and 4.735 ÷ 2 = 2.3675

2.3625 m ⩽ Radius < 2.3675 m

Using a Calculator

1. The Kind of Calculator You Need

For GCSE mathematics you need a **scientific calculator**. Buy an inexpensive, basic model that can display only one number at a time (more sophisticated models often come with complicated, thick instruction manuals). Make sure it has trigonometry keys [sin][cos][tan] and statistics keys [Σx][Σx²][x̄][n][σ]. The calculator steps given in this book are for a basic calculator.

2. The Keys of a Basic Calculator

Here are the keys found on a basic calculator. Some of the symbols may look different on your calculator or may be printed above or below another key. Check your instruction manual.

Numerical [0][1][2][3][4][5][6][7][8][9][·][π][x] Used to enter numbers into the calculator.

Arithmetical [+][−][×][÷][(][)] Used to combine two or more numbers into a single number.

Functions [+/−][√][x²][x^y][x^{1/y}][1/x][INV][sin][cos][tan][EXP][Σx][Σx²][x̄][n][σ] Used to modify the displayed number in some way.

Memory [Min][M+][MR] Used to store, change and retrieve the memory.

Others [=][C][AC] Used to finish and start a calculation, correct a mistake, etc.

3. Before You Start a Calculation

Calculator Modes

Calculators can work in several different **modes**, depending on the type of calculation. For example, **statistics mode** for statistical calculations; **degrees mode** for calculating with angles measured in degrees. Make sure your calculator is in the *correct working mode* before you begin a calculation; the mode is usually displayed on the screen, e.g. DEG for degrees mode (read your instruction manual).

Memory

The memory of your calculator starts with 0 when you switch it on. More sophisticated calculators can store numbers after they are switched off.

If you are performing several calculations involving the memory, *clear* the memory each time or replace it with a number you want to store (see Box 12, p24)

4. Entering Numbers into a Calculator

To enter the number 52.63 into your calculator, press

[5][2][·][6][3] which will be displayed as 52.63

To enter the number 0.58 into your calculator, press

[0][·][5][8] which will be displayed as 0.58

or simply press [·][5][8]

To enter the negative number −40, use [+/−] to change 40 into −40. Press

[4][0][+/−] which will be displayed as −40.

5. If You Make a Mistake ....

[C] undoes the last number or function entered.

[AC] clears the entire calculation (but ***not*** the memory), ready to start a new calculation.

6. Addition and Subtraction

To calculate 16+31, press the following keys:

[1][6] enters the number 16 — 16.

[+] ready for the next number — 16.

[3][1] enters the number 31 — 31.

[=] displays the answer — 47.

To calculate −15+12, press the following keys:

[1][5] enters the number 15 — 15.

[+/−] changes 15 to −15 — −15.

[+][1][2][=] displays the answer — −3.

To calculate 5−7+4−11+3, press the following keys:

[5][−][7][+][4][−][1][1][+][3][=] gives — −6.

7. Multiplication

To calculate 16.3×0.04, press the following keys:

[1][6][·][3][×][0][·][0][4][=] — 0.652

To calculate −7×3×2, press the following keys:

[7][+/−][×][3][×][2][=] — −42.

8. Division

To calculate 16.3÷0.04, press the following keys:

[1][6][·][3][÷][0][·][0][4][=] — 407.5

To convert $\frac{7}{8}$ to a decimal, press the following keys:

[7][÷][8][=] — 0.875

See also Box 13, p24

Using a Calculator (Contd)

9. Accuracy

Your calculator works to a high degree of accuracy. The displayed answer is often more accurate than you need. For example, if £52.39 is divided equally between 7 people, each person would receive £52.39÷7. Using a calculator,

[5][2][·][3][9][÷][7][=] gives the answer (7.4842857)

The displayed answer is too accurate, since money is usually expressed correct to 2 decimal places, i.e. correct to the nearest p.
So we would write £52.39÷7 = £7.48
or more strictly £52.39÷7 ≈ £7.48

10. BoDMAS and Brackets

Your calculator obeys the rules of BoDMAS (see Box 4, p11). This means it will correctly calculate any allowable combination of numbers and arithmetical symbols +, −, ×, ÷, (,) when the corresponding keys are pressed.

To calculate 2+3×4, press the following keys:

[2][+][3][×][4][=] giving the answer (14.)

To calculate 15÷(2+3), press the following keys:

[1][5][÷][(][2][+][3][)][=] (3.)

To calculate 16+4(−5−12÷2)+6×4, press:

[1][6][+][4][×][(][5][+/-][−][1][2][÷][2][)][+][6][×][4][=] (-4.)

4(means 4×(— Changes 5 to −5

Combinations of × and ÷ signs are carried out by the calculator in the order they are entered

To calculate 24÷2×3÷9, press the following keys:

[2][4][÷][2][×][3][÷][9][=] (4.)

11. Function Keys

Most function keys modify the number on the calculator display.

To calculate 15^2, press the following keys:

[1][5] enters the number 15 (15.)

[x^2] squares the displayed number (225.)

To calculate $\sqrt{16}$, press the following keys:

[1][6] enters the number 16 (16.)

[√] square roots the displayed number (4.)

To calculate $\frac{1}{8}$, press the following keys:

[8][$\frac{1}{x}$] (0.125)

To calculate sin 30°, press the following keys:

[3][0][sin] (0.5)

12. Using the Calculator Memory

You can temporarily store a number in the memory of your calculator. This saves having to write the number down and is also more accurate.

Question *Bricks cost 87p each and are sold in packs of 856.*
(a) How much does a pack cost?
(b) How many packs can a builder buy with £5000?

(a) Cost of one pack = 856×£0.87 = £744.72

[8][5][6][×][0][·][8][7][=] (744.72)

[Min] 744.72 is now stored in the memory

(b) Number of packs that can be bought for £5000
= 5000÷744.72

[5][0][0][0][÷] (5000.)

[MR] recalls 744.72 from the memory (744.72)

[=] gives the answer (6.7139328)

So, the builder can buy 6 complete packs.

To clear the memory, press [0][Min]. This puts 0 into the memory.

Use the [M+] key to add the displayed number to the contents of the memory.

Question *Pens cost 60p each, pencils 45p, erasers 80p. Calculate the cost of 12 pens, 4 pencils and 2 erasers.*

Keys		Display
[0][Min]	clear the memory	0.
[1][2][×][6][0]	cost of pens	720.
[M+]	.... added to the memory	720.
[4][×][4][5][M+]	cost of pens added	180.
[2][×][8][0][M+]	cost of erasers added	160.
[MR]	retrieves the total cost	1060.

Total cost is £10.60.

13. Calculations Involving Fractions

For calculations involving simple fractions, replace the dividing line by the divide sign ÷

To calculate $\frac{28}{5} - \frac{2}{0.63}$, write as 28÷5−2÷0.63 and press:

[2][8][÷][5][−][2][÷][0][·][6][3][=] (2.4253968)

So, $\frac{28}{5} - \frac{2}{0.63}$ = 2.43 (correct to 2 dp)

For more complicated fractions, bracket the numerator and denominator.

To calculate $\frac{17.4-2.8}{3.6+4.9}$, write as $\frac{(17.4-2.8)}{(3.6+4.9)}$, then as (17.4−2.8)÷(3.6+4.9) and press:

[(][1][7][·][4][−][2][·][8][)][÷][(][3][·][6][+][4][·][9][)][=]

So, $\frac{17.4-2.8}{3.6+4.9}$ = 1.72 (2 dp) (1.7176471)

Alternatively, calculate the denominator first and store it in the memory for later:

[3][·][6][+][4][·][9][=][Min][1][7][·][4][−][2][·][8][=][÷][MR][=]

Denominator — Numerator

Percentages

1. Percentages, Fractions and Decimals

75% is a short way of writing the fraction $\frac{75}{100}$. So,

$$75\% = \frac{75}{100} = 75 \div 100 = 0.75$$

Percentage ↑ Fraction ↑ Decimal ↑

To convert a percentage to a fraction, divide by 100.

Question *Express 60% as a fraction in its lowest terms.*

$60\% = \frac{60}{100} = \frac{6^3}{10_5} = \frac{3}{5}$

Question *Place the numbers 88%, $\frac{7}{8}$ and 0.808 in increasing order of size.*

Convert the non-decimals to decimals.

$88\% = 88 \div 100 = 0.88$ $\quad \frac{7}{8} = 7 \div 8 = 0.875$

Place the decimals in increasing order of size (see Box 5, p18).

0.808 0.875 0.88

Largest 0.88
0.875
Smallest 0.808

Write down the *original* numbers in increasing order of size.

0.808 $\frac{7}{8}$ 88%

To convert a decimal or fraction to a percentage, multiply by 100.

Question *Convert 0.45 to a percentage.*

$0.45 = 0.45 \times 100\% = 45\%$

Question *Convert 0.05 to a percentage.*

$0.05 = 0.05 \times 100\% = 5\%$

Question *$\frac{5}{14}$ of Joan's teeth have fillings. What percentage of her teeth are filled?*

$\frac{5}{14} = \frac{5}{14} \times 100\% = 5 \div 14 \times 100\% = 35.7\%$ (1 dp)

NOTE You get the same answer by calculating $5 \times 100 \div 14$ or $100 \div 14 \times 5$.

2. Common Percentages and Fractions

$100\% = \frac{100}{100} = 1$	**100%** represents a **whole**
$25\% = \frac{25^1}{100_4} = \frac{1}{4}$	**25%** represents a **quarter**
$50\% = \frac{50^1}{100_2} = \frac{1}{2}$	**50%** represents a **half**
$75\% = \frac{75^3}{100_4} = \frac{3}{4}$	**75%** represents **three quarters**
$10\% = \frac{10^1}{100_{10}} = \frac{1}{10}$	**10%** represents **one tenth**
$20\% = \frac{20^2}{100_{10}} = \frac{2}{10}$	**20%** represents **two tenths**
etc.	
$1\% = \frac{1}{100}$	**1%** represents **one hundredth**
$5\% = \frac{5^1}{100_{20}} = \frac{1}{20}$	**5%** represents **one twentieth**
$\frac{1}{3} = \frac{1}{3} \times 100\% = \frac{100}{3}\% = 33\frac{1}{3}\%$	**$33\frac{1}{3}$%** is **one third**
$\frac{2}{3} = \frac{2}{3} \times 100\% = \frac{200}{3}\% = 66\frac{2}{3}\%$	**$66\frac{2}{3}$%** is **two thirds**

3. Expressing One Quantity as a Percentage of Another Quantity

Question *A bottle contains 70 cl of wine. Bob drinks 15 cl. What percentage of the wine does Bob drink?*

Bob drinks 15 cl *out of* 70 cl.

$= \frac{15\text{ cl}}{\text{out of } 70\text{ cl}} = \frac{15}{70}$ As a fraction

$= \frac{15}{70} \times 100\%$ Converting to a percentage

$= 15 \div 70 \times 100$

$= 21.4\%$ (1 dp)

Question *Ahmed buys a car for £6500 (the cost price) and sells it 2 years later to a dealer for £4000 (the selling price). Express the selling price as a percentage of the cost price.*

Selling price *as a percentage of* cost price

= £4000 as a percentage of £6500

$= \frac{£4000}{\text{as a percentage of } £6500} = \frac{4000}{6500}$

$= \frac{4000}{6500} \times 100\%$

$= 4000 \div 6500 \times 100$

$= 61.5\%$ (1 dp)

Question *A dealer buys a car for £4000 (the cost price) and sells it for £4600 (the selling price). Express the selling price as a percentage of the cost price.*

£4600 as a percentage of £4000

$= \frac{£4600}{£4000} = \frac{4600}{4000} \times 100\% = 115\%$

4. Finding a Percentage of a Quantity

Question *Calculate 20% of 150 kg.*

20% of 150 kg

$= \frac{20}{100} \times 150$ kg **of means ×**

$= 20 \div 100 \times 150$

$= 30$ kg

Question *A salesman of double glazed windows earns $6\frac{1}{4}$% commission. How much does he earn on a sale of £1700?*

Commission $= 6\frac{1}{4}\%$ of £1700

= 6.25% of £1700

$= \frac{6.25}{100} \times £1700$

$= 6.25 \div 100 \times £1700$

= £106.25

Question *The share price of a gold mine was 128p. Share prices rose by 400% when a new gold vein was discovered. By how much did the share price rise?*

Rise in price = 400% of 128p

$= \frac{400}{100} \times 128$p

$= 4 \times 128$p

= 512p

(Each share would then be worth 128+512 = 640p)

Percentages (Contd)

5. Finding the Percentage Change of a Quantity

$$\text{Percentage change} = \frac{\text{Change in quantity}}{\text{Original quantity}} \times 100\%$$

Question *During a fever, the temperature of a child increased from 98.4°C to 104°C. Find the percentage increase in temperature.*

NOTE *Percentage increase* can be written briefly as *% increase*

Original temperature = 98.4 °C

Change in temperature (increase) = 104 − 98.4
= 5.6 °C

$$\% \text{ increase} = \frac{\text{Increase in temperature}}{\text{Original temperature}} \times 100\%$$
$$= \frac{5.6}{98.4} \times 100\%$$
$$= 5.6 \div 98.4 \times 100\%$$
$$= 5.69\% \text{ (2 dp)}$$

The child's temperature increased by 5.69%.

Question *Alex and Grace bought their house in 1982 for £67 000 and sold it in 1994 for £98 000. Calculate:*
(a) the profit on the sale
(b) the percentage profit.

(a) Profit = Selling price − Cost price
= £98 000 − £67 000
= £31 000

$$\text{(b) \% profit} = \frac{\text{Profit (change in price)}}{\text{Cost price (original price)}} \times 100\%$$
$$= \frac{31\,000}{67\,000} \times 100\%$$
$$= 31\,000 \div 67\,000 \times 100\%$$
$$= 46.3\% \text{ (1 dp)}$$

7. Reversing an Increase or Decrease

Question *In a store sale all prices are discounted by 15%. If a customer pays £2300 for a three-piece suite, what would the price of the suite have been before the discount?*

NOTE A **discount** is a reduction in price.

Let 100% represent the original price of £2300, *before* the discount. Then the original price has been reduced by 15% to 85% of itself, as shown in the diagram

Original price	−	Discount	=	£2300
100%	−	15%	=	85%

We need to find the original price, i.e. 100%.

From the diagram, 85% of original price = £2300

So, 1% of original price = £2300 ÷ 85 = £27.06 (2 dp)

Then, original price = 100% = 100 × 1%
= 100 × £27.06
= £2705.88

6. Increasing or Decreasing a Quantity by a Given Percentage

Question *The shop price of a television set is £350. Value added tax (VAT) at $17\frac{1}{2}$% is added to this price. How much does the TV cost?*

VAT = $17\frac{1}{2}$% of £350

= 17.5% of £350 = $\frac{17.5}{100}$ × £350 = £61.25

So, cost of television set = Shop price + VAT
= £350 + £61.25
= £411.25

Question *£3000 is invested in a bank account and earns 7% interest per annum. The interest is added to the account at the end of each year. How much money will be in the account*
(a) at the end of the first year
(b) at the end of the second year.

(a) Interest earned at end of first year
= 7% of £3000
= $\frac{7}{100}$ × £3000 = 7 ÷ 100 × £3000 = £210
Account after 1 yr = £3000 + £210 = £3210

(b) Interest earned at end of second year
= 7% of £3210
= $\frac{7}{100}$ × £3210 = 7 ÷ 100 × £3210 = £224.70
Account after 2 yr = £3210 + £224.70 = £3434.70

The above calculations can be shortened using a **multiplier**.

(a) Let 100% represent the initial amount of £3000, i.e. 100% of £3000 is £3000.
This increases by 7% to 107% at the end of the year, as shown in the diagram:

£3000	+	Interest	=	Amount after 1 year
100%	+	7%	=	107%

So, increased amount
= 107% of £3000
= $\frac{107}{100}$ × £3000 = 1.07 × £3000 = £3210
The number 1.07 is called a **multiplier**. It increases whatever it multiplies by 7%.

(b) During the second year, £3210 increases by 7%.
So, increased amount = 1.07 × £3210 = £3434.70

Question *A pond contains 50 litres of water. Each day 3% of its water evaporates. What will its volume be in 3 days?*

Let 100% represent the original 50 litres.
In 1 day, 100% reduces by 3% to 97%.

50 ℓ	−	Evaporation	=	Volume after 1 day
100%	−	3%	=	97%

Reduced amount = 97% of 50 = 0.97 × 50 = 48.5 ℓ
Here the multiplier is 0.97.
So, after 2 days, volume = 0.97 × 48.5 = 47.045 ℓ
and after 3 days, volume = 0.97 × 47.045 ≈ 45.6 ℓ

An even quicker method is:

Volume after 3 days = $0.97^3 \times 50 \approx 45.6$ ℓ

Ratio

1. Ratio

The wrapper of a 250 g pack of butter is marked into 5 equal parts. A cook uses 2 parts for frying and 3 parts for baking. We say that the butter has been divided in the **ratio** 2 parts to 3 parts, written 2 : 3.

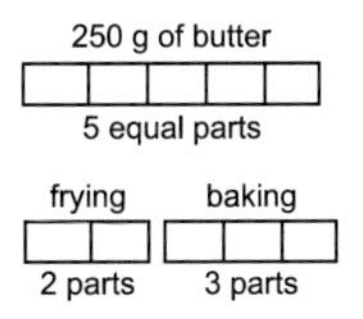

We can also say that the ratio of frying butter to baking butter is 2 : 3 and write

Frying butter : baking butter = 2 : 3

We can find the amount of butter used for frying by first *finding* 1 *part*.

We know 5 parts = 250 g
and so 1 part = 250 g ÷ 5 = 50 g
So, frying butter = 2 parts = 2 × 50 g = 100 g
and baking butter = 3 parts = 3 × 50 g = 150 g

Question *Yogurt flip is made from a mixture of yogurt, orange juice and sparkling water in the ratio 7:3:2.*
(a) How much orange juice does a 30 cl glass contain?
(b) A jug of flip contains 20 cl of sparkling water. How much yogurt does it contain?

Sparkling water 2 parts
Orange juice 3 parts
Yogurt 7 parts
30 cl

(a) 7:3:2 means 7 parts : 3 parts : 2 parts, giving a total of 7 + 3 + 2 = 12 parts (the whole glass).
So, 12 parts = 30 cl
Thus, 1 part = 30 cl ÷ 12 = 2.5 cl
Orange juice = 3 parts
= 3 × 2.5 cl = 7.5 cl

(b) Sparkling water = 2 parts = 20 cl
So, 1 part = 20 cl ÷ 2 = 10 cl
Yogurt = 7 parts = 7 × 10 cl = 70 cl

2. Equivalent Ratios

Multiplying or dividing the numbers of a ratio by the *same* number gives an **equivalent** ratio.

Examples

2 : 5 = 6 : 15 (×3) 12 : 20 = 6 : 10 = 3 : 5 (÷2, ÷2) $\frac{1}{2} : \frac{1}{4} = 2 : 1$ (×4)

Question *A builder mixes together $1\frac{1}{4}$ buckets of sand, $\frac{1}{2}$ of a bucket of cement and $\frac{1}{4}$ of a bucket of water. Express the ratio of sand to cement to water, using whole numbers.*

Sand : Cement : Water = $1\frac{1}{4} : \frac{1}{2} : \frac{1}{4} = 2\frac{1}{2} : 1 : \frac{1}{2} = 5 : 2 : 1$ (×2, ×2)

Question *Lemonade is sold in small bottles costing 90p and large bottles costing £1.35. Express the ratio of these prices in its lowest terms.*

First, convert £1.35 to 135p.

When comparing quantities, make sure they have the *same* units of measurement.

Then, Small : Large = 90 : 135 = $\frac{90}{} : \frac{135}{}$ (cancelled to 18 : 45, then 2 : 3) = 2 : 3

3. Increasing/Decreasing a Quantity in a Given Ratio

Question *Mandy was given this recipe for rock cakes by her grandmother. These quantities make 6 rock cakes.*

Rock Cakes
240 g flour
150 g sugar
150 g margarine
210 g dried fruit
2 large eggs

(a) How much sugar does Mandy need to make 8 rock cakes?
(b) Mandy has only 100 g of margarine but has plenty of all the other ingredients. How many rock cakes can she make?

(a) To increase the recipe from 6 to 8 cakes, we must increase each ingredient in the ratio 6 : 8, i.e. 3 : 4

Before increase : After increase
3 parts : 4 parts
150 g sugar : Sugar needed?

3 parts = 150 g and so 1 part = 150 g ÷ 3 = 50 g
4 parts = 4 × 1 part = 4 × 50 g = 200 g
Mandy needs 200 g of sugar.

(b) Decreasing the margarine from 150 g to 100 g will decrease the number of rock cakes in the ratio 150 : 100, i.e. 3:2

Before decrease : After decrease
3 parts : 2 parts
6 cakes : How many cakes?

3 parts = 6 cakes and so 1 part = 6 ÷ 3 = 2 cakes
2 parts = 2 × 1 part = 2 × 2 cakes = 4 cakes
Mandy can make 4 cakes.

4. Scale Factors

Question *A photograph measuring 18 cm by 12 cm was enlarged to 45 cm by 30 cm. Write down the ratio of the enlargement in the form 1:n.*

Photo : Enlargement
18 cm : 45 cm
$= \frac{18}{18} : \frac{45}{18}$ (cancelled to $\frac{5}{2}$) Divide both sides by 18 to make the left-hand side equal to 1
$= 1 : \frac{5}{2}$
$= 1 : 2\frac{1}{2}$ ← This number is called the **scale factor** of the enlargement

The height and width of the enlargement are $2\frac{1}{2}$ times the height and width of the original photograph.

5. Ratios as Fractions

A ratio can be written as a fraction, e.g. $5 : 7 = \frac{5}{7}$

Question *The ratio of the volume of a cup to a mug is 2 : 3. If the volume of a mug is 45 cl, calculate the volume of a cup.*

Cup : Mug = 2 : 3, which can be written as a fraction:

$\frac{\text{Cup}}{\text{Mug}} = \frac{2}{3}$ and so Cup = $\frac{2}{3}$ × Mug = $\frac{2}{3}$ × 45 = 30 cl

Units of Measurement

1. Metric Units

These are the basic units of measurement used in the UK today.

Length	Weight (Mass)	Capacity (Volume)	Money
kilometre (km)	kilogram (kg)	litre (ℓ)	pound (£)
metre (m)	gram (g)	centilitre (cℓ)	penny (p)
centimetre (cm)	milligram (mg)	millilitre (mℓ)	
millimetre (mm)			

2. Imperial Units

These are the most common units of measurement used before the introduction of the metric system.

Length	Weight (Mass)	Capacity	Money
inch (in *or* ")	ounce (oz)	fluid ounce (fl oz)	pound (£)
foot (ft *or* ')	pound (lb)	pint (pt)	shilling (s)
yard (yd)	stone (st)	quart (qt)	penny (d)
mile (m)	hundredweight (cwt)	gallon (gal)	
	ton (t)		

3. Prefixes

A **prefix** is a word or letter placed before a basic unit to make a smaller or larger new unit.

kilo (k) means **thousand (1000)**

So, kilometre (km) means thousand metres (1000 m)
kilogram (kg) means thousand grams (1000 g)
kilowatt (kW) means thousand watts (1000 W)

centi (c) means **hundredth** ($\frac{1}{100}$)

So, centimetre (cm) means hundredth of a metre ($\frac{1}{100}$ m)
centilitre (cℓ) means hundredth of a litre ($\frac{1}{100}$ ℓ)

milli (m) means **thousandth** ($\frac{1}{1000}$)

So, milliimetre (mm) means thousandth of a metre ($\frac{1}{1000}$ m)
millilitre (mℓ) means thousandth of a litre ($\frac{1}{1000}$ ℓ)
milligram (mg) means thousandth of a gram ($\frac{1}{1000}$ g)

4. Estimating

You may be asked to estimate the measurement of an everyday object. Here are a few examples:

Height of a door	2 m
Length of a car	3 m
Height of a work surface	1 m
Capacity of a wine glass	10 cℓ
Weight of an apple	150 g

Take a good look at a ruler to estimate the following

Width of this page	20 cm
Diameter of a 2p coin	2 cm
Thickness of a credit card	1 mm

5. Equivalent Metric Units

Length	Weight	Capacity
1 km = 1000 m	1 kg = 1000 g	1 ℓ = 100 cℓ
1 m = 100 cm	1 g = 1000 mg	1 ℓ = 1000 mℓ
1 m = 1000 mm	1 tonne (t) = 1000 kg	1 cℓ = 10 mℓ
1 cm = 10 mm		

6. Converting Metric Units

To convert a big unit to a small unit, *multiply*

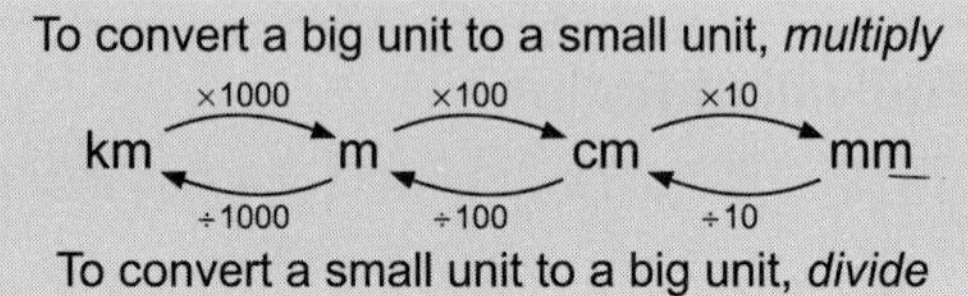

To convert a small unit to a big unit, *divide*

Question *Convert 0.13 kg to g.*

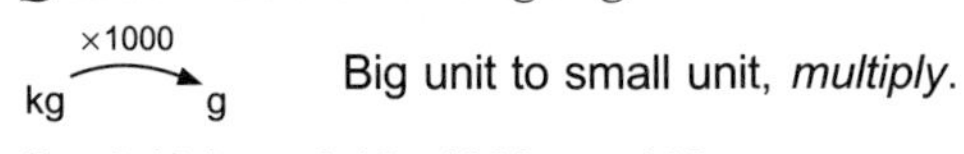

Big unit to small unit, *multiply*.

So, 0.13 kg = 0.13×1000 g = 130 g

Question *Convert 15 mm to cm.*

cm ← mm (÷10) Small unit to big unit, *divide*.

So, 15 mm = 15÷10 cm = 1.5 cm

Convert measurements to the *same* unit before starting a calculation. Look at the question to see which unit is required.

Question *Patrick made some ginger ale by mixing together 1.25 ℓ of lemonade, 30 cℓ of ginger syrup and 250 mℓ of rum. Calculate the volume of ginger ale he made, giving your answer in cℓ.*

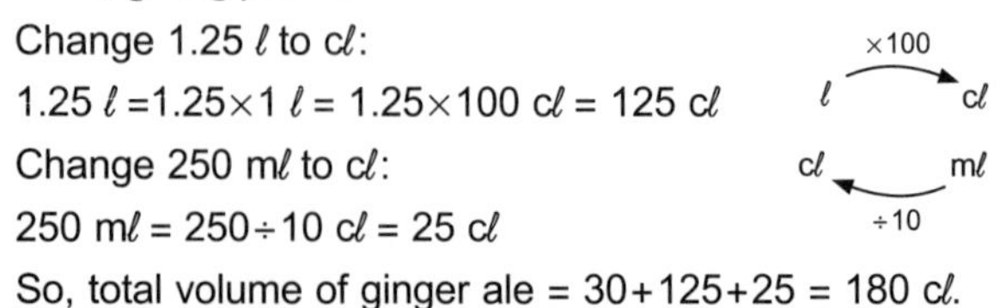

Change 1.25 ℓ to cℓ:

1.25 ℓ = 1.25×1 ℓ = 1.25×100 cℓ = 125 cℓ

Change 250 mℓ to cℓ:

250 mℓ = 250÷10 cℓ = 25 cℓ

So, total volume of ginger ale = 30+125+25 = 180 cℓ.

7. Converting Metric and Imperial Units

Length	Weight	Capacity
1 m ≈ 3 ft = 1 yd	1 kg ≈ 2 lb	1 ℓ ≈ $1\frac{3}{4}$ pt
1 in ≈ 25 mm	500 g ≈ 1 lb	1 gallon ≈ 4.5 ℓ
1 ft ≈ 30 cm	250 g ≈ $\frac{1}{2}$ lb	
5 miles ≈ 8 km		

Question *Suna is 5 ft 2 in tall. Given that 1 in ≈ 2.5 cm and 1 ft = 12 in, calculate Suna's height in metres.*

5 ft 2 in = 5 ft + 2 in = 5×12 in + 2 in = 62 in
62 in = 62×1 in ≈ 62×2.5 cm = 155 cm
155 cm = 155÷100 m = 1.55 m
Suna is approximately 1.55 m tall

Question *Jeremy weighs 134 lb. Estimate his weight in kilograms.*

Rough estimate	Better estimate
1 kg ≈ 2 lb	1 kg ≈ 2.2 lb
134 lb ≈ 134÷2 kg	134 lb ≈ 134÷2.2 kg
= 67 kg	≈ 61 kg

8. Currency Conversion

The exchange rates in this table are used in the questions that follow.

Currency Conversion Table
£1 = DM 2.68 (German marks)
£1 = FFr 9.03 (French francs)
£1 = L 2685 (Italian liras)
£1 = BFr 55.37 (Belgian francs)
£1 = $ 1.59 (US dollars)

Question *Convert £25 to German marks (DM).*

The exchange rate for German marks is £1 = DM 2.68.

So, £25 = 25×£1 = 25×DM 2.68 = DM 67

Question *Convert FFr 165 to pounds sterling.*

The exchange rate for French francs is £1 = FFr 9.03.

So, FFr 165 = £165÷9.03 = £18.27

Question *Convert L 500 000 to US dollars ($)*

First, convert liras to £ and then £ to $.

The exchange rate for Italian liras is £1 = L 2685.

So, L 500 000 = £500 000÷2685 = £186.22

The exchange rate for US dollars is £1 = $1.59.

So, £186.22 = 186.22×$1.59 = $296.09

Question *Mary converted £300 to German marks (DM) and £400 to Belgian francs (BFr). She spent DM 535 in Germany and BFr 13 400 in Belgium and converted the rest back to pounds sterling. How many pounds did she receive?*

Mary started with £300+£400 = £700

The quickest method is to convert the spent DM and BFr to £ and subtract both from £700

DM 535 = £535÷2.68 = £199.63
BFr 13 400 = £13 400÷55.37 = £242.01

Mary received £700−£199.63−£242.01 = £258.36

Question *Gunter changed £200 into DM 548. What was the exchange rate from £ to DM?*

£200 = DM 548 and so £1 = DM 548÷200 = DM 2.74
The exchange rate is £1 = DM 2.74

9. Compound Units

Examples of compound units are:

Speed 5 km/h means 5 km travelled in 1 hour

Cost 85p/kg means 1 kg costs 85p

Density 5 g/cm^3 means 1 cm^3 weighs 5 g

Fuel efficiency 15 km/ℓ means 15 km travelled on 1 ℓ of fuel

10. Best Buy

Question *Baked beans are sold in small and large cans, as shown in the diagram. Which can is better value for money?*

275 g BEANS 38p

<u>Small can</u> 15p buys 125 g
So, 1p buys 125 g÷15 = 8.33g (2 dp)
1p buys 8.33 g

Large can 38p buys 275 g
So, 1p buys 275 g÷38 = 7.24g (2 dp)
1p buys 7.24 g

The small can is better value since you get more weight per penny.

Question *Suggest a size and corresponding price for a medium box of washing powder. You must give reasons for your answers and show your working.*

1 kg WASHO £1.25 | ? kg WASHO £? | 4 kg WASHO £4.20

The weight of a medium box could be halfway between 1 kg and 4 kg, i.e. $\frac{1+4}{2} = \frac{5}{2} = 2.5$ kg

To find a reasonable price of a 2.5 kg pack, we must first find a reasonable cost per kg.

Small size 1 kg costs £1.25
So, cost per kg is £1.25/kg

<u>Large size</u> 4 kg costs £4.20
So, cost of 1 kg = £4.20÷4 = £1.05
So, cost per kg is £1.05/kg

A reasonable price per kg would be halfway between £1.25p/kg and £1.05p/kg, i.e. $\frac{1.25+1.05}{2} = \frac{2.30}{2} =$ £1.15p/kg

Price of medium box = 2.5×£1.15 = £2.875 ≈ £2.88

Powers, Roots, Reciprocals and Surds

1. Calculating Powers

To calculate 1.7^2, press:

[1] [·] [7] [x^2] → 2.89

To calculate 5^7, press:

[5] [x^y] [7] [=] → 78125.

Power key

2. Calculating Roots

To calculate $\sqrt{2.9}$, press:

[2] [·] [9] [$\sqrt{\ }$] → 1.7029386

To calculate $\sqrt[5]{32}$, press:

[3] [2] [$x^{1/y}$] [5] [=] → 2.

Root key

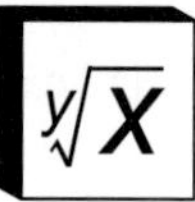

3. Two Special Powers

5^0 means 1

5^1 means 5

4. Negative Indices

5^{-1} means $\frac{1}{5}$ $\quad$ 5^{-2} means $\frac{1}{5^2}$ $\quad$ 5^{-3} means $\frac{1}{5^3}$

Question *Write 6^{-2} as a fraction.*

$6^{-2} = \frac{1}{6^2} = \frac{1}{36}$

Question *Write 10^{-3} as a decimal.*

$10^{-3} = \frac{1}{10^3} = \frac{1}{1000} = 0.001$

Question *Calculate the value of 1.5^{-3} correct to 2 dp.*

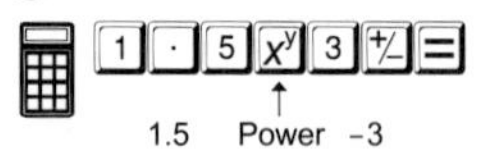

[1] [·] [5] [x^y] [3] [+/−] [=] → 0.2962963

1.5 $\quad$ Power $\quad$ −3

So, $1.5^{-3} = 0.30$ correct to 2 dp

See also Box 5

5. Fractional Indices

$9^{\frac{1}{2}}$ means $\sqrt{9}$ $\quad$ $8^{\frac{1}{3}}$ means $\sqrt[3]{8}$ $\quad$ $16^{\frac{1}{4}}$ means $\sqrt[4]{16}$

Question *Find the value of $8^{\frac{1}{3}}$ without using a calculator.*

$8^{\frac{1}{3}} = \sqrt[3]{8} = 2$ because $2 \times 2 \times 2 = 8$ (see Box 9, p12)

Question *Write $81^{-\frac{1}{2}}$ as a fraction.*

$81^{-\frac{1}{2}} = \frac{1}{81^{\frac{1}{2}}}$ $\quad$ (see Box 4)

$= \frac{1}{\sqrt{81}} = \frac{1}{9}$

$8^{\frac{2}{3}}$ means $(\sqrt[3]{8})^2$ or equivalently $\sqrt[3]{8^2}$ $\quad$ $8^{\frac{2}{3}}$ ← power (2), ← root (3)

Question *Find the value of $8^{\frac{2}{3}}$ without using a calculator.*

$8^{\frac{2}{3}} = (\sqrt[3]{8})^2$ $\quad$ Finding the root first is easier

$= (2)^2 = 2^2 = 4$

6. More Difficult Calculations

Question *Calculate the value of $\sqrt{1-0.8^2}$.*

$\sqrt{1-0.8^2}$ means $\sqrt{(1-0.8^2)}$. So, calculate the bracket, then square root the answer.

[1] [−] [0] [·] [8] [x^2] [=] [$\sqrt{\ }$] → 0.6

So, $\sqrt{1-0.8^2} = 0.6$

Question *Calculate the value of $(2\pi)^{\frac{3}{4}}$, correct to 3 decimal places.*

[2] [×] [π] [=] [x^y] [3] [=] [$x^{1/y}$] [4] [=] → 3.9685778

3rd power $\quad$ 4th root

So, $(2\pi)^{\frac{3}{4}} = 3.969$ correct to 3 dp.

7. Reciprocals

The **reciprocal** of a number is $\frac{1}{\text{number}}$.

Examples

The reciprocal of 2 is $\frac{1}{2}$.

The reciprocal of 0.4 is $\frac{1}{0.4}$.

Question *Calculate the value of $\frac{1}{0.4} + \frac{1}{0.5}$.*

[0] [·] [4] [$\frac{1}{x}$] [+] [0] [·] [5] [$\frac{1}{x}$] [=] → 4.5

Reciprocal key

So, $\frac{1}{0.4} + \frac{1}{0.5} = 4.5$

8. Summary

$8^0 = 1$

$8^1 = 8$

$8^3 = 8 \times 8 \times 8$

$8^{-1} = \frac{1}{8}$

$8^{-3} = \frac{1}{8^3}$

$8^{\frac{1}{2}} = \sqrt[2]{8} = \sqrt{8}$

$8^{\frac{1}{3}} = \sqrt[3]{8}$

$8^{\frac{2}{3}} = (\sqrt[3]{8})^2 = \sqrt[3]{8^2}$

$8^{-\frac{1}{3}} = \frac{1}{8^{\frac{1}{3}}} = \frac{1}{\sqrt[3]{8}}$

$8^{-\frac{2}{3}} = \frac{1}{8^{\frac{2}{3}}} = \frac{1}{(\sqrt[3]{8})^2}$

9. Surds

H

A **surd** is the root of a whole number which produces an irrational number (it also refers to an expression that involves one). Here are a few examples:

$\sqrt{2}$ $\quad 3+\sqrt{2}$ $\quad 4\sqrt{2}$ $\quad 5-3\sqrt{2}$ $\quad \frac{4}{\sqrt{2}}$ $\quad \frac{1}{4+3\sqrt{2}}$

NOTE Surds are *irrational* numbers (see Box 13, p20).
So, $\sqrt{9}$ is ***not*** a surd, because $\sqrt{9}=3$

Surds involving the *same* root can be simplified by adding, subtracting, multiplying and dividing.

Adding/Subtracting Surds

$3\sqrt{5}$ means $3\times\sqrt{5}$

$3\sqrt{5}+4\sqrt{5}=7\sqrt{5}$ This is like $3a+4a=7a$

$4+5+6\sqrt{7}=9+6\sqrt{7}$ This cannot be further simplified

$(3+6\sqrt{3})+(5-2\sqrt{3}) = 3+5+6\sqrt{3}-2\sqrt{3}$ Rearrange
$= 8+4\sqrt{3}$ Combine

Multiplying Surds

$\sqrt{3}\sqrt{3}=3$ or equivalently $(\sqrt{3})^2=3$ (see Box 10, p12)

$5(2-4\sqrt{7}) = 5\times2-5\times4\sqrt{7} = 10-20\sqrt{7}$

$(5-2\sqrt{3})(4-\sqrt{3}) = 20-5\sqrt{3}-8\sqrt{3}+2\sqrt{3}\sqrt{3}$
$= 20-13\sqrt{3}+2\times3$ Since $\sqrt{3}\sqrt{3}=3$
$= 26-13\sqrt{3}$

Dividing Surds

Only simple examples will be set at this level

$\frac{6}{\sqrt{3}} = \frac{6\times\sqrt{3}}{\sqrt{3}\times\sqrt{3}}$ Multiply top and bottom by $\sqrt{3}$ to eliminate the root on the bottom

$= \frac{\cancel{6}^{2}\times\sqrt{3}}{\cancel{3}_{1}}$

$= 2\sqrt{3}$

Question *Simplify* $\sqrt{48}+2\sqrt{3}$.

$\sqrt{48}=\sqrt{16\times3}=\sqrt{16}\times\sqrt{3}=4\sqrt{3}$ (see Box 11, p34)

So, $\sqrt{48}+2\sqrt{3} = 4\sqrt{3}+2\sqrt{3} = 6\sqrt{3}$

Standard Form

1. What is Standard Form Used For?

Standard form is a convenient way of writing *very small* and *very large* numbers. It is sometimes called **standard index form** because it is based on powers of 10.

2. Multiplying Decimals by Powers of 10

Multiplying a number by a *positive* power of 10 gives a *bigger* number.

2.8×10^5

$= 280\,000$ Move the decimal point 5 places right

Multiplying a number by a *negative* power of 10 gives a *smaller* number.

2.8×10^{-5}

$= 0.000\,028$ Move the decimal point 5 places left

Question *The mass of a meteorite is* 3.61×10^7 *kg. Write this as an ordinary number.*

3.61×10^7

$= 36\,100\,000$ kg

3. Standard Form

These numbers are written in **standard form**.

2.8×10^5
1.76×10^{-5}

(Number between 1 and 10) (Power of 10)

The power of 10 is called the **order of magnitude** and indicates the overall size of the number.

The number between 1 and 10 gives more detail about the number.

NOTE The number 29.6×10^3 is ***not*** in standard form because 29.6 does not lie between 1 and 10.

4. Writing Numbers in Standard Form

Question *Write the number 150 000 in standard form*

150 000. Put in the decimal point if it is missing

1.50 000. Move the decimal point 5 places to make a number between 1 and 10

So, $150\,000 = 1.5\times10^5$ ← Number of decimal places moved
(Big number) (Positive power)

Question *Write the number 0.000 004 in standard form.*

0.000 004. Move the decimal point 6 places to make a number between 1 and 10

So, $0.000\,004 = 4\times10^{-6}$ ← Number of decimal places moved
(Small number) (Negative power)

Standard Form (Contd)

5. Comparing Numbers in Standard Form

The powers of 10 below are arranged in increasing order of size.

10^{-3}	10^{-2}	10^{-1}	10^{0}	10^{1}	10^{2}	10^{3}
$\frac{1}{1000}$	$\frac{1}{100}$	$\frac{1}{10}$	1	10	100	1000

To compare numbers in standard form, compare their powers of 10.
For example, 5.8×10^3 is bigger than 7.2×10^2 because 10^3 is bigger than 10^2.
Similarly, 2.84×10^{-1} is bigger than 9.75×10^{-3} because 10^{-1} is bigger than 10^{-3}.

Question *Place the following numbers in increasing order of magnitude (size):*

5.4×10^6 9.4×10^4 3.6×10^6 2.4×10^{-9}

The correct order is shown below

2.4×10^{-9} 9.4×10^4 3.6×10^6 5.4×10^6

Although 5.4×10^6 and 3.6×10^6 have the same power of 10, 5.4×10^6 is bigger than 3.6×10^6 because 5.4 is bigger than 3.6.

6. Standard Form and Calculators

To enter the number 5.8×10^5 into the calculator:

NOTE The EXP key is pressed *instead of* the × 1 0 keys.

To enter the number 3.4×10^{-12} into the calculator:

3 · 4 EXP 1 2 +/−   3.4 −12

NOTE The display looks like the power 3.4^{-12} but actually means 3.4×10^{-12}.

7. Standard Form and Significant Figures

Question *The mass of the Moon is 7.38×10^{19} tonnes. The mass of the Earth is 81 times the mass of the Moon. Calculate the mass of the Earth, expressing your answer in standard form correct to 2 significant figures.*

Mass of Earth = $81\times7.38\times10^{19}$

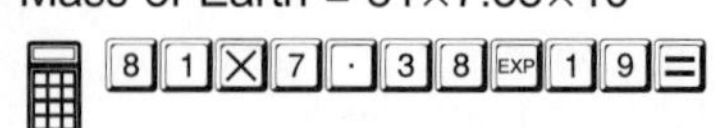

5.978 21

So, mass of Earth = 6.0×10^{21} tonnes, correct to 2 significant figures.

8. Questions Involving Standard Form

Question *The Sun is approximately 149.6 million km from the Earth.*
(a) Write this number in standard form.
(b) If light travels 1.80×10^7 km in 1 minute, how many minutes does light from the Sun take to reach the Earth? Give your answer to the nearest minute.

(a) 149.6 million = $149.6\times1\ 000\ 000$

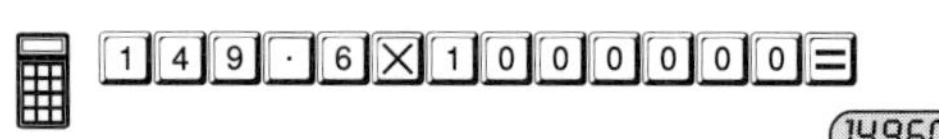

149600000

So, 149.6 million km = 149 600 000 km
= 1.496×10^8 km

(b) Number of minutes = $1.496\times10^8\div1.80\times10^7$

So, it takes approximately 8 minutes.

Question *The number 10^{100} is called a googol. Write 50 googols in standard form.*

50 googols = 50×10^{100}

Now, this number is too big for your calculator. Try pressing 5 0 EXP 1 0 0 =. A basic calculator will not have space for three-digit indices like 100. So we must do without a calculator:

$50\times10^{100} = 5\times10\times10^{100} = 5\times10^1\times10^{100}$
$= 5\times10^{1+100} = 5\times10^{101}$

Basic Algebra

1. Algebra and Arithmetic

Algebra uses the same rules as arithmetic.

Always remember that letters represent numbers.

An **algebraic expression** is any allowable combination of letters (*a, b, c, x, y, C, N*), numbers (1, 2, $\frac{1}{2}$, 5.7) and arithmetical symbols (+, ×, −, ÷, ( ), √). Here are a few simple examples:

$a+b$ Sum of the numbers a and b

$N-2$ Number 2 subtracted from the number N

$5y$ Product of 5 and y
NOTE $5y$ is an abbreviation of $5 \times y$.

ab Product of the numbers a and b
(ab is short for $a \times b$ and is the same as ba)

$\frac{m}{n}$ Number m divided by the number n
NOTE write $\frac{m}{n}$ rather than $m \div n$.

$\sqrt{n}$ Square root of the number n

$1x$ is usually written simply as x.

2. Making Algebraic Expressions

Question *Apples cost 15p each. Write down an expression for the cost of n apples.*

First, write down the expression using words.

Cost = Number of apples × Price of an apple
= $n \times 15$ pence Replace words with symbols
= $n15$ pence Omit the × sign
= $15n$ pence Write numbers before letters

Question *Mary starts with a number, x, doubles it, adds 6 and divides the result by 2. Write down an expression for the number she ends up with.*

Mary starts with x.

She doubles x to give $2x$.

Then she adds 6, giving $2x+6$ or $6+2x$

She divides the result by 2, giving $\frac{2x+6}{2}$

NOTE If you really must use the ÷ sign, this answer could also be written $(2x+6) \div 2$.
But ***not*** $2x+6 \div 2$, where only the 6 is being divided by 2

3. Powers

Powers of letters have the same meaning as powers of numbers (see Box 7, p.11 and Boxes 3, 4, 5, p.30).

Since $2^3 = 2 \times 2 \times 2$ then $a^3 = a \times a \times a$

Similarly $2^1 = 2$ and so $a^1 = a$
$2^0 = 1$ and so $a^0 = 1$
$2^{-3} = \frac{1}{2^3}$ and so $a^{-3} = \frac{1}{a^3}$

See also Box 9, p34.

4. Substituting Numbers for Letters

Replacing letters by numbers enables us to calculate the **value** of an algebraic expression.

Question *Find the value of the expression 2(b+w) given that b = 4 and w = 6.*

Replacing b by 4 and w by 6 gives

$2(b+w) = 2 \times (b+w) = 2 \times (4+6) = 2 \times (10) = 2 \times 10 = 20$

Question *Find the value of u+at given that u = 4, a = −3 and t = 2.5.*

Put negative numbers in brackets to avoid mistakes.

$u+at = u+a \times t = 4+(-3) \times 2.5 = 4+-7.5 = 4-7.5 = -3.5$
Multiply first

Question *Find the value of* $2\pi\sqrt{\frac{L}{g}}$ *when L = 15, g = 9.81.*

$2\pi\sqrt{\frac{L}{g}} = 2 \times \pi \times \sqrt{\frac{15}{9.81}} = 7.77$ (correct to 2 dp)

Start with the most difficult part of the calculation

5. Multiplying Numbers and Letters

Simplify by multiplying numbers together.

Examples

$2 \times 5a = 10a$

$-3(2xy) = -3 \times 2xy = -6xy$

Group together numbers before multiplying.

Examples

$2a3b = 2 \times a \times 3 \times b = 2 \times 3 \times a \times b = 6 \times a \times b = 6ab$

$(4pq)(-3t) = 4 \times p \times q \times -3 \times t = 4 \times -3 \times p \times q \times t = -12pqt$

Multiplying letters and numbers by 0 gives 0.

Examples

$0 \times 3 \times 2 = 0$ $0ab = 0 \times a \times b = 0$ $0(x-y) = 0$

6. Multiplying Powers

$a^2a^3 = a^2 \times a^3 = a \times a \times a \times a \times a = a^5$

So, $a^2a^3 = a^{2+3}$

RULE When **multiplying** powers of the *same* letter or number, **add** their indices.

Examples

$m^2m^3 = m^2 \times m^3 = m^{2+3} = m^5$

$xx^2x^3 = x^1x^2x^3 = x^{1+2+3} = x^6$ x can be written x^1

$v^5v^{-2} = v^{5+-2} = v^{5-2} = v^3$ Remember: +− gives −

$p^{12}p^n = p^{12+n}$

$a^2b^5a^3b^{-4} = a^2a^3b^5b^{-4}$ Group the same letters
$= a^{2+3} \times b^{5+-4}$
$= a^5b^{5-4} = a^5b^1 = a^5b$

$10^3 \times 10^5 = 10^{3+5} = 10^8$ $10^3 \times 10^{-5} = 10^{3+-5} = 10^{-2}$

Question *Without using a calculator, find the value of* $(3 \times 10^7) \times (2 \times 10^{-4})$ *in standard form.*

$(3 \times 10^7) \times (2 \times 10^{-4}) = 3 \times 2 \times 10^7 \times 10^{-4} = 6 \times 10^{7+-4} = 6 \times 10^3$

Basic Algebra (Contd)

7. Dividing Powers

Just as $\frac{\not{5}^1}{\not{5}_1} = \frac{1}{1} = 1$ so $\frac{\not{a}^1}{\not{a}_1} = \frac{1}{1} = 1$

That is, letters can also be cancelled.

So, $\frac{a^5}{a^3} = \frac{\not{a}\times\not{a}\times\not{a}\times a\times a}{\not{a}\times\not{a}\times\not{a}} = \frac{1\times1\times1\times a\times a}{1\times1\times1} = \frac{a^2}{1} = a^2$

So, $\frac{a^5}{a^3} = a^{5-3} = a^2$ or $a^5\div a^3 = a^{5-3} = a^2$

A common way of writing cancelling is: $\frac{a^{\not{5}\,2}}{a^{\not{3}}\,1} = \frac{a^2}{1} = a^2$

RULE When **dividing** powers of the *same* letter or number, **subtract** their indices.

Examples

$\frac{y^5}{y^7} = y^5\div y^7 = y^{5-7} = y^{-2}$ Which can be written $\frac{1}{y^2}$

Alternatively:

$\frac{\not{y^5}\,1}{y^{\not{7}\,2}} = \frac{1}{y^2}$ Which can be written y^{-2}

$10^{15}\div10^{11} = 10^{15-11} = 10^4$

$a^6\div a^{-2} = a^{6--2} = a^{6+2} = a^8$

Special case:

$\frac{1}{x^{-3}} = \frac{x^0}{x^{-3}} = x^{0--3} = x^{0+3} = x^3$ So, $\frac{1}{x^{-3}} = x^3$

Question *Evaluate* $\frac{1}{5^{-2}}$ *without using a calculator.*

$\frac{1}{5^{-2}} = 5^2 = 25$

8. Power of a Power

$(\text{Number})^3 = (\text{Number})\times(\text{Number})\times(\text{Number})$

So, $(a^2)^3 = (a^2)\times(a^2)\times(a^2)$
$= (a\times a)\times(a\times a)\times(a\times a)$
$= a\times a \times a\times a \times a\times a$
$= a^6$

So, $(a^2)^3 = a^{2\times3} = a^6$

RULE When a power is **raised** to a power, **multiply** the indices.

Examples

$(p^4)^{-3} = p^{4\times(-3)} = p^{-12}$

$(10^2)^3 = 10^{2\times3} = 10^6$

$(m^{12})^{\frac{3}{4}} = m^{12\times\frac{3}{4}} = m^{\frac{12}{1}\times\frac{3}{4}} = m^{\frac{36}{4}} = m^9$

9. Powers and Roots

H

Since $9^{\frac{1}{2}} = \sqrt{9}$ then $a^{\frac{1}{2}} = \sqrt{a}$ (see Box 5, p30)

Similarly, $8^{\frac{1}{3}} = \sqrt[3]{8}$ and so $a^{\frac{1}{3}} = \sqrt[3]{a}$

$8^{-\frac{1}{3}} = \frac{1}{8^{\frac{1}{3}}} = \frac{1}{\sqrt[3]{8}}$ and so $a^{-\frac{1}{3}} = \frac{1}{a^{\frac{1}{3}}} = \frac{1}{\sqrt[3]{a}}$

$8^{\frac{2}{3}} = \sqrt[3]{8^2} = (\sqrt[3]{8})^2$ and so $a^{\frac{2}{3}} = \sqrt[3]{a^2} = (\sqrt[3]{a})^2$

Replace roots by fractional powers.

Examples

$\sqrt[5]{n^2} = n^{\frac{2}{5}}$ $\sqrt{n^4} = n^{\frac{4}{2}} = n^2$ $\sqrt[4]{x^2} = x^{\frac{2}{4}} = x^{\frac{1}{2}}$

$r\sqrt{r} = r^1r^{\frac{1}{2}} = r^{1+\frac{1}{2}} = r^{1\frac{1}{2}} = r^{\frac{3}{2}}$

$\frac{x^2}{\sqrt[3]{x}} = \frac{x^2}{x^{\frac{1}{3}}} = x^2\div x^{\frac{1}{3}} = x^{2-\frac{1}{3}} = x^{\frac{5}{3}}$

$x^{\frac{1}{2}}x^{\frac{1}{3}} = x^{\frac{1}{2}+\frac{1}{3}} = x^{\frac{3}{6}+\frac{2}{6}} = x^{\frac{5}{6}}$

Special cases

$\sqrt{n^2} = n$ and $(\sqrt{n})^2 = n$

$\sqrt[3]{n^3} = n$ and $(\sqrt[3]{n})^3 = n$

Powers and roots cancel each other

10. Powers and Brackets

$(ab)^3 = (ab)\times(ab)\times(ab) = a\times b\times a\times b\times a\times b$
$= a\times a\times a\times b\times b\times b$
$= a^3b^3$

NOTE ab^3 is ***not*** $(ab)^3$ because $ab^3 = a\times b\times b\times b$.

Similarly, $\left(\frac{a}{b}\right)^3 = \frac{a^3}{b^3}$

The power of a product (or quotient) is the product (or quotient) of powers.

$(2xy)^3 = 2^3x^3y^3 = 8x^3y^3$

$(p^2q)^4 = (p^2)^4q^4 = p^{2\times4}q^4 = p^8q^4$

$(8x^6)^{\frac{1}{3}} = 8^{\frac{1}{3}}(x^6)^{\frac{1}{3}} = \sqrt[3]{8}\,x^{6\times\frac{1}{3}} = 2x^2$

11. Roots of Products and Quotients

$\sqrt{9\times16} = \sqrt{9}\times\sqrt{16} = 3\times4 = 12$

Similarly, $\sqrt{ab} = \sqrt{a}\sqrt{b}$

The root of a product (or quotient) is the product (or quotient) of roots.

Examples

$\sqrt[3]{8p^6} = \sqrt[3]{8}\sqrt[3]{p^6} = 2(p^6)^{\frac{1}{3}} = 2p^{6\times\frac{1}{3}} = 2p^2$

$\sqrt{9x^2y^4} = \sqrt{9}\sqrt{x^2}\sqrt{y^4} = 3(x^2)^{\frac{1}{2}}(y^4)^{\frac{1}{2}} = 3x^1y^2 = 3xy^2$

$\sqrt[4]{\frac{m^8}{16}} = \frac{\sqrt[4]{m^8}}{\sqrt[4]{16}} = \frac{(m^8)^{\frac{1}{4}}}{2} = \frac{m^{8\times\frac{1}{4}}}{2} = \frac{m^2}{2}$

12. Index Equations

If two powers are equal, their indices are also equal.

Question *Find n when* $(x^n)^2 = \frac{1}{x^4}$.

$(x^n)^2 = x^{2n}$ and $\frac{1}{x^4} = x^{-4}$ and so $x^{2n} = x^{-4}$

For the powers x^{2n} and x^{-4} to be equal, their indices $2n$ and -4 must also be equal, i.e. $2n = -4$, so $n = -2$.

13. Terms of an Algebraic Expression

Terms are algebraic quantities that are separated from each other by + or – signs.

$2x^2-3x+4$ — Terms

$\frac{2a}{3}+a-4b$ — Terms

Like terms are multiples of the same algebraic quantity.

$a \quad 2a \quad 3a \quad \frac{1}{2}a$ — Like terms

$2xy \quad 3xy \quad \frac{3xy}{2}$ — Like terms

$3p \quad 2q \quad 5x \quad 7$ — Unlike terms

$1 \quad x \quad x^2 \quad x^3$ — Unlike terms

Like terms can be combined into a single term.

Examples

$2a+3a = 5a$

$4p-7p = -3p$ Because $4-7 = -3$

$5x+2+3x+4 = 5x+3x+2+4$ Group like terms

$= 8x+6$ Combine like terms

NOTE $8x+6$ cannot be simplified any further.

$2p-3q-7p+q = 2p-7p-3q+1q = -5p-2q$

$5x^2+7x-2x^2+4 = 5x^2-2x^2+7x+4 = 3x^2+7x+4$

14. Simplifying Algebraic Expressions

To **simplify** an algebraic expression means to combine terms and powers where possible. This usually results in a shorter expression.

Question *Simplify* $(3x)^2+4x-2x^2+x$ *as far as possible.*

$(3x)^2+4x-2x^2+x$

$= 3^2x^2+4x-2x^2+x$ Power of a bracket

$= 9x^2-2x^2+4x+1x$ Group like terms

$= 7x^2+5x$ Combine like terms

Question *Simplify* $(ab)^2+a^2b+4a^2b^2-3a(ba)+ab^2$

$(ab)^2+a^2b+4a^2b^2-3a(ba)+ab^2$

$= a^2b^2+a^2b+4a^2b^2-3aba+ab^2$ See Box 10, p34

$= 1a^2b^2+4a^2b^2-3aab+a^2b+ab^2$ Group like terms

$= 5a^2b^2-3a^2b+1a^2b+ab^2$ Combine terms

$= 5a^2b^2-2a^2b+ab^2$ Combine terms

Question *Simplify* $\frac{3}{6a}$.

$\frac{3}{6a} = \frac{\not{3}^1}{{}_2\not{6}a} = \frac{1}{2a}$ Cancel numbers

Question *Simplify* $\frac{4a^3b^2}{6ab^4}$.

$\frac{4a^3b^2}{6ab^4} = \frac{{}^2\not{4}a^3b^2}{{}_3\not{6}a^1b^4} = \frac{2a^{\not{3}2}\not{b^2}}{3\not{a}^1b^{\not{4}2}} = \frac{2a^2}{3b^2}$ Cancel numbers and powers

Question *Simplify* $(6p^2q)(2pq)^2$.

$(6p^2q)(2pq)^2$

$= 6p^2q^1\times2^2p^2q^2$ Power of a bracket

$= 6\times2^2\times p^2\times p^2\times q^1\times q^2$ Rearrange

$= 6\times4\times p^{2+2}q^{1+2}$ Combine powers

$= 24p^4q^3$

15. More Difficult Questions

H

Question *The algebraic expression* $2\pi\sqrt{\frac{L}{g}}$ *can be written in the form* kL^x*. Find the values of k and x given that g = 9.81.*

$2\pi\sqrt{\frac{L}{g}} = 2\times\pi\times\sqrt{\frac{L}{9.81}}$ Replace g by 9.81

$= 2\times\pi\times\frac{\sqrt{L}}{\sqrt{9.81}}$ Root of a quotient (see Box 11, p34)

$= 2\times\pi\times\frac{L^{\frac{1}{2}}}{3.13}$ Change root to a power

$= 2\times\pi\div3.13\,L^{\frac{1}{2}}$ Combine numbers

$= 2.01\,L^{0.5}$

So, $k = 2.01$ and $x = 0.5$.

Question *Given* $v = 3.2\times10^{-1}$ *calculate the value of the algebraic expression* $\frac{2\pi}{\sqrt{1-v^2}}$ *correct to 2dp.*

$\frac{2\pi}{\sqrt{1-v^2}} = \frac{2\times\pi}{\sqrt{1-(3.2\times10^{-1})^2}} = 6.63$ (6.6319073)

1 − 3 · 2 EXP 1 +/- x² = √ Min 2 × π = ÷ MR =

Calculate the denominator and store it in the memory

Calculate the numerator and divide by the recalled denominator

Question *The formula for the population, P, of mice with a growth rate of r% per year, in time t months, is given by the formula*

$$P = P_0\left(1+\frac{r}{100}\right)^t$$

where P_0 *is the population this month. Calculate the population of mice in 6 months given that the population this month is 24 and the growth rate is 12% per month.*

The question tells us that $P_0 = 24$, $t = 6$ and $r = 12$.

Substitute these values into the formula:

$P = P_0\left(1+\frac{r}{100}\right)^t = 24\left(1+\frac{12}{100}\right)^6 = 47.37 \approx 47$

(47.371745)

The population will have 47 mice in 6 months time.

Question *Find the value of y for which* $2\times4^y = 64$.

Notice that the numbers 2, 4 and 64 are all powers of 2, i.e. $2 = 2^1$, $4 = 2^2$ and $64 = 2^6$. So we can rewrite the equation using powers of 2:

$2\times4^y = 64$

$\therefore 2^1\times(2^2)^y = 2^6$ Rewrite using powers of 2

$\therefore 2^1\times2^{2y} = 2^6$ Power of a power: multiply indices

$\therefore 2^{1+2y} = 2^6$ Multiplying powers: add indices

$\therefore 1+2y = 6$ Indices are equal

$\therefore 2y = 5$

$\therefore y = \frac{5}{2} = 2.5$

Equations

1. Equations

$$1+2+3 = 6$$

This is an **equation** and tells us that the sum 1+2+3 is equal to the number 6.

An equation can be thought of as a balanced pair of weighing scales, with numbers as weights.

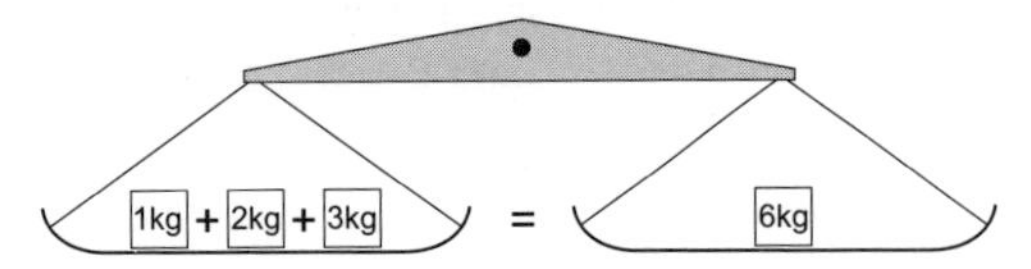

If we change one side of an equation, we must change the other side in exactly the same way in order for the equation to remain true.

For example, if we add 4 to the left-hand side (LHS) we must also add 4 to the right-hand side (RHS):

$$1+2+3+4 = 6+4$$

The scales are still balanced (the equation is still true).

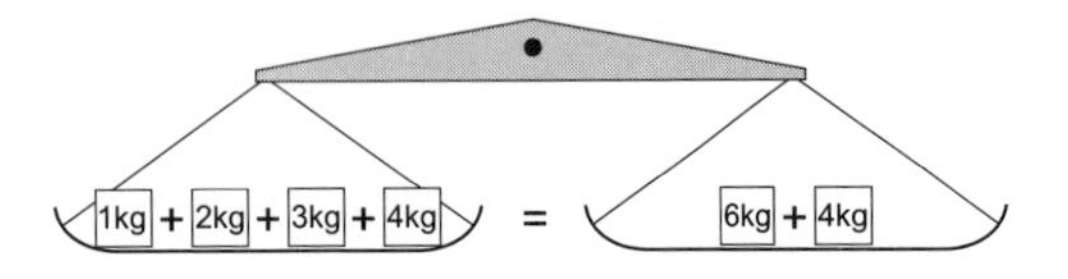

2. Solving Equations

$$x+2 = 5$$

This equation involves an **unknown** number x. **Solving** the equation means finding the number x which makes it true. The scales below show that x must be 3. So we can write $x = 3$.

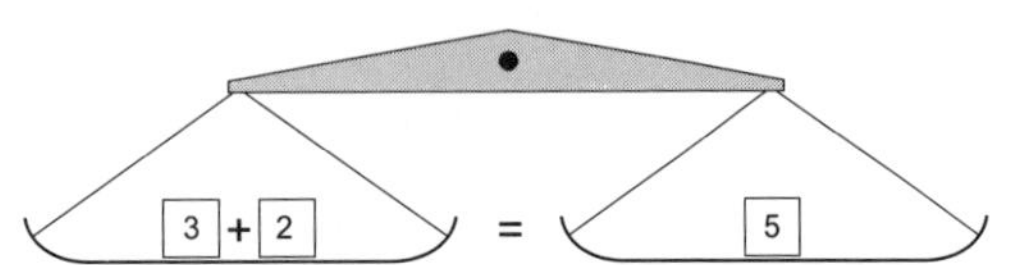

We say that $x = 3$ is the **solution** of the equation. We also say that $x = 3$ **satisfies** the equation.

3. Equations Requiring Addition or Subtraction

Question *Solve the equation $x+2 = 5$.*

The aim is to find the number x which makes the equation true. We do this by changing both sides of the equation until we get x = *number*.

$x+2 = 5$	Write down the equation
$\therefore x+2-2 = 5-2$	Subtract 2 from *both* sides,
$\therefore x+\cancel{2}-\cancel{2} = 5-2$	to leave x on its own
$\therefore x = 5-2$	Simplify RHS, to give the solution
$\therefore x = 3$	

The sign ∴ means **therefore** and shows that the current line follows from the previous line

more

3. Equations Requiring Addition or Subtraction (Contd)

In practice, we simply move the +2 to the RHS and change it to −2

$x+2 = 5$	Rewrite the equation each time
$\therefore x = 5-2$	you change it. Write each equation
$\therefore x = 3$	on a new line if there is space

Question *Solve the equation $5 = y-2$.*

$5 = y-2$	Write down the equation
$\therefore 5+2 = y$	Move −2 to LHS and change it
$\therefore 7 = y$	to +2. Simplify LHS
$\therefore y = 7$	Turn the answer around. It does not matter which way around you write an equation

Question *Solve the equation $2+T = 7$.*

$2+T = 7$	2 is another way of writing +2 and
$\therefore T = 7-2$	so it changes to −2 when it moves
$\therefore T = 5$	to RHS

4. Equations Requiring Division

Question *Solve the equation $5x = 35$.*

The 5 multiplies the number x. So we must divide both sides by 5 to cancel it out, leaving x on its own.

$5x = 35$	Write down the equation
$\therefore \frac{5x}{5} = \frac{35}{5}$	Divide both sides by 5
$\therefore \frac{\cancel{5}x}{\cancel{5}} = \frac{35}{5}$	Cancel
$\therefore x = \frac{35}{5}$	Simplify RHS
$\therefore x = 7$	

In practice, we simply move the 5× to the RHS and change it to ÷5.

$5x = 35$	Move the 5× to RHS ....
$\therefore x = \frac{35}{5}$	.... and change it to ÷5
$\therefore x = 7$	

Question *Solve the equation $-4p = 7$.*

The negative number −4 is *multiplying* the number p (there is no subtraction on the LHS).

$-4p = 7$	Move the −4× to RHS ....
$\therefore p = \frac{7}{-4}$	.... and change it to ÷(−4)
$\therefore p = -1.75$	

Question *Solve the equation $\frac{1}{4}m = 2$.*

$\frac{1}{4}m = 2$	Move the $\frac{1}{4}$× to RHS ....
$\therefore m = 2 \div \frac{1}{4}$	.... and change it to $\div\frac{1}{4}$
$\therefore m = 2 \times 4$	
$\therefore m = 8$	

5. Equations Requiring Multiplication

Question *Solve the equation* $\frac{x}{2} = 7$

The 2 divides the number x. So we must multiply both sides by 2 to cancel it out, leaving x on its own.

$\frac{x}{2} = 7$	Write down the equation
$\therefore 2\times\frac{x}{2} = 2\times7$	Multiply both sides by 2
$\therefore \cancel{2}\times\frac{x}{\cancel{2}} = 2\times7$	Cancel
$\therefore x = 2\times7$	Simplify
$\therefore x = 14$	

In practice, we simply move the $\div2$ to the RHS and change it to $\times2$.

$\frac{x}{2} = 7$	Move $\div2$ to the other side ....
$\therefore x = 7\times2$	.... changing to $\times2$
$\therefore x = 14$	

6. Equations Requiring Multiplication and Division

Question *Solve the equation* $\frac{3t}{4} = 2$.

The 3 multiplies the number t and the 4 divides it. Moving the $3\times$ and the $\div4$ to the RHS changes them to $\div3$ and $\times4$, leaving t on its own.

$\frac{3t}{4} = 2$	Move $3\times$ and $\div4$ to RHS ....
$\therefore t = \frac{2\times4}{3}$	.... changing to $\div3$ and $\times4$
$\therefore t = \frac{8}{3}$	Simplify
$\therefore t = 2\frac{2}{3}$	

Cross Multiplying

Cross multiplying is a quick way of solving equations where one fraction equals another

Question *Solve the equation* $\frac{2p}{3} = \frac{5}{6}$.

$\frac{2p}{3} \times \frac{5}{6}$	Cross multiply
$\therefore 2p\times6 = 3\times5$	
$\therefore 12p = 15$	Simplify. Move $12\times$ to RHS ....
$\therefore p = \frac{\cancel{15}^{5}}{\cancel{12}_{4}}$	.... changing to $\div12$. Cancel
$\therefore p = \frac{5}{4}$	Simplify
$\therefore p = 1\frac{1}{4}$	

7. Equations Requiring Addition, Subtraction, Multiplication, Division

RULE Add and subtract numbers from both sides before multiplying and dividing.

Question *Solve the equation* $3y+2 = 11$.

$3y+2 = 11$	Move +2 to RHS and change it to −2.
$\therefore 3y = 11-2$	
$\therefore 3y = 9$	Simplify. Move $3\times$ to RHS ...
$\therefore y = \frac{9}{3}$	... and change it to $\div3$
$\therefore y = 3$	Simplify

Question *Solve the equation* $\frac{3x}{2} - 5 = 1$.

$\frac{3x}{2} - 5 = 1$	Move −5 to RHS ....
$\therefore \frac{3x}{2} = 1+5$	.... and change it to +5. Simplify
$\therefore \frac{3x}{2} = 6$	Move $3\times$ and $\div2$ to RHS ....
$\therefore x = \frac{2\times6}{3}$	.... and change to $\div3$ and $\times2$
$\therefore x = \frac{12}{3}$	Simplify
$\therefore x = 4$	

8. Equations with the Unknown in the Denominator

Question *Solve the equation* $\frac{3}{t} = 8$.

The 3 is divided by t. So we must move the $\div t$ to the RHS and change it to $\times t$.

$\frac{3}{t} = 8$	Move $\div t$ to RHS ....
$\therefore 3 = 8\times t$	.... and change it to $\times t$
$\therefore \frac{3}{8} = t$	Now move $8\times$ to LHS and change it to $\div8$
$\therefore t = \frac{3}{8}$	Turn the equation around

9. Equations Involving −*x*

Question *Solve the equation* $-x = 5$.

Here we need to eliminate the minus sign. The trick is to multiply both sides by −1.

$-x = 5$	
$\therefore -1\times-x = -1\times5$	Multiply both sides by −1
$\therefore +x = -5$	Remember: $-\times- = +$
$\therefore x = -5$	$+x$ can be written as x

A quicker method is to put a minus sign in front of the LHS and RHS.

$-x = 5$	
$\therefore --x = -5$	Put a minus sign on both sides
$\therefore +x = -5$	Remember: $-- = +$
$\therefore x = -5$	$+x$ can be written as x

Equations (Contd)

10. Terms of an Equation

The **terms** of an equation are separated from each other by +, − and = signs.

$3x + 2 = 5$ (Terms: $3x$, 2, 5)

$\frac{5t}{6} - 4 = \frac{3}{5}$ (Terms: $\frac{5t}{6}$, 4, $\frac{3}{5}$)

11. Rearranging Terms of an Equation

Question *Solve the equation* $3x+2x = 10$.

$3x+2x = 10$	Combine the x-terms
$\therefore 5x = 10$	Move the 5× to RHS ....
$\therefore x = \frac{10}{5}$	.... changing it to ÷5
$\therefore x = 2$	

Question *Solve the equation* $9x+6 = 30-3x$.

Move all the x-terms to one side and all the number terms to the other side.

$9x+6 = 30-3x$	Move $-3x$ to LHS and ....
$\therefore 9x+6+3x = 30$	.... change it to $+3x$. Move $+6$
$\therefore 9x+3x = 30-6$	to RHS and change it to -6
$\therefore 12x = 24$	Combine terms
$\therefore x = \frac{24}{12}$	
$\therefore x = 2$	

12. Using Equations to Solve Problems

Question *Pencils cost 15 pence each and erasers cost 20 pence each. Paul buys n pencils and 2n erasers, costing £2.20 altogether. Write down an equation in n and solve it to find the number of pencils and erasers Paul bought.*

Write down the equation using words first. Then replace the words by symbols.

Cost of pencils + Cost of erasers = £2.20

Now, cost of pencils = Number × Price
= $n \times 15$ pence = $15n$ pence

and cost of erasers = Number × Price
= $2n \times 20$ pence = $40n$ pence

The equation can now be written using algebra:

$15n$ pence $+ 40n$ pence = £2.20

Convert £ to pence, to make all the units the same:

$15n$ pence + $40n$ pence = 220 pence

Now we can leave out the units (pence):

$15n+40n = 220$

$\therefore 55n = 220$

$\therefore n = \frac{220}{55}$

$\therefore n = 4$

So, Paul bought 4 pencils and $2 \times n = 2 \times 4 = 8$ erasers

Formulas

1. Formulas

A **formula** is an equation involving several letters, each letter representing a different quantity. For example, the formula connecting speed (s), distance (d) and time (t) is:

$$s = \frac{d}{t}$$

The letter, s, on the LHS of a formula is called the **subject** of the formula. We say that s is **expressed in terms of *d* and *t***.

2. Making Formulas

You may be asked to find the formula connecting the quantities involved in a real situation (see also Box 12 above).

Question *Snak Bars cost 26 pence each. Write down the cost, C pence, of n Snak Bars.*

Write down the formula in words first:

Cost = Number of bars × Price of a Snak Bar

Now replace the words by letters:

C pence = $n \times 26$ pence

$\therefore C = n \times 26$	Drop the units, pence
$\therefore C = 26n$	

3. Replacing Letters by Numbers (Substitution)

Question *The formula below can be used to convert temperatures measured in degrees Celsius (°C) into degrees Fahrenheit (°F)*

$$F = \frac{9}{5}C + 32$$

(a) Convert 25 °C to Fahrenheit.
(b) Convert −4 °F to Celsius.

(a) Replace C by 25 in the formula (this is called **substitution**).

$F = \frac{9}{5}C+32$	Replace C by 25
$F = \frac{9}{5} \times 25+32$	
$= 45+32$	
$= 77$	

So, 25 °C is equivalent to 77 °F.

(b) Replace F by −4 in the formula:

$F = \frac{9}{5}C+32$	
$-4 = \frac{9}{5}C+32$	Solve equation to find C
$\therefore -4-32 = \frac{9}{5}C$	

more

3. Replacing Letters by Numbers (Contd)

$\therefore -36 = \frac{9}{5}C$

$\therefore \frac{-36 \times 5}{9} = C$

$\therefore -20 = C$

$\therefore C = -20$

So, −4 °F is equivalent to −20 °C.

4. Rearranging Formulas

Formulas can be rearranged (**transposed**) using the same methods as for equations.

Question *Rearrange the formula $F = 25G+250$ to make G the subject.*

We must rearrange the formula to get G on its own on the LHS:

$F = 25G+250$	Turn the formula around
$\therefore 25G+250 = F$	Move 250 to RHS
$\therefore 25G = F-250$	Move 25× to RHS ....
$\therefore G = \frac{F-250}{25}$	.... changing to ÷25

G is now the subject, on its own on the LHS.

NOTE Don't use the ÷ sign when rearranging equations and formulas. Use a dividing line, as in the above example.

Question *Transpose the formula $v = u+at$ to make t the subject.*

$v = u+at$	
$\therefore u+at = v$	Turn the formula around
$\therefore at = v-u$	Move u to RHS, changing to $-u$
$\therefore t = \frac{v-u}{a}$	Move $a\times$ to RHS, changing to $\div a$

Question *Given that $T = \frac{\lambda x}{L}$, express x in terms of λ, T and L.*

$T = \frac{\lambda x}{L}$	
$\therefore \frac{\lambda x}{L} = T$	Turn formula around to get x on LHS
$\therefore \lambda x = TL$	Move $\div L$ to RHS, changing to $\times L$
$\therefore x = \frac{TL}{\lambda}$	Move $\lambda\times$ to RHS, changing to $\div\lambda$

Question *Make A the subject of the formula $\frac{1}{A} + B = C$.*

$\frac{1}{A} + B = C$	
$\therefore \frac{1}{A} = C-B$	Move $+B$ to RHS, changing to $-B$
$\therefore \frac{1}{A} = \frac{C-B}{1}$	Make RHS a fraction
$\therefore \frac{A}{1} = \frac{1}{C-B}$	Turn both sides upside down
$\therefore A = \frac{1}{C-B}$	

5. Equations and Formulas Involving Powers and Roots

When rearranging formulas that involve powers or roots, remember that powers and roots cancel each other out, e.g. squaring cancels out a square root.

Question *Find the value of n if $\sqrt{4n} = 5$.*

$\sqrt{4n} = 5$	
$\therefore (\sqrt{4n})^2 = 5^2$	Square both sides to eliminate
$\therefore 4n = 25$	square root
$\therefore n = \frac{25}{4}$	
$\therefore n = 6.25$	

Question *Make M the subject of the formula $F = \sqrt{3M}$.*

$F = \sqrt{3M}$	
$\therefore F^2 = (\sqrt{3M})^2$	Square both sides to cancel
$\therefore F^2 = 3M$	out the square root
$\therefore 3M = F^2$	Turn the equation around
$\therefore M = \frac{F^2}{3}$	

Question *The time, T, for a pendulum of length, L, to swing back and forth once is given by the formula $T = 2\pi\sqrt{\frac{L}{g}}$. Express L in terms of T and g.*

$T = 2\pi\sqrt{\frac{L}{g}}$	
$\therefore T^2 = 2^2\pi^2\left(\sqrt{\frac{L}{g}}\right)^2$	Square *all* of RHS
$\therefore T^2 = 4\pi^2\frac{L}{g}$	Move g and $4\pi^2$ to LHS
$\therefore \frac{T^2g}{4\pi^2} = L$	
$\therefore L = \frac{T^2g}{4\pi^2}$	Turn the equation around

Question *The volume, V, of a sphere is given by the formula $V = \frac{4}{3}\pi r^3$.*

(a) Rearrange the formula to express r in terms of V.

(b) Find the radius of a sphere whose volume is 54 cm^3, correct to 2 decimal places.

(a) $V = \frac{4}{3}\pi r^3$

$\therefore \frac{4}{3}\pi r^3 = V$	Turn the equation around
$\therefore r^3 = \frac{3V}{4\pi}$	Move 4π and 3 to RHS
$\therefore \sqrt[3]{r^3} = \sqrt[3]{\frac{3V}{4\pi}}$	Take 3rd root of both sides
$\therefore r = \sqrt[3]{\frac{3V}{4\pi}}$	

(b) Put $V = 54$ in the formula:

$\therefore r = \sqrt[3]{\frac{3\times54}{4\pi}} = 2.34$ cm

2.3447779

Expanding Brackets and Factorisation

1. Expanding Brackets

To **expand** brackets means to remove them.

We have already done this in arithmetic using the BoDMAS rule

$5(3+4) = 5\times(3+4) = 5\times(7) = 5\times7 = 35$

Calculate bracket first — Drop bracket

You can get the same answer by multiplying each number in the bracket by 5.

$5(3+4) = 5\times(3+4) = 5\times3 + 5\times4 = 15+20 = 35$

Similarly

$6(5-3) = 6\times(5-3) = 6\times5 - 6\times3 = 30-18 = 12$

This method can also be used to expand brackets in algebra.

$5(a+3) = 5\times(a+3) = 5\times a + 5\times3 = 5a+15$

Simplify the result after expanding.

Examples

$y(y-4) = y\times y - y\times4 = y^2-4y$

$2m(3m+4) = 2m\times3m + 2m\times4 = 6m^2+8m$

$\frac{1}{2}(4p+6) = \frac{1}{2}\times4p+\frac{1}{2}\times6 = 2p+3$

Question *Expand and simplify $2(x-3)+4(2x+1)$.*

$2(x-3)+4(2x+1)$

$= 2x-6+8x+4$ — Expand both brackets

$= 2x+8x+4-6$ — Group like terms

$= 10x-2$ — Combine terms

When multiplying a bracket by a negative number, use these rules: $- - = +$, $- \times - = +$, $- + = -$, $- \times + = -$

Examples

$-2(a+3) = -2\times a + -2\times3$ — Expand bracket

$= -2a+-6$ — Use the rule $-\times+ = -$

$= -2a-6$ — Use the rule $+- = -$

$-y(1-y) = -y\times1 - -y\times y$ — Expand bracket

$= -1y--y^2$ — Use the rule $-\times+ = -$

$= -y+y^2$ — Use the rule $-- = +$

$-(a-b) = -a--b$ — Expand bracket

$= -a+b$

NOTE The above example shows that a minus sign before a bracket changes the signs of the terms in the bracket, e.g. $-(-2-x) = +2+x$

Question *Expand and simplify $8y-2(1-3y)$*

$8y-2(1-3y)$

$= 8y-2\times1--2\times3y$ — Expand bracket

$= 8y-2+6y$

$= 14y-2$

Question *Expand and simplify $4t(t+1)-t(4t-1)$.*

$4t(t+1)-t(4t-1)$

$= 4tt+4t1-t4t--t1$ — Expand both brackets

$= 4t^2+4t-4tt+t$ — Use the rule $-- = +$

$= \cancel{4t^2}+4t-\cancel{4t^2}+t$ — Cancel

$= 4t+t$

$= 5t$

2. Equations and Formulas Involving Brackets

Question *Solve the equation $3(2x-1) = 2(x-4)$.*

$3(2x-1) = 2(x-4)$

$\therefore 6x-3 = 2x-8$ — Expand brackets

$\therefore 6x-2x = -8+3$ — Rearrange terms

$\therefore 4x = -5$ — Simplify

$\therefore x = \frac{-5}{4}$ — Remember that $-\div+ = -$

$\therefore x = -\frac{5}{4}$ (or -1.25)

Question *Paper cups cost n pence each. Paper plates cost 2 pence more.*

(a) Write down an algebraic expression for the price of a plate in terms of n.

(b) George bought 4 cups and 2 plates for 34 pence. Write down an equation in n.

(c) Solve your equation to find the value of n.

(d) State the price of a cup and the price of a plate.

(a) Cup price = n pence

Plate price = Cup price + 2 pence

= n pence + 2 pence

= $(n+2)$ pence

Use brackets to contain the number of pence

(b) 4 cups plus 2 plates cost 34 pence

$\therefore$ $4\times n$ pence + $2\times(n+2)$ pence = 34 pence

$\therefore 4\times n + 2\times(n+2) = 34$ — Leave out the units

$\therefore 4n + 2(n+2) = 34$

(c) $\therefore 4n+2n+4 = 34$ — Expand brackets

$\therefore 6n+4 = 34$ — Simplify

$\therefore 6n = 34-4$ — Rearrange terms

$\therefore 6n = 30$ — Simplify

$\therefore n = 5$

(d) Price of cup = n pence = 5 pence

Price of plate = $(n+2)$ pence = $(5+2)$ pence = 7 pence

Question *Rearrange the formula $P = 2(L+B)$ to make L the subject.*

Method 1

$P = 2(L+B)$

$\therefore 2(L+B) = P$ — Turn the formula around

$\therefore 2L+2B = P$ — Expand bracket

$\therefore 2L = P-2B$ — Rearrange terms

$\therefore L = \frac{P-2B}{2}$ — Move $2\times$ to RHS, changing to $\div2$

Method 2

$P = 2(L+B)$

$\therefore 2(L+B) = P$ — Turn formula around

$\therefore 2\times(L+B) = P$ — Move $2\times$ to RHS ....

$\therefore (L+B) = \frac{P}{2}$ — .... changing to $\div2$

$\therefore L+B = \frac{P}{2}$ — Drop the bracket

$\therefore L = \frac{P}{2} - B$

NOTE These two methods give the same formula, even though they look different; one is a rearrangement of the other.

3. Multiplying Two Brackets

We do this in arithmetic using the BoDMAS rule:

$(5+2)(3+4) = (5+2)\times(3+4) = (7)\times(7) = 7\times7 = 49$

Calculate brackets first — Drop brackets

We can get the same answer by using each number in the first bracket to multiply the second bracket:

$(5+2)(3+4) = 5\times(3+4) + 2\times(3+4)$
$= 5\times3+5\times4 + 2\times3+2\times4$
$= 15+20+6+8$
$= 49$

Another way is to multiply each number in the first bracket by each number in the second bracket:

$(5+2)(3+4) = 5\times3+5\times4+2\times3+2\times4 = 15+20+6+8 = 49$

These methods can also be used to expand brackets in algebra.

Examples

$(a+2)(b+c)$	a and 2 multiply bracket $(b+c)$
$= a(b+c)+2(b+c)$	
$= ab+ac+2b+2c$	Expand brackets
$(x+3)(x+4)$	x and 3 multiply bracket $(x+4)$
$= x(x+4)+3(x+4)$	
$= xx+x4+3x+3\times4$	Expand brackets
$= x^2+4x+3x+12$	Simplify
$= x^2+7x+12$	Simplify
$(y-3)(y-2)$	y and -3 multiply $(y-2)$
$= y(y-2)-3(y-2)$	
$= yy-y2-3y--3\times2$	Expand brackets
$= y^2-2y-3y+6$	Simplify
$= y^2-5y+6$	Simplify

4. Squaring Brackets

$(x+3)^2$ means $(x+3)(x+3)$ and so

$(x+3)^2 = (x+3)(x+3)$
$= x(x+3)+3(x+3)$
$= xx+x3+3x+3\times3$
$= x^2+3x+3x+9$
$= x^2+6x+9$

Examples

$(y-4)^2 = (y-4)(y-4)$
$= y(y-4)-4(y-4)$
$= yy-y4-4y--4\times4$
$= y^2-4y-4y+16$
$= y^2-8y+16$

$(3a+2)^2 = (3a+2)(3a+2)$
$= 3a(3a+2)+2(3a+2)$
$= 3a3a+3a2+2\times3a+2\times2$
$= 3\times3aa+3\times2a+6a+4$
$= 9a^2+6a+6a+4$
$= 9a^2+12a+4$

Question *Simplify* $(x+3)^2-x^2$.

$(x+3)^2-x^2 = (x+3)(x+3)-x^2$
$= x(x+3)+3(x+3)-x^2$
$= x^2+3x+3x+9-x^2$
$= x^2-x^2+3x+3x+9$
$= 3x+3x+9$
$= 6x+9$

5. Factors of an Algebraic Expression

Every number can be expressed as a product of its prime factors (see also Box 15, p12).

For example: $12 = 2\times2\times3$ (Prime factors)

We can find the highest common factor of two numbers using this method. For example, to find the highest common factor of 12 and 18:

$12 = 2\times2\times3$
$18 = 2\times3\times3$

Common prime factors are 2 and 3.
So, HCF $= 2\times3 = 6$

Some algebraic expressions can also be **broken down** into their constituent parts.

For example: $12a = 2\times2\times3\times a$
$9tw = 3\times3\times t\times w$
$10p^2q = 2\times5\times p\times p\times q$

This helps us to find the highest common factor of two algebraic expressions, such as $4ab$ and $6ac$.

$4ab = 2\times2\times a\times b$
$6ac = 2\times3\times a\times c$

The common factors are 2 and a.
So, the HCF $= 2\times a = 2a$

Question *Find the highest common factor of* $6y^2$ *and* $8y$.

$6y^2 = 2\times3\times y\times y$
$8y = 2\times2\times2\times y$

The common factors are 2 and y.
So, the HCF $= 2\times y = 2y$

Question *Find the highest common factor of 12 and* $4x$.

$12 = 2\times2\times3$
$4x = 2\times2\times x$

The common factors are 2 and 2.
So, the HCF $= 2\times2 = 4$

6. Factorisation

Expanding removes brackets. **Factorising** does the opposite by *inserting* brackets. For example:

expanding $3(a+b)$ gives $3a+3b$, whereas factorising $3a+3b$ gives $3(a+b)$

Question *Factorise* $4a+6$.

① Find the HCF of the terms $4a$ and 6:

$4a = 2\times2\times a$
$6 = 2\times3$
HCF = 2

② Write down the HCF multiplying an empty bracket:

$4a+6 = 2(\ \ +\ \ )$

③ Remove the HCF from the original terms and put what is left in the bracket:

$4a = 2\times2\times a$ leaves $2a$
$6 = 2\times3$ leaves 3

So, $4a+6 = 2(2a+3)$

NOTE $2(2a+3)$ is the answer to the question.

④ Check your answer by expanding the bracket. You should get back to where you started from:

$2(2a+3) = 2\times2a+2\times3 = 4a+6$ ✓

more

Expanding Brackets and Factorisation (Contd)

6. Factorisation (Contd)

Question *Factorise $2a-6a^2$.*

$2a = 2 \times a$
$-6a^2 = -2 \times 3 \times a \times a$ HCF $= 2\times a = 2a$

Notice that the HCF is the same as one of the terms.

So, $2a-6a^2 = 2a\,(1-3a)$

HCF Must be 1 here so that $2a\times 1 = 2a$

Check: $2a(1-3a) = 2a\times 1-2a\times 3a = 2a-6a^2$ ✓

Question *Factorise $-12-8b$.*

$-12 = -2\times 2\times 3$
$-8b = -2\times 2\times 2\times b$ HCF $= -2\times 2 = -4$

So, $-12-8b = -4(3+2b)$

Check: $-4(3+2b) = -4\times 3+-4\times 2b = -12-8b$ ✓

7. Factorising Quadratic Expressions

A **quadratic** expression contains x^2 as its highest power. Here are the different types:

$5x^2$	Contains just an x^2-term
$10x^2-15x$	Contains an x^2-term and an x-term
$4x^2-9$	Contains an x^2-term and a number term
x^2+5x+4	Contains an x^2-term, x-term and number term

The last three types can sometimes be factorised.

Expressions with an x^2-term and x-term

To factorise $10x^2-15x$, use the same method as shown in Box 6.

$10x^2 = 2\times 5\times x\times x$
$-15x = -3\times 5\times x$ HCF $= 5\times x = 5x$

So, $10x^2-15x = 5x(2x-3)$

Check: $5x(2x-3) = 5x\times 2x-5x\times 3 = 10x^2-15x$ ✓

Expressions with an x^2-term and a number term

To factorise $4x^2-9$:

Notice that 4, x^2 and 9 are squares, i.e. $4 = 2^2$, x^2 and then $9 = 3^2$.

① Write each term as the square of a quantity:

$4x^2 = 2x\times 2x = (2x)^2$
$9 = 3^2$

② Write down the product of two brackets that contain the sum and difference of these quantities:

$4x^2-9 = (2x)^2-3^2 = (2x+3)(2x-3)$ (Sum, Difference)

③ Check by expanding the brackets:

$(2x+3)(2x-3) = 2x(2x-3)+3(2x-3)$
$= 2x\times 2x-2x\times 3+3\times 2x-3\times 3$
$= 4x^2-6x+6x-9$
$= 4x^2-9$ ✓

NOTE $(2x)^2-3^2$ is called the **difference of two squares**.

For any two squares a^2 and b^2, we have the general result:

$a^2-b^2 = (a+b)(a-b)$

more

7. Factorising Quadratic Expressions (Contd)

Question *Factorise $9x^2-16y^2$.*

$9x^2-16y^2 = 3^2x^2-4^2y^2 = (3x)^2-(4y)^2 = (3x+4y)(3x-4y)$

Compare with result: $a^2 - b^2 = (a+b)(a-b)$

Question *Factorise a^4-25.*

$a^4-25 = (a^2)^2-5^2 = (a^2+5)(a^2-5)$

Question *Factorise $18-2t^2$.*

Notice that 18 and $-2t^2$ have a common factor, 2. Take out this common factor first:

$18-2t^2 = 2(9-t^2) = 2(3^2-t^2) = 2(3-t)(3+t)$

Expressions with an x^2-term, x-term and a number term

To factorise x^2+5x+4.

① Write down two empty brackets:

( )( )

② Fill in the first term of each bracket so that their product is the x-term (there may be several alternatives):

$(x\ \ )(x\ \ )$ Because $x\times x = x^2$

③ Fill in the last term of each bracket so that their product is the number term (there may be several alternatives):

$(x+2)(x+2)$ Because $2\times 2 = 4$
or $(x+4)(x+1)$ Because $4\times 1 = 4$

④ Expand the brackets to find which gives the original quadratic expression:

$(x+2)(x+2) = x(x+2)+2(x+2)$
$= xx+x2+2x+2\times 2$
$= x^2+2x+2x+4$
$= x^2+4x+4$ ✗

$(x+4)(x+1) = x(x+1)+4(x+1)$
$= xx+x1+4x+4\times 1$
$= x^2+1x+4x+4$
$= x^2+5x+4$ ✓

⑤ Write down your answer:

$x^2+5x+4 = (x+4)(x+1)$

Question *Factorise $2x^2+5x-3$.*

② $(2x\ \ )(x\ \ )$ Because $2x\times x = 2x^2$

③ $(2x+3)(x-1)$ Because $+3\times -1 = -3$
$(2x-3)(x+1)$ Because $-3\times +1 = -3$
$(2x+1)(x-3)$ Because $+1\times -3 = -3$
$(2x-1)(x+3)$ Because $-1\times +3 = -3$

④ $(2x+3)(x-1) = 2x(x-1)+3(x-1)$
$= 2x^2-2x+3x-3$
$= 2x^2+x-3$ ✗

$(2x-3)(x+1) = 2x(x+1)-3(x+1)$
$= 2x^2+2x-3x-3$
$= 2x^2-x-3$ ✗

$(2x+1)(x-3) = 2x(x-3)+1(x-3)$
$= 2x^2-6x+1x-3$
$= 2x^2-5x-3$ ✗

$(2x-1)(x+3) = 2x(x+3)-1(x+3)$
$= 2x^2+6x-1x-3$
$= 2x^2+5x-3$ ✓

⑤ So, $2x^2+5x-3 = (2x-1)(x+3)$

Quadratic Equations

1. Quadratic Equations

A **quadratic** equation has x^2 as its highest power. There are three different types:

$x^2 = 9$	Contains an x^2-term and a number term
$10x^2 - 15x = 0$	Contains an x^2-term and a x-term
$x^2 + 5x + 4 = 0$	Contains an x^2-term, x-term and a number term

Quadratic equations may have no solution, one solution or two solutions.

There are five methods of solving quadratic equations that you need to know: direct, factorisation, formula, graphical, iteration (the last two methods are dealt with on p45 and p63).

Sometimes you will be told which to use. Otherwise you have to choose the most appropriate method.

2. Direct Method

This method can be used if the quadratic equation can be rearranged to look like: $x^2 = number$.

Question *Solve the equation* $x^2 = 9$.

$x^2 = 9$

$\therefore \sqrt{x^2} = \sqrt{9}$ Square root both sides to change x^2 into x

$\therefore x = 3$

This method gives you one solution, *but there is another.*

3 is a solution because $3^2 = 9$

-3 is also a solution because $(-3)^2 = (-3)\times(-3) = 9$

So, the two solutions are: $x = 3$ and $x = -3$.

These two solutions are written briefly as: $x = \pm 3$.

$\pm$ means $+$ *or* $-$

The correct way of writing the solution is:

$x^2 = 9$

$\therefore \sqrt{x^2} = \pm\sqrt{9}$ Write the $\pm$ sign when taking the square root of both sides.

$\therefore x = \pm 3$

3. Factorisation Method

If you have difficulty with this method, use the formula method described in Box 4.

Question *Solve the equation* $10x^2 = 15x$.

① Rearrange the equation, if necessary, to get 0 on the RHS:

$10x^2 = 15x$

$\therefore 10x^2 - 15x = 0$ Move $15x$ to LHS

② Factorise the LHS:

$5x(2x-3) = 0$ See Box 7, p42

③ When the product of several numbers is 0, one of them must be 0:

$5 \times x \times (2x-3) = 0$

Number × Number × Number

We know that 5 is not 0. So, either x is 0 or the number in the bracket $(2x-3)$ is 0.

$\therefore x = 0$ or $2x - 3 = 0$

$\therefore x = 0$ or $2x = 0 + 3$

more

3. Factorisation Method (Contd)

$\therefore x = 0$ or $2x = 3$

$\therefore x = 0$ or $x = \frac{3}{2}$

Question *Solve the equation* $x^2 = 4x - 3$.

① $x^2 = 4x - 3$

$\therefore x^2 - 4x + 3 = 0$ Rearrange to get 0 on RHS

② $\therefore (x-1)(x-3) = 0$ Factorise LHS (see Box 7, p42)

Number × Number

③ $\therefore x - 1 = 0$ or $x - 3 = 0$

$\therefore x = 0 + 1$ or $x = 0 + 3$

$\therefore x = 1$ or $x = 3$

Question *Solve the equation* $x^2 - 9 = 0$.

$x^2 - 9 = 0$

$\therefore x^2 - 3^2 = 0$ Notice the LHS is the difference of two squares

$\therefore (x+3)(x-3) = 0$ Factorise the LHS (see Box 7, p42)

$\therefore x + 3 = 0$ or $x - 3 = 0$

$\therefore x = 0 - 3$ or $x = 0 + 3$

$\therefore x = -3$ or $x = 3$

$\therefore x = \pm 3$

4. The Formula Method

H

This method works for *all* quadratic equations, provided they are arranged in the following form:

$$ax^2 + bx + c = 0$$

(x^2-term, x-term, Number term)

where a, b and c are numbers. For example, in the equation $3x^2 + 2x - 6 = 0$, a is 3, b is 2 and c is -6.

Always use this method when the question asks for an approximate answer, e.g. correct to 2 dp.

Question *Solve the equation* $2x^2 - 6x = 1$ *correct to 2 decimal places.*

① Rearrange the equation to get 0 on the RHS:

$2x^2 - 6x = 1$

$\therefore 2x^2 - 6x - 1 = 0$

② Write down the values of a, b and c:

$2x^2 - 6x - 1 = 0$:

$a = 2$, $b = -6$ and $c = -1$ Don't forget the - signs

③ Substitute the values of a, b and c into the formula:

$$x = \frac{-b \pm \sqrt{b^2 - 4ac}}{2a}$$

This formula will be given on the question paper

Use brackets to avoid errors with minus signs:

$$x = \frac{-(-6) \pm \sqrt{(-6)^2 - 4(2)(-1)}}{2(2)}$$

Dividing line must go right across the fraction

④ Calculate the two values of x:

$x = \frac{6 \pm \sqrt{36 - -8}}{4}$ Because $4(2)(-1) = 8(-1) = -8$

$= \frac{6 \pm \sqrt{44}}{4}$ Remember: $- - = +$

$= \frac{6 \pm 6.633}{4}$ Store the answer to $\sqrt{44}$ in your calculator

$= \frac{6 + 6.633}{4}$ or $\frac{6 - 6.633}{4}$

$= 3.16$ or -0.16 Correct to 2 dp

Quadratic Equations (Contd)

5. Solving Problems Using Quadratic Equations

Question *A golfer hits a golf ball a horizontal distance d metres. The ball rises to a height of h metres given by the formula* $h = d - 0.004d^2$.

(a) How high will the ball have risen when it has travelled a distance of 90 metres?

(b) How far will the ball have travelled when it first reaches a height of 50 metres?

(a) Put $d = 90$ into the formula to find the height, h.

$h = 90 - 0.004 \times 90^2 = 57.6$ metres

(b) Put $h = 50$ into the formula to find the distance, d.

$50 = d - 0.004d^2$

Now solve this quadratic equation to find d:

H

$0.004d^2 - d + 50 = 0$ Rearrange into the form

$\therefore\ 0.004d^2 - 1d + 50 = 0$ $ax^2 + bx + c = 0$

Here, $a = 0.004$, $b = -1$ and $c = 50$.

$$\therefore\ d = \frac{-b \pm \sqrt{b^2 - 4ac}}{2a} = \frac{-(-1) \pm \sqrt{(-1)^2 - 4(0.004)(50)}}{2(0.004)} = \frac{1 \pm \sqrt{1 - 0.8}}{0.008} = \frac{1 \pm \sqrt{0.2}}{0.008} = \frac{1 + 0.447}{0.008} \text{ or } \frac{1 - 0.447}{0.008}$$

≈ 181 m or 69 m

The ball reaches a height of 50 m when it has travelled 69 m and 181 m. So it first reaches this height when it has travelled 69 m.

Convergence and Iteration

1. Convergence of a Sequence

The terms of the sequence 1.9, 1.99, 1.999, 1.9999, ... are getting closer and closer to the number 2. We say that the sequence **converges** to the **limit** 2.

If a sequence is convergent, the differences between successive terms gets smaller. For example:

1.9 1.99 1.999 1.9999

0.09 0.009 0.0009

Differences getting smaller

A sequence that is not convergent is said to be **divergent**. Here are two examples:

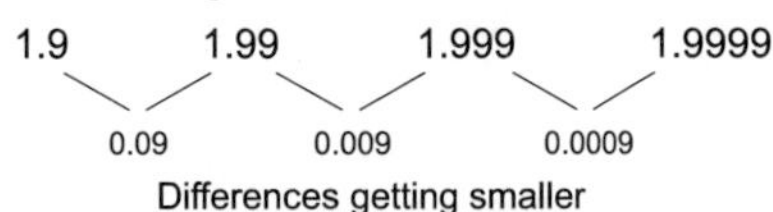

1 −1 1 −1 1 ...

Numbers *oscillate* between −1 and 1

Question *Is the sequence below convergent? If so, what is its limit?*

$\frac{1}{2}$ $\frac{3}{4}$ $\frac{5}{6}$ $\frac{7}{8}$ $\frac{9}{10}$ $\frac{11}{12}$ ....

Convert the terms to decimals and calculate the differences between successive terms:

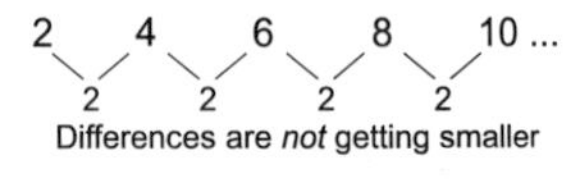

The differences are getting smaller, so the sequence is convergent.

To be sure of the limit, calculate a few more terms of the sequence:

$\frac{31}{32} \approx 0.97$ $\frac{47}{48} \approx 0.98$ $\frac{99}{100} = 0.99$ $\frac{999}{1000} = 0.999$

You can see that the terms are getting closer and closer to 1. So, the limit of the sequence is 1.

2. Iteration

H

Iteration is a way of finding any term of a sequence using the previous term(s). Each term in the sequence below can be found by adding 2 to the previous term.

5 →(Add 2) 7 →(Add 2) 9 →(Add 2) 11 →(Add 2) 13

This process can be described in words:

term = previous term + 2, with the first term 5

or algebraically using an **iterative formula**:

$u_{n+1} = u_n + 2$, starting with $u_1 = 5$

Using this formula we can generate the sequence:

$u_1 = 5$

$u_2 = u_1 + 2 = 5 + 2 = 7$

$u_3 = u_2 + 2 = 7 + 2 = 9$ etc.

Question *Investigate the sequence generated by the iterative formula* $u_{n+1} = \frac{u_n + 2}{5}$, *given that* $u_1 = 3$.

$u_1 = 3$ $u_2 = \frac{u_1 + 2}{5} = \frac{3 + 2}{5} = \frac{5}{5} = 1$

$u_3 = \frac{u_2 + 2}{5} = \frac{1 + 2}{5} = \frac{3}{5} = 0.6$

$u_4 = \frac{u_3 + 2}{5} = \frac{0.6 + 2}{5} = \frac{2.6}{5} = 0.52$ etc.

The sequence converges because the differences become smaller:

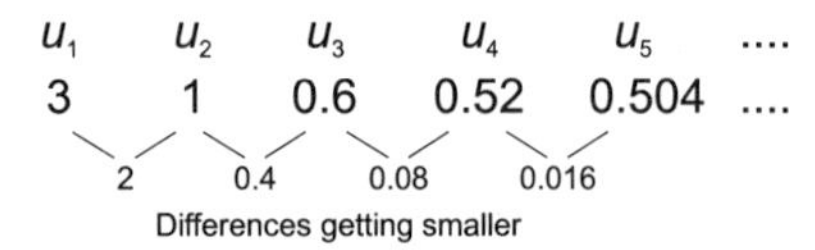

To find the limit of a convergent sequence, replace x_{n+1} and u_n by x and then solve the equation.

So, $u_{n+1} = \frac{u_n + 2}{5}$ becomes $x = \frac{x + 2}{5}$

$\therefore\ 5x = x + 2 \Rightarrow 5x - x = 2 \Rightarrow 4x = 2 \Rightarrow x = \frac{2}{4} = \frac{1}{2}$

So the limit of the sequence is 0.5.

Numerical Methods for Solving Equations

1. Trial and Improvement Method

With this method, you estimate the solution of an equation and then gradually improve your estimate.

Suppose that you have to find the solution of the equation $x^2+2x = 10$ correct to 1 decimal place. Your first guess might be $x = 2$. You will normally be given the first estimate in the question. Check how close this guess is by replacing x with 2 in the LHS of the equation. You are aiming for 10 on the RHS:

$x^2+2x = 2^2+2\times2 = 4+4 = 8$

Since the result is too low (less than 10), try increasing your estimate slightly, say to $x = 2.5$:

$x^2+2x = 2.5^2+2\times2.5 = 6.25+5 = 11.25$

Since the result is too high (greater than 10), the correct solution must lie somewhere between your two estimates of 2 and 2.5. Try $x = 2.3$:

$x^2+2x = 2.3^2+2\times2.3 = 5.29+4.6 = 9.89$

You are now getting much closer to 10. Since 9.89 is less than 10, the correct solution must lie somewhere between the last two estimates of 2.5 and 2.3. Try $x = 2.4$. Continue with more calculations until you obtain two estimates that are the same correct to 1 decimal place, one giving the RHS greater than 10, the other giving it as less than 10. The results are shown in the table below

Trial	Trial value (Guess)	x^2+2x (LHS)	Comment
1	2	8	Too low
2	2.5	11.25	Too high
3	2.3	9.89	Too low
4	2.4	10.56	Too high
5	2.34	10.1556	Too high
6	2.31	9.9561	Too low

The last two estimates are 2.34 and 2.31. These are both equal to 2.3, correct to 1 decimal place, and so the solution to the equation is $x = 2.3$ (1 dp).

Question *Given that $2^x = 20$, use the method of trial and improvement to find the value of x, correct to 1 dp.*

Try $x = 4$ to start with: $2^4 = 16$ Too low

So, try a larger value, say $x = 5$: $2^5 = 32$ Too high

Try a value in between 4 and 5, say $x = 4.5$. To calculate the value of $2^{4.5}$, use the power key x^y of your calculator:

So, $2^{4.5} \approx 22.6$ Too high

The last two estimates in the table are $x = 4.34$ (too high) and $x = 4.32$ (too low). These are both equal to 4.3, correct to 1 decimal place, and so the solution to the equation is $x \approx 4.3$ (1 dp).

Trial	Trial value (Guess)	2^x (LHS)	Comment
1	4	16	Too low
2	5	32	Too high
3	4.5	22.6274	Too high
4	4.4	21.1121	Too high
5	4.3	19.6983	Too low
6	4.34	20.2521	Too high
7	4.32	19.9733	Too low

2. Using Iteration to Solve an Equation H

With this method, the equation is rearranged to produce an iterative formula (see Box 2, p44) that can be used to find an approximate solution.

Suppose we want to solve the equation $x^2+2x = 10$ correct to 2 decimal places. This is the same equation as in Box 1.

First, rearrange the equation to get x on its own on the LHS. There are several ways of doing this; some work better than others:

(a) $x^2+2x = 10$
$\therefore\ 2x = 10-x^2$
$\therefore\ x = \dfrac{10-x^2}{2}$

(b) $x^2+2x = 10$
$\therefore\ x(x+2) = 10$
$\therefore\ x = \dfrac{10}{x+2}$

(c) $x^2+2x = 10$
$\therefore\ x^2 = 10-2x$
$\therefore\ x = \sqrt{10-2x}$ Ignore the $\pm$ sign

Equations involving a fraction with x in the denominator often work well, so we will choose equation (b).

To change an equation into an iterative formula, replace x by x_{n+1} and x_n. For equation (b):

$$x = \frac{10}{x+2} \quad \text{becomes} \quad x_{n+1} = \frac{10}{x_n+2}$$

(You will probably be given the iterative formula in the question, as well as the first value, x_1).

If the values of x_n converge, they converge to the solution of the equation.

Question *Solve the equation $x^2+2x = 10$, correct to 2 dp, using the iterative formula $x_{n+1} = \dfrac{10}{x_n+2}$ starting with $x_1 = 2.3$.*

$x_1 = 2.3$

$$x_2 = \frac{10}{x_1+2} = \frac{10}{2.3+2} = \frac{10}{4.3} \approx 2.32558$$

NOTE Store this accurate value in the memory of your calculator, ready for the next step.

$$x_3 = \frac{10}{x_2+2} = \frac{10}{2.32558+2} = \frac{10}{4.32558} = 2.31183$$

Continue calculating values of x_n until the 3rd decimal place stops changing (one more decimal place than required in the question).

The values of x_n are summarised in the table below.

x_1	x_2	x_3	x_4	x_5	x_6	x_7	x_8
2.3	2.32558	2.31183	2.31920	2.31524	2.31737	2.31623	2.31684

The table shows that the values of x_n are converging. The last two values both begin 2.316.... So, we can safely say that the solution of the equation is $x = 2.32$, correct to 2 decimal places.

Flow Charts

1. Flow Charts

A **flow chart** is a series of instructions and questions arranged in the form of a diagram.

Instructions and questions are contained in shaped boxes, as shown below:

Finish | Instruction

Arrows show you which box to go to next. Sometimes this depends on the answer to a question.

Question *Use this flow chart to calculate*
(a) the output, when the input is 7
(b) the two possible inputs when the output is 6.

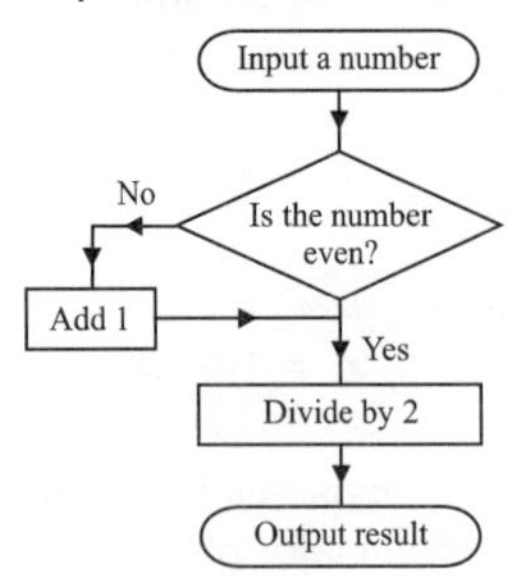

(a)

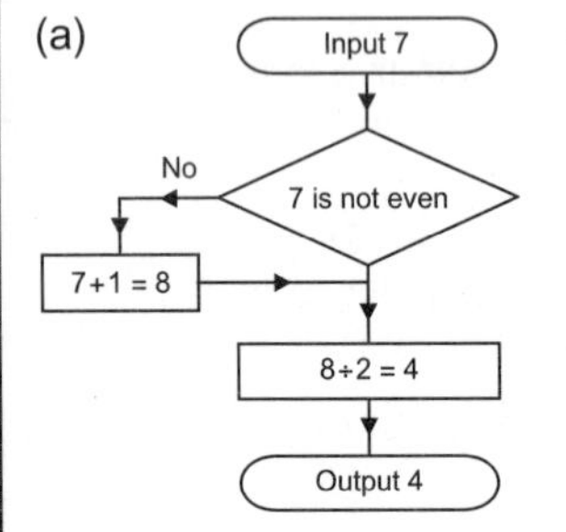

(b) Work from the bottom up, reversing the instructions.

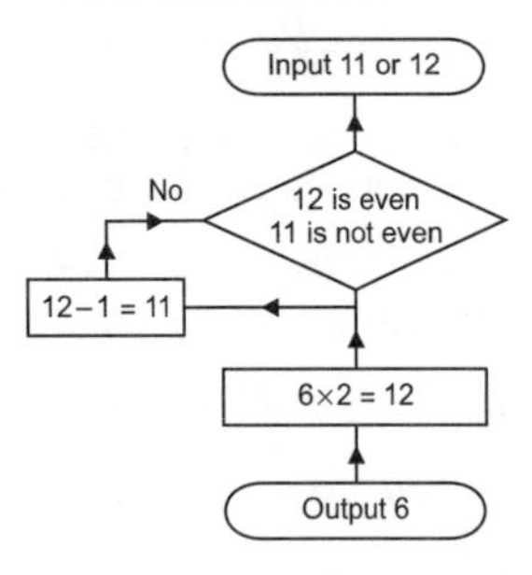

2. Flow Charts and Algebra

Most flow charts use algebra to describe the instructions and questions.

Question *Use the flow chart below to calculate the output when $x = 2$ and $y = 3$*

Solution

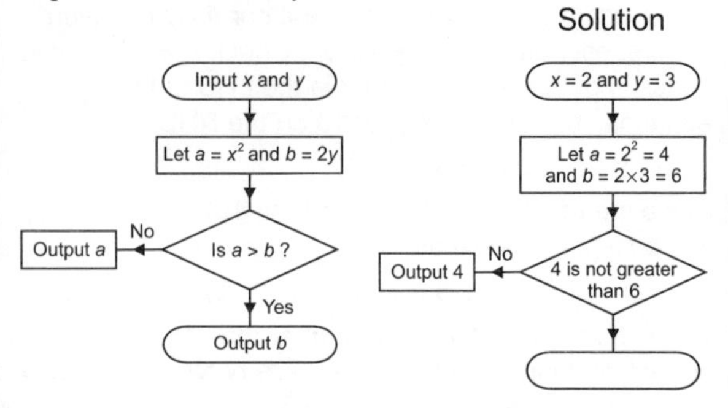

Question *What does the flow diagram below do?*

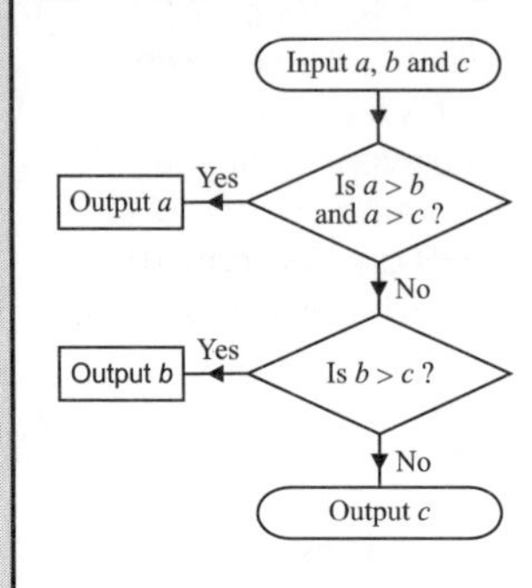

Input a few numbers to get some idea of what the flow diagram does.

Try $a = 2$, $b = 5$, $c = 3$. a is not greater than both b and c, but b is greater than c. So, the output is $b = 5$. You can see that the flow diagram has output the biggest number.

Try a few more numbers to be sure.

So, the flow diagram finds the greatest of any three numbers.

3. Flow Charts with Loops

A **loop** repeats a set of instructions until a certain condition is met, e.g. keep on adding 2 until you reach 100.

Question *The flow chart below can be used to find the cube root of 24. Use the diagram to complete the table of values.*

x	y
2.5	

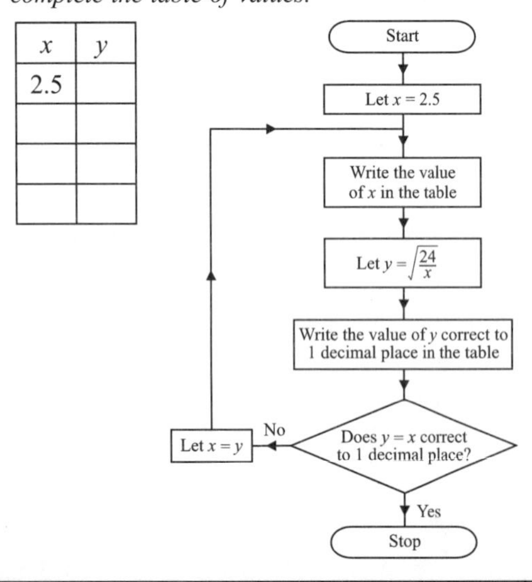

Solution

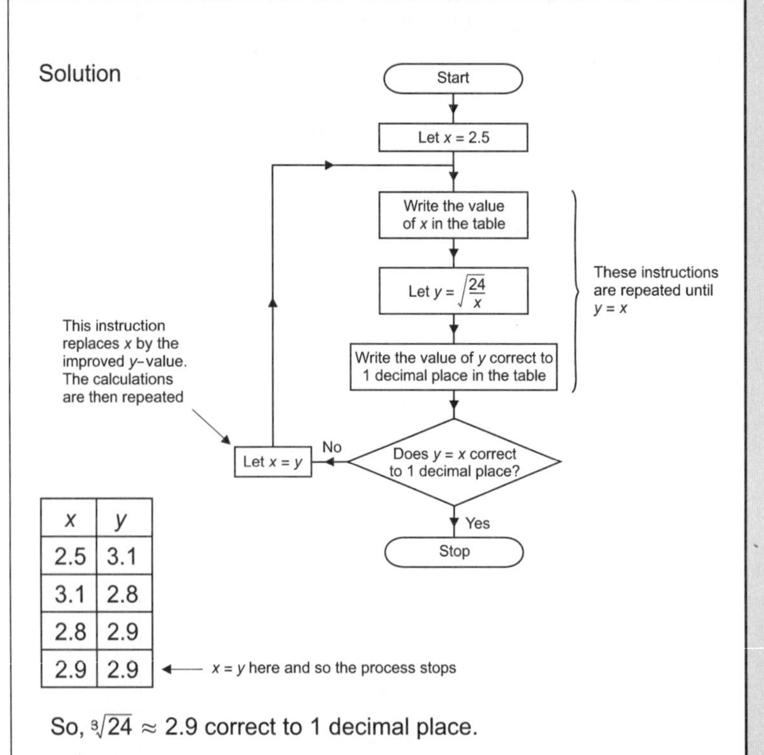

x	y
2.5	3.1
3.1	2.8
2.8	2.9
2.9	2.9

← $x = y$ here and so the process stops

So, $\sqrt[3]{24} \approx 2.9$ correct to 1 decimal place.

Simultaneous Equations

1. Simultaneous Equations

Simultaneous equations involve *two* unknown numbers, x and y say. You need two equations to be able to find the values of x and y. For example:

$$3x+2y = 11$$
$$2x+y = 6$$

Solving these equations means finding the values of x and y which make the LHS equal to the RHS in *both* equations.

The solution of the above two equations is $x = 1$ and $y = 4$. We can check this by substituting these values in the LHS of each equation:

$$3\times1+2\times4 = 3+8 = 11 \checkmark$$
$$2\times1+4 = 2+4 = 6 \checkmark$$

2. Solving by Subtracting Equations

The method of solving simultaneous equations involves eliminating the x-terms or y-terms by adding or subtracting the equations.

Question *Solve the simultaneous equations:*

$$2x+3y = 11$$
$$2x+y = 5$$

① Label the equations (A) and (B):

$$2x+3y = 11 \text{ .... (A)}$$
$$2x+y = 5 \text{ .... (B)}$$

② Subtract one equation from the other when either the x-terms or the y-terms are exactly the same.

Here, the x-terms are both $2x$:

$$2x+3y = 11 \text{ .... (A)}$$
$$2x+y = 5 \text{ .... (B)}$$
(A)−(B) gives: $$2y = 6$$

③ Solve the new equation:

$2y = 6$
$\therefore\ y = \frac{6}{2}$
$\therefore\ y = 3$

④ Substitute this solution into either of the original equations (A) or (B).

Putting $y = 3$ into equation (A) gives:

$2x+3\times3 = 11$
$\therefore\ 2x+9 = 11$
$\therefore\ 2x = 11-9$
$\therefore\ 2x = 2$
$\therefore\ x = 1$

⑤ Write down the solution to the simultaneous equations:

$x = 1$ and $y = 3$

⑥ Check the solution by substituting the values of x and y into the original equations:

Equation (A): $2\times1+3\times3 = 2+9 = 11$ ✓

Equation (B): $2\times1+3 = 2+3 = 5$ ✓

3. Solving by Adding Equations

Question *Solve the simultaneous equations*

$$4x-2y = 7$$
$$3x+2y = 7$$

① Label the equations:

$$4x-2y = 7 \text{ .... (A)}$$
$$3x+2y = 7 \text{ .... (B)}$$

② Add the equations when either the x-terms or the y-terms are the same except for their signs.

Here, the y-terms are $-2y$ and $+2y$

$$4x-2y = 7 \text{ .... (A)}$$
$$3x+2y = 7 \text{ .... (B)}$$
(A)+(B): $$7x = 14$$

NOTE $-2y$ and $+2y$ cancel each other when added together: $(-2y)+(+2y) = -2y+2y = 0$

③ Solve the new equation:

$7x = 14$
$\therefore\ x = 2$

④ Substitute this solution into equation (A) or (B).

Putting $x = 2$ into equation (B) gives:

$3\times2+2y = 7$
$\therefore\ 6+2y = 7$
$\therefore\ 2y = 7-6$
$\therefore\ 2y = 1$
$\therefore\ y = \frac{1}{2}$

⑤ Write down the solution to the simultaneous equations:

$x = 2$ and $y = \frac{1}{2}$

⑥ Check the solution by substituting the values of x and y into the original equations:

Equation (A): $4\times2-2\times\frac{1}{2} = 8-1 = 7$ ✓

Equation (B): $3\times2+2\times\frac{1}{2} = 6+1 = 7$ ✓

4. More Difficult Subtraction

Question *Solve the simultaneous equations*

$$3x+4y = 34$$
$$3x-2y = 10$$

The x-terms are the same and so we must subtract the equations:

$$3x+4y = 34 \text{ .... (A)}$$
$$3x-2y = 10 \text{ .... (B)}$$
(A)−(B): $$6y = 24$$

NOTE Take care when subtracting negative terms: $(+4y)-(-2y) = +4y+2y = 6y$

$\therefore\ y = \frac{24}{6}$
$\therefore\ y = 4$

Putting $y = 4$ into equation (A) gives:

$3x+4\times4 = 34$
$\therefore\ 3x+16 = 34$
$\therefore\ 3x = 18$
$\therefore\ x = 6$ and $y = 4$

Simultaneous Equations

5. Equations Requiring Multiplication

When neither the x-terms nor the y-terms of the equations are the same, we must make either pair of terms the same by multiplying the equations by numbers. Then we can use the previous methods.

Question *Solve the simultaneous equations*

$$2x-y = 3 \quad .... (A)$$
$$3x+2y = 22 \quad .... (B)$$

The x-terms are different and so are the y-terms. We can make the y-terms the same by multiplying equation (A) by 2:

$2x-y = 3$ .... (A)

$2\times$(A): $4x-2y = 6$ .... (C) Label new equation

$3x+2y = 22$ .... (B)

Equations (B) and (C) now have the same y-terms, apart from their signs. Adding the equations eliminates y (see Box 3, p47):

$4x-2y = 6$ .... (C)

$3x+2y = 22$ .... (B)

(C)+(B): $7x = 28$

$\therefore x = 4$

Putting $x = 4$ into equation (B) gives:

$3\times4+2y = 22$

$\therefore 12+2y = 22$

$\therefore 2y = 22-12$

$\therefore 2y = 10$

$\therefore y = 5$

Solution to equation is $x = 4$, $y = 5$.

Check: Equation (A): $2\times4-5 = 8-5 = 3$ ✓

Equation (B): $3\times4+2\times5 = 12+10 = 22$ ✓

Question *Solve the simultaneous equations*

$$2p-3q = 5 \quad .... (A)$$
$$5p-2q = 40 \quad .... (B)$$

The p-terms are different and so are the q-terms. We can make both the p-terms $10p$ by multiplying equation (A) by 5 and equation (B) by 2:

$2p - 3q = 5$ .... (A)

$5\times$(A): $10p - 15q = 25$ .... (C) Label new equation

$5p - 2q = 40$ .... (B)

$2\times$(B): $10p - 4q = 80$ .... (D) Label new equation

Rewrite equations (C) and (D) and subtract (D) from (C) to eliminate the p-terms:

$10p - 15q = 25$ .... (C)

$10p - 4q = 80$ .... (D)

(C)−(D): $-11q = -55$

NOTE: $(-15q)-(-4q) = -15q+4q = -11q$

$\therefore q = \frac{-55}{-11} = 5$

Putting $q = 5$ into equation (A) gives:

$2p-3\times5 = 5$

$\therefore 2p-15 = 5$

$\therefore 2p = 20$

$\therefore p = 10$

Solution to equation is $p = 10$, $q = 5$.

Check: Equation (A): $2\times10-3\times5 = 20-15 = 5$ ✓

Equation (B): $5\times10-2\times5 = 50-10 = 40$ ✓

6. Solving Problems Using Simultaneous Equations

Question *Toffees cost x pence each and chocolates cost y pence each. Lee bought 7 toffees and 5 chocolates, paying £2.00 altogether. He spent 80 pence more on the toffees than the chocolates.*

(a) Write down two equations in x and y.

(b) Solve your equations to find the values of x and y.

Write down the equations in words first; then replace the words with symbols.

Cost of 7 toffees and 5 chocolates is £2.00

$7\times x$ pence + $5\times y$ pence = 200 pence

$7x + 5y = 200$

Label this first equation (A):

$7x+5y = 200$ .... (A)

Now make the second equation:

7 toffees cost 80 pence more than 5 chocolates

$7\times x$ pence = 80 pence + $5\times y$ pence

$7x = 80 + 5y$

Label this equation (B):

$7x = 80+5y$ .... (B)

Write down the equations above each other:

$7x+5y = 200$ .... (A)

$7x = 80+5y$ .... (B)

Rearrange the equations, if necessary, to get the x and y terms on the LHS and the number term on the RHS.

Equation (B) needs rearranging

$7x = 80+5y$

$7x-5y = 80$ .... (C)

Write down the equations again and solve them

$7x+5y = 200$ .... (A)

$7x-5y = 80$ .... (C)

(A)+(C): $14x = 280$

$\therefore x = \frac{280}{14} = 20$

Putting $x = 20$ into equation (A) gives:

$7\times20+5y = 200$

$\therefore 140+5y = 200$

$\therefore 5y = 200-140$

$\therefore 5y = 60$

$\therefore y = 12$

Solution to equation is $x = 20$, $y = 12$. So, toffees cost 20 pence each and chocolates cost 12 pence each.

Check: Eqn (A): $7\times20+5\times12 = 140+60 = 200$ ✓

Eqn (B): $7\times20 = 80+5\times12$ ✓

Algebraic Fractions

1. Multiplying and Dividing Fractions

Question *Simplify* $\dfrac{4a^2c}{3b} \times \dfrac{21b^3}{2ac^2}$.

$\dfrac{\overset{2}{\cancel{4}}a^2c}{\cancel{3}b} \times \dfrac{\overset{7}{\cancel{21}}b^3}{\cancel{2}ac^2}$ Cancel numbers

$= \dfrac{2a^{\cancel{2}1}\cancel{c}}{\cancel{b}1} \times \dfrac{7b^{\cancel{3}2}}{\cancel{a}c^{\cancel{2}1}}$ Cancel letters

$= \dfrac{2a}{1} \times \dfrac{7b^2}{c}$

$= \dfrac{2a \times 7b^2}{1 \times c}$ Multiply numerators and denominators

$= \dfrac{14ab^2}{c}$

Question *Simplify* $\dfrac{1}{6x} \div \dfrac{1}{3x^2}$.

$\dfrac{1}{6x} \div \dfrac{1}{3x^2}$

$= \dfrac{1}{6x} \times \dfrac{3x^2}{1}$ Change ÷ to × and invert $\frac{1}{3x^2}$

$= \dfrac{1}{{}_2\cancel{6}\cancel{x}} \times \dfrac{\cancel{3}x^{\cancel{2}1}}{1}$ Cancel numbers and letters

$= \dfrac{1 \times x}{2 \times 1}$ Multiply

$= \dfrac{x}{2}$

2. Adding and Subtracting Fractions

Fractions that have numbers as denominators can be added and subtracted the same way as in arithmetic (see Box 8, p17).

Question *Express* $\dfrac{7a}{15} - \dfrac{3a}{10}$ *as a single fraction in its lowest terms.*

The LCM of 15 and 10 is 30. So, we must convert each fraction to an equivalent fraction whose denominator is 30.

$\dfrac{7a}{15} \overset{\times 2}{=} \dfrac{14a}{30}$ $\dfrac{3a}{10} \overset{\times 3}{=} \dfrac{9a}{30}$

Now we can add the fractions:

$\dfrac{7a}{15} - \dfrac{3a}{10} = \dfrac{14a}{30} - \dfrac{9a}{30} = \dfrac{14a - 9a}{30} = \dfrac{\overset{1}{\cancel{5}}a}{\cancel{30}_6} = \dfrac{a}{6}$

When the denominators contain letters, their LCM contains the highest power of each letter.

Question *Express* $\dfrac{7}{15a^2} - \dfrac{3}{10ab}$ *as a single fraction.*

The LCM of $15a^2$ and $10ab$ is $30a^2b$ because 30 is the LCM of 15 and 10, a^2 is the highest power of a, and b is the highest power of b. Now convert each fraction to an equivalent fraction whose denominator is $30a^2b$:

$\dfrac{7}{15a^2} \overset{\times 2b}{=} \dfrac{14b}{30a^2b}$ $\dfrac{3}{10ab} \overset{\times 3a}{=} \dfrac{9a}{30a^2b}$

more

2. Adding•Subtracting Fractions (Contd)

Now we can subtract the fractions:

$\dfrac{7}{15a^2} - \dfrac{3}{10ab} = \dfrac{14b}{30a^2b} - \dfrac{9a}{30a^2b} = \dfrac{14b - 9a}{30a^2b}$

NOTE You cannot further simplify the answer by cancelling. For example, although 14 and 30 can be divided by 2, 9 cannot.

Question **H** *Express* $\dfrac{7}{(x+2)} - \dfrac{3}{(x-3)}$ *as a single fraction, simplifying your answer.*

When a denominator contains a bracket, the LCM also contains this bracket.

The LCM of $(x+2)$ and $(x-3)$ is $(x+2)(x-3)$. So, we must convert each fraction to an equivalent fraction whose denominator is $(x+2)(x-3)$:

$\dfrac{7}{(x+2)} \overset{\times (x-3)}{=} \dfrac{7(x-3)}{(x+2)(x-3)}$ $\dfrac{3}{(x-3)} \overset{\times (x+2)}{=} \dfrac{3(x+2)}{(x+2)(x-3)}$

Now we can subtract the fractions

$$\dfrac{7}{(x+2)} - \dfrac{3}{(x-3)} = \dfrac{7(x-3)}{(x+2)(x-3)} - \dfrac{3(x+2)}{(x+2)(x-3)}$$

$$= \dfrac{7(x-3) - 3(x+2)}{(x+2)(x-3)}$$

$$= \dfrac{7x - 21 - 3x - 6}{(x+2)(x-3)}$$

$$= \dfrac{4x - 27}{(x+2)(x-3)}$$

3. Equations Involving Fractions

Question *Solve the equation* $\dfrac{2x}{5} + \dfrac{x}{4} = \dfrac{3}{2}$.

Multiply each term by the LCM of the denominators (the lowest common denominator).

The LCM of 5, 4 and 2 is 20

$\dfrac{2x}{5} + \dfrac{x}{4} = \dfrac{3}{2}$ Write the equation

$\therefore\ \overset{4}{\cancel{20}} \times \dfrac{2x}{\cancel{5}_1} + \overset{5}{\cancel{20}} \times \dfrac{x}{\cancel{4}_1} = \overset{10}{\cancel{20}} \times \dfrac{3}{\cancel{2}_1}$ Multiply each term by 20 and then cancel

$\therefore\ 4 \times 2x + 5 \times x = 10 \times 3$ Simplify

$\therefore\ 8x + 5x = 30$

$\therefore\ 13x = 30$

$\therefore\ x = \frac{30}{13}$

Question *Solve the equation* $\dfrac{t-2}{3} + \dfrac{t+1}{2} = \dfrac{3}{4}$.

The LCM of 3, 2 and 4 is 12.

$\dfrac{(t-2)}{3} + \dfrac{(t+1)}{2} = \dfrac{3}{4}$ Bracket numerators

$\therefore\ \overset{4}{\cancel{12}} \times \dfrac{(t-2)}{\cancel{3}_1} + \overset{6}{\cancel{12}} \times \dfrac{(t+1)}{\cancel{2}_1} = \overset{3}{\cancel{12}} \times \dfrac{3}{\cancel{4}_1}$ Multiply by 12 and then cancel

$\therefore\ 4 \times (t-2) + 6 \times (t+1) = 3 \times 3$

$\therefore\ 4t - 8 + 6t + 6 = 9$

$\therefore\ 10t - 2 = 9$

$\therefore\ 10t = 11$

$\therefore\ t = \frac{11}{10}$ (or 1.1)

Inequalities

1. Inequalities

An **inequality** states that one number is greater (or smaller) than another.

The inequality '5 is less than 6' can be written algebraically as $5 < 6$. The symbol $<$ means 'less than' when read from left to right.

'5 is less than 6' is the same as saying '6 is greater than 5', which can be written algebraically as $6 > 5$. The symbol $>$ means 'greater than' when read from left to right.

So, inequalities can be turned around

$5 < 6$ means the same as $6 > 5$

2. Rules of Inequalities

Inequalities can be manipulated in a similar way to equations.

A number can be added or subtracted from both sides of an inequality.

For example, we know $5 < 6$ is true. Adding 2 to both sides gives $5+2 < 6+2$ or $7 < 8$ which is also true.

A **positive** number can multiply or divide both sides of an inequality.

For example, we know $10 < 12$ is true. Dividing both sides by 2 gives $\frac{10}{2} < \frac{12}{2}$ or $5 < 6$, which is also true.

Similarly, multiplying both sides by 3 gives $3\times10 < 3\times12$ or $30 < 36$, which is also true.

Multiplying or dividing both sides of an inequality by a **negative** number reverses the inequality sign.

For example, we know $5 < 6$ is true. Multiplying both sides by -2 gives $-2\times5 < -2\times6$ or $-10 < -12$, which is ***not*** true. However, reversing the inequality sign gives $-10 > -12$, which is true.

Similarly, we know $10 < 12$ is true. Dividing both sides by -2 and reversing the inequality sign gives $\frac{10}{-2} > \frac{12}{-2}$ or $-5 > -6$, which is also true.

3. Algebraic Inequalities

The inequality $x < 3$ tells us that x is a number less than 3, as shown on the number line below:

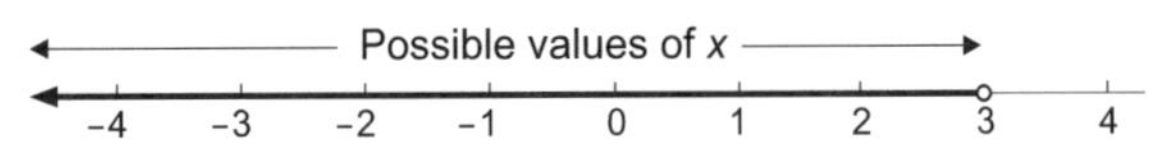

The empty circle indicates that x cannot be 3; x is **strictly less than** 3.

The inequality $x \leqslant 3$ tells us that x is a number less than or equal to 3, as shown on the number line below:

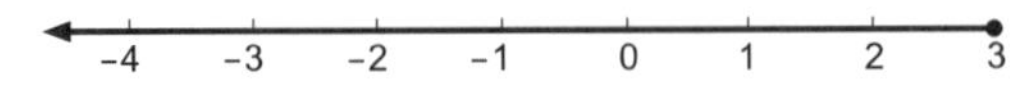

The solid circle indicates that x can be 3.

more

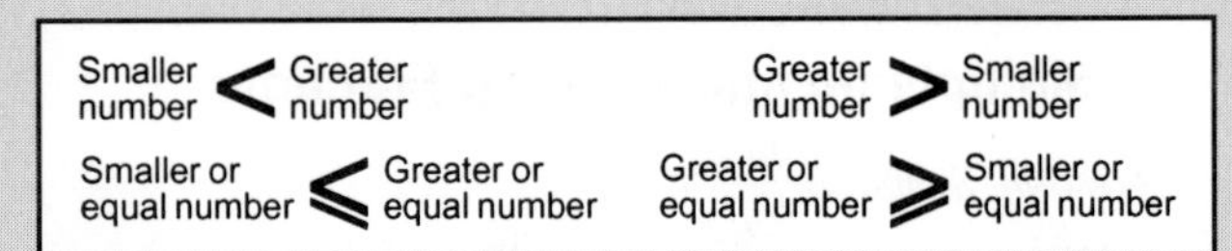

3. Algebraic Inequalities (Contd)

Sometimes x is on the RHS. You can either reverse the inequality or read the inequality from right to left.

The inequality $-2 < x$ states that -2 is less than the number x; or, equivalently, x is a number greater than -2, which could be written $x > -2$.

The inequality $-2 < x \leqslant 3$ states that x is a number greater than -2 (read the inequality from right to left) but less than or equal to 3, as shown on the number line below.

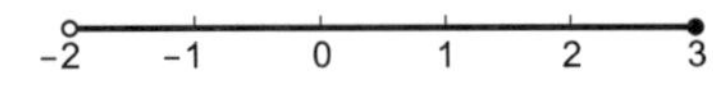

Question *Write down the positive integers, n, satisfying the inequality $n < 5$.*

We can see from the number line that the positive integers (whole numbers) less than 5 are: 1, 2, 3 and 4.

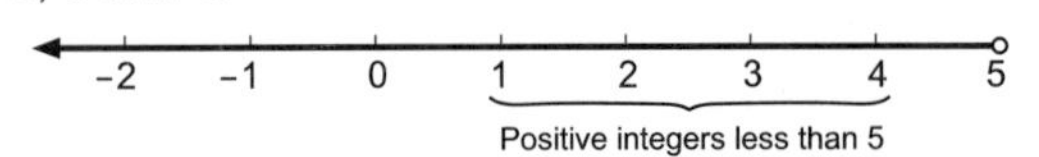

4. Solving Inequalities

To solve an inequality means to find the values of x which make it true. This involves rearranging the inequality to get x on its own on one side, using the rules in Box 2.

Question *Solve the inequality $x-2 < 5$.*

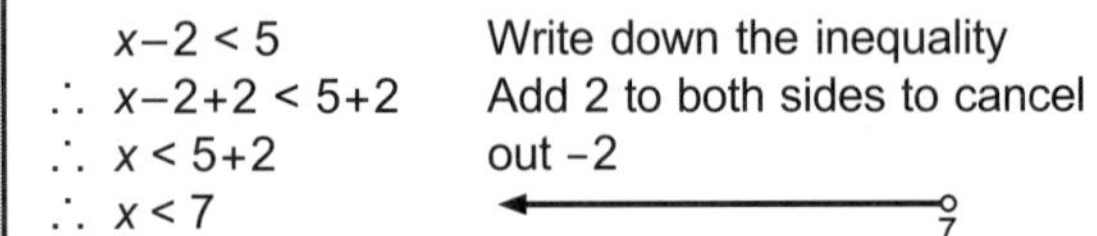

$x-2 < 5$	Write down the inequality
$\therefore x-2+2 < 5+2$	Add 2 to both sides to cancel out -2
$\therefore x < 5+2$	
$\therefore x < 7$	

As with equations, moving the -2 to the RHS and changing it to $+2$ gives the same result:

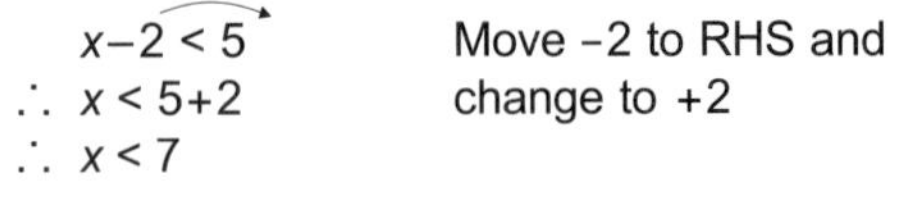

$x-2 < 5$	Move -2 to RHS and change to $+2$
$\therefore x < 5+2$	
$\therefore x < 7$	

Question *Solve the inequality $3x \geqslant 12$.*

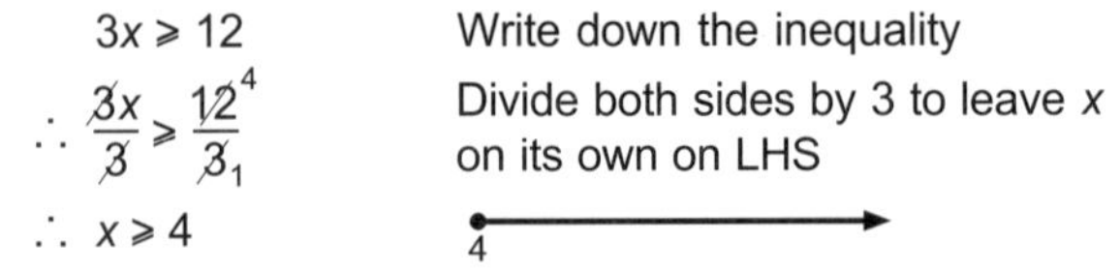

$3x \geqslant 12$	Write down the inequality
$\therefore \frac{3x}{3} \geqslant \frac{12}{3}$	Divide both sides by 3 to leave x on its own on LHS
$\therefore x \geqslant 4$	

As with equations, moving the $3\times$ to the RHS and changing it to $\div 3$ gives the same result:

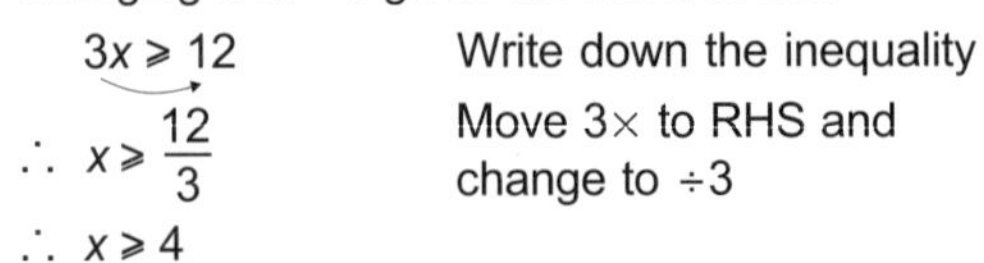

$3x \geqslant 12$	Write down the inequality
$\therefore x \geqslant \frac{12}{3}$	Move $3\times$ to RHS and change to $\div3$
$\therefore x \geqslant 4$	

more

4. Solving Inequalities (Contd)

Question *Solve the inequality* $-2x \geqslant 6$.

$-2x \geqslant 6$	Write down the inequality
$\therefore \frac{-2x}{-2} \leqslant \frac{6}{-2}$	Divide both sides by −2 and reverse the ⩾ sign
$\therefore x \leqslant \frac{6}{-2}$ (cancelled to −3)	
$\therefore x \leqslant -3$	(number line: arrow to the left from −3)

Question *Solve the inequality* $4n+3 < 18$.

$4n+3 < 18$	Move +3 to RHS, change to −3
$\therefore 4n < 18-3$	
$\therefore 4n < 15$	Move 4× to RHS, change to ÷4
$\therefore n < \frac{15}{4}$	
$\therefore n < 3\frac{3}{4}$	

5. Inequalities Involving x^2

Question *Solve the inequality* $x^2 \leqslant 9$.

The largest value of x satisfying this inequality is $x = 3$ since $3^2 = 9$. This value is calculated by $\sqrt{9}$.

The smallest value of x satisying this inequality is $x = -3$ since $(-3)^2 = (-3)\times(-3) = 9$.

So, x can be any number between −3 and 3:

$-3 \leqslant x \leqslant 3$

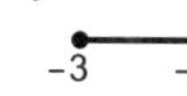
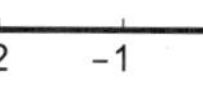
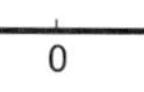

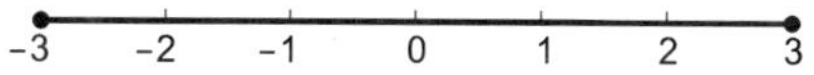

6. Using Inequalities to Solve Problems

Question *Pencils cost 27 pence each and erasers cost 30 pence each. Jim has £2.00 to spend on pencils and erasers. He buys n pencils and 2 erasers.*
(a) Write down an inequality in n.
(b) What is the largest number of pencils Jim bought?

(a) Cost of n pencils and 2 erasers is less than or equal to 200 pence.

We can write this algebraically as an inequality:

Cost of n pencils + Cost of 2 erasers ⩽ 200 pence

$n\times 27$ pence + 2×30 pence ⩽ 200 pence

$\therefore 27n+2\times 30 \leqslant 200$

(b) Solve the inequality as usual:

$27n+60 \leqslant 200$

$\therefore 27n \leqslant 200-60$

$\therefore 27n \leqslant 140$

$\therefore n \leqslant \frac{140}{27}$

$\therefore n \leqslant 5.19$ (2 dp)

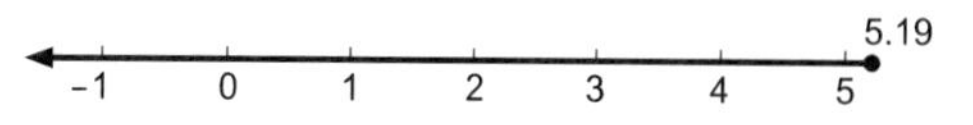

Now n is the number of pencils Jim bought and so it must be a whole number. From the number line we can see that n is 5. So, Jim bought 5 pencils.

Direct and Inverse Proportion

1. Direct Proportion

Suppose apples cost 10 pence each. Then:

Cost of 2 apples = 10×2 pence = 20 pence
Cost of 3 apples = 10×3 pence = 30 pence etc.

The more apples bought, the greater the cost.

Generally:

Cost of apples = 10 pence × Number of apples

If N apples cost C pence, we have the formula:

C pence = 10 pence × N

or simply $C = 10N$

As the number of apples, N, increases, their cost, C pence, also increases. We say that the cost, C pence, is **directly proportional** to the number of apples, N. To indicate that C is directly proportional to N, we write:

$$C \propto N$$

Two quantities, C and N, are said to be directly proportional if they are related by the formula:
C = Fixed number × N

The fixed number is called the **constant of proportionality**. In the above example, the constant of proportionality is 10.

1. Direct Proportion (Contd)

Question *The voltage, V, in an electrical circuit is directly proportional to the current flowing, A. Given that V = 12 when A = 5.*
(a) Write down an equation expressing V in terms of A.
(b) Find the value of V when A = 7.

(a) V is directly proportional to A and so:

V = Fixed number × A

We are told that $V = 12$ when $A = 5$. Substitute these values into the equation to find the fixed number.

12 = Fixed number × 5

$\therefore \frac{12}{5}$ = Fixed number

$\therefore$ Fixed number = $\frac{12}{5} = 2.4$

We can now rewrite the equation connecting V and A:

$V = 2.4\times A$ or simply $V = 2.4A$

(b) Putting $A = 7$ into the formula gives:

$V = 2.4\times 7 = 16.8$

more

Direct and Inverse Proportion (Contd)

1. Direct Proportion (Contd)

Question *When a stone is thrown upwards with an initial speed s metres per second, it reaches a maximum height, h metres. Given that h varies directly as the square of s and that h = 5 when s = 10:*
(a) Work out a formula connecting h and s.
(b) Calculate the value of s when h = 20.

(a) h **varies directly** as the square of s is another way of saying that h is directly proportional to s^2 and so we can write:

h = Fixed number $\times s^2$

When $s = 10$, $h = 5$ and so:

5 = Fixed number $\times 10^2$

$\therefore$ Fixed number $= 5 \div 10^2 = 0.05$

So, the formula connecting h and s is: $h = 0.05s^2$.

(b) Putting $h = 20$ in the formula gives:

$20 = 0.05s^2$
$\therefore s^2 = 20 \div 0.05$
$\therefore s^2 = 400$
$\therefore s = \sqrt{400} = 20$ m/s

2. Inverse Proportion

Suppose it takes 8 men 6 hours to dig a hole. Common sense tells us that 4 men would take twice as long as 8 men, i.e. 12 hours. And 2 men would take twice as long as 4 men, i.e. 24 hours.

If we multiply the number of men by the number of hours they take to dig the hole, the result is always the same:

8 men taking 6 hours: $8 \times 6 = 48$
4 men taking 12 hours: $4 \times 12 = 48$
2 men taking 24 hours: $2 \times 24 = 48$

The fewer the men, the longer they take to dig the hole. Generally:

Number of men $\times$ Number of hours = 48

If M men take T hours to dig the hole, we have the formula:

$$M \times T = 48$$

This formula can be rearranged as:

$$M = \frac{48}{T}$$

As the number of men, M, decreases, the number of hours, T, they take to dig the hole increases. We say that the number of men, M, is **inversely proportional** to the number of hours, T, they take to dig the hole. To indicate that M is inversely proportional to T, we write:

$$M \propto \frac{1}{T}$$

Two quantities, M and T, are said to be inversely proportional if they are related by the formula:

$M \times T$ = Fixed number or $M = \dfrac{\text{Fixed number}}{T}$

Here also, the fixed number is called the **constant of proportionality**, and is 48 in the above example.

more

2. Inverse Proportion (Contd)

Question *The pressure, P, of a gas is inversely proportional to its volume, V. Given that P = 50 when V = 200, express P in terms of V and find the value of P when V = 250.*

P is inversely proportional to V and so we can write:

$P \times V$ = Fixed number

We are told that $P = 50$ when $V = 200$. Substitute these values into the equation to find the fixed number:

50×200 = Fixed number
$\therefore$ Fixed number $= 50 \times 200 = 10\,000$

We can now rewrite the equation connecting P and V:

$P \times V = 10\,000$

We can use this formula to find the value of P when $V = 250$:

$P \times 250 = 10\,000$

$\therefore P = \dfrac{10\,000}{250}$

$\therefore P = 40$

3. Inverse Square Law

H

Two quantities, A and B, satisfy the **inverse square law** if A is inversely proportional to B^2, written briefly as:

$$A \propto \frac{1}{B^2}$$

This means that A and B are related by the formula:

$$A = \frac{k}{B^2} \quad \text{or} \quad A \times B^2 = k$$

where k is the constant of proportionality.

Question *The force, F, between two objects is inversely proportional to the square of the distance, d, between them. Given that F = 0.75 when d = 3.8, find the value of d when F = 12.*

The force F is inversely proportional to d^2 and so:

$F \times d^2 = k$

We are given that $F = 0.75$ when $d = 3.8$. Put these values in the equation to find k:

$\therefore 0.75 \times 3.8^2 = k$
$\therefore k = 0.75 \times 3.8^2 = 10.83$

We can now rewrite the equation connecting F and d:

$F \times d^2 = 10.83$

So, when $F = 12$:

$12 \times d^2 = 10.83$
$\therefore d^2 = 10.83 \div 12$
$\therefore d^2 = 0.9025$
$\therefore d = \sqrt{0.9025}$
$\therefore d = 0.95$ (2 dp)

Plotting and Reading Graphs

1. Coordinates and Graphs

A **graph** is a diagram that shows the relationship between two quantities. Each quantity is represented by a straight line called an **axis**.

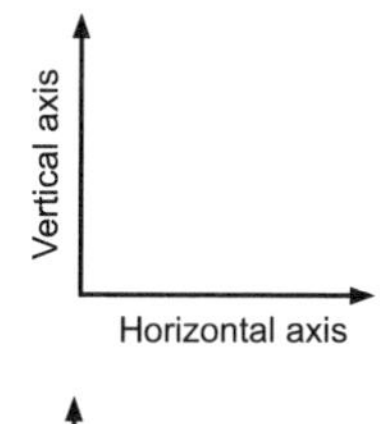

Suppose we are interested in the relationship between Ann's age and weight. We could let the horizontal axis represent her age and the vertical axis represent her weight.

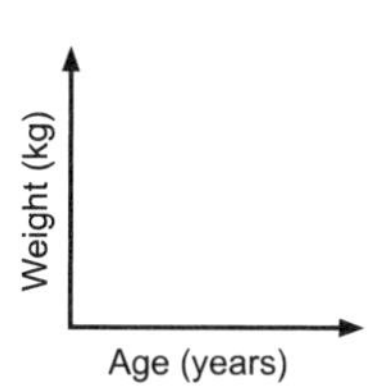

When Ann was 5 years old she weighed 20 kg. The point on the graph represents Ann's age and weight.

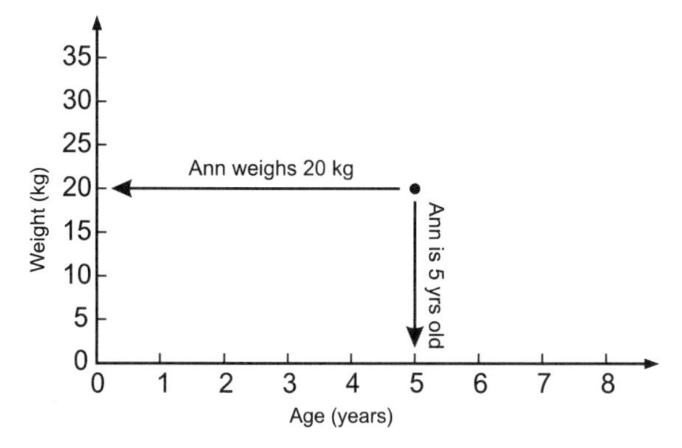

Ann's age and weight can be summarised as (5 yr, 20 kg) or more simply as (5, 20). These numbers are called the **coordinates** of the point on the graph.

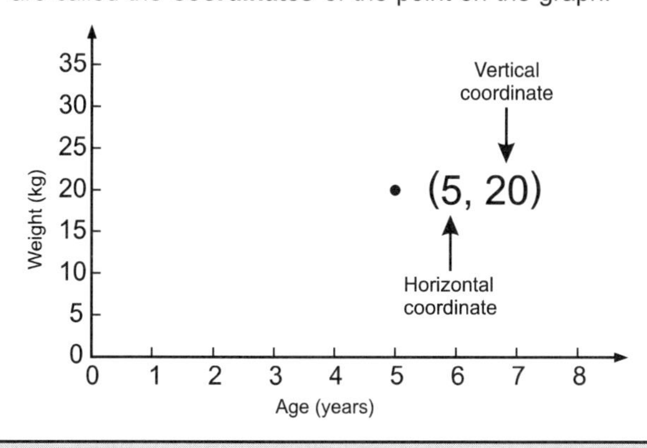

The table below shows Ann's weight at different ages. This is called a **table of values**.

Age (years)	0 (birth)	1	2	3	4	5	6	7	8
Weight (kg)	4	10	13	15	17	20	24	28	32

Each (age, weight) pair of values corresponds to a point on the graph. These points have been plotted on the graph below.

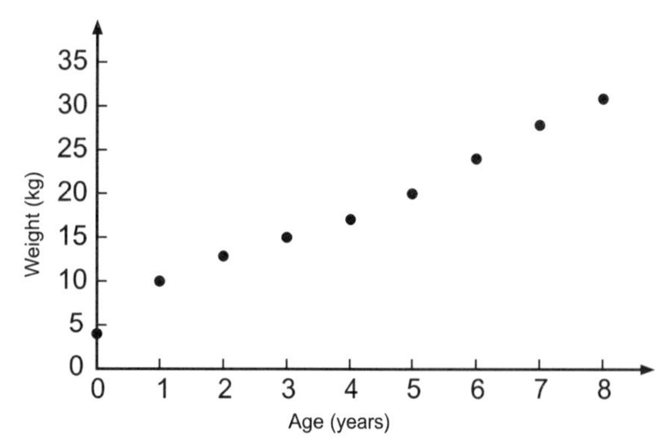

Joining up the dots with a smooth line improves the appearance of the graph and can be very useful (see Boxes 2 and 5).

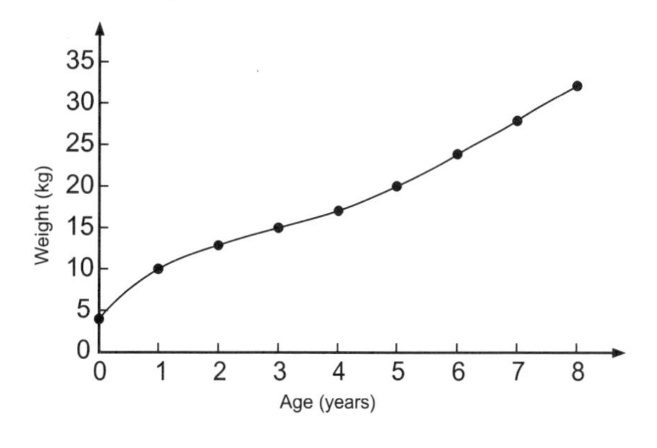

2. Reading Graphs

The graph opposite is called a **currency converter**. It can be used to convert German marks (DM) into pounds sterling (£), and vice-versa.

The dashed lines show that:

£20 is equivalent to 60 DM

120 DM is equivalent to £40

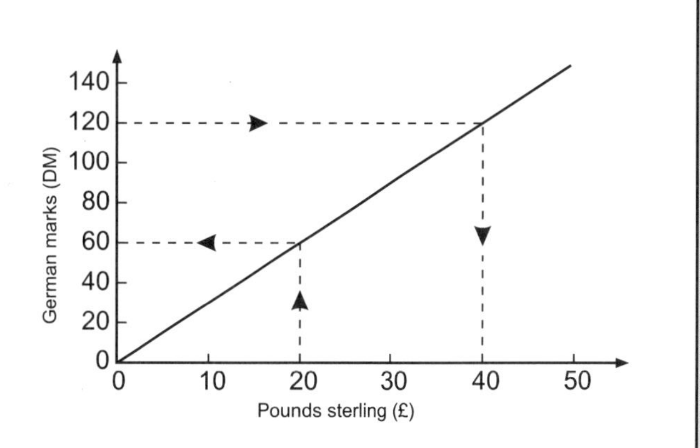

Plotting and Reading Graphs (Contd)

3. The Origin

The axes usually cross at a point called the **origin**, whose coordinates are (0, 0).

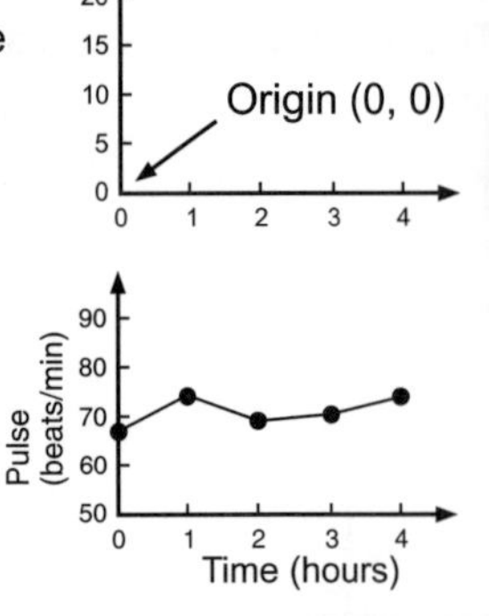

The axes do not need to cross at the origin. For example, the pulse rate of a person at rest is usually somewhere between 50 and 90.

4. Graph Paper

Graph paper is usually divided into 1 cm squares.

Each 1 cm square is further divided into either 5 or 10 smaller squares. There are 5 or 10 small squares along each edge of a 1 cm square.

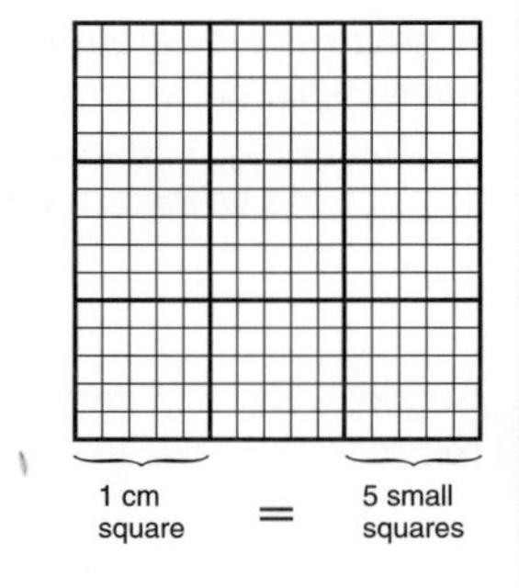

5. Scales

A **scale** states what 1 cm represents on an axis.

The scale for the horizontal axis is:

1 cm represents 1 gallon of petrol

The scale for the vertical axis is:

1 cm represents 100 km

So, 5 small squares represents 100 km

So, 1 small square represents 100 km÷5 = 20 km

From the dashed line we can see that the Vista travels 160 km on 2 gallons of petrol.

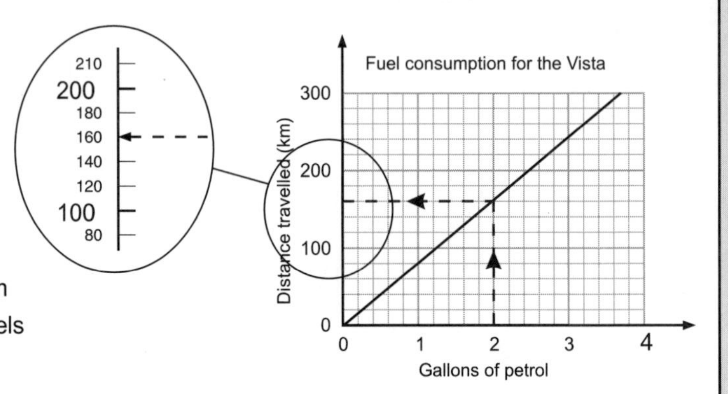

6. *x* and *y* Coordinates

You will come across abstract graphs whose axes do not represent real-life quantities

The horizontal axis is called the ***x*–axis**.

The vertical axis is called the ***y*–axis**.

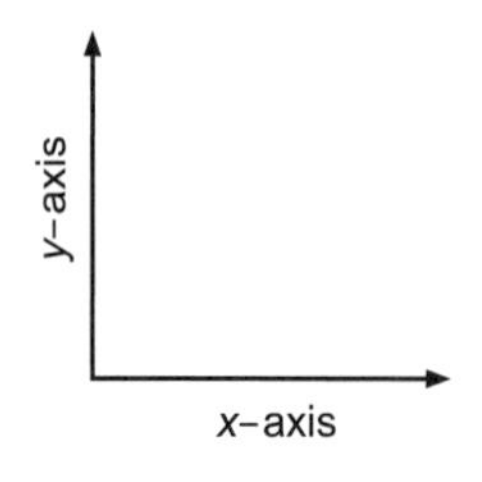

Every point on the graph has an *x* and *y* coordinate.

Remember the order for writing coordinates:

(*x*–coordinate, *y*–coordinate)

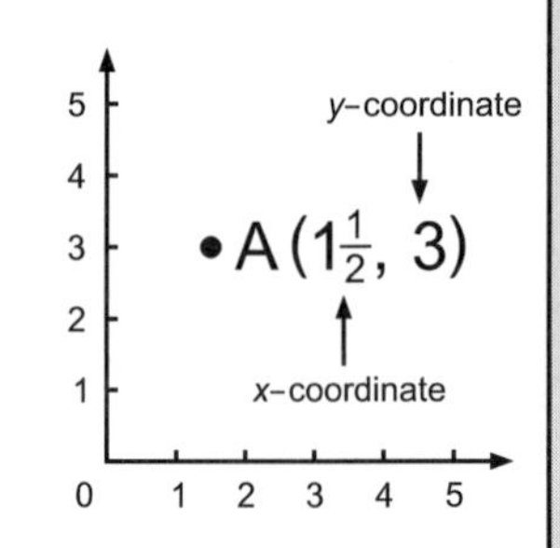

7. Negative Coordinates

The *x* and *y* axes can be extended to include negative numbers.

Point A has coordinates (–2, 4).

Point B has coordinates (1, –4).

Point C has coordinates (–3, –4).

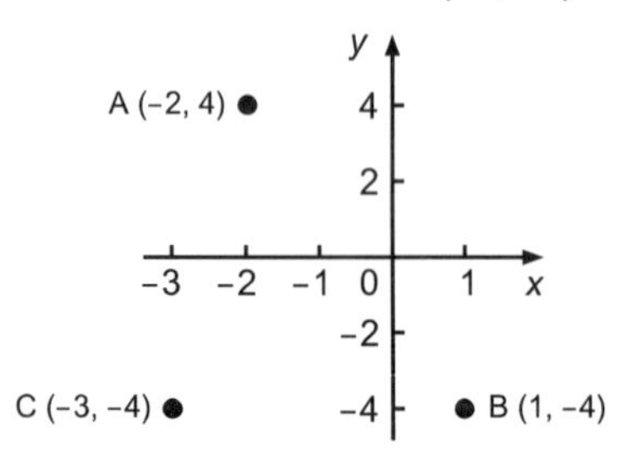

Question *Plot the points A (–3, 2), B (1, 2) and C (1, –2). If ABCD is a rectangle, what are the coordinates of point D?*

There is only one possible rectangle that has A, B and C as corners. The fourth corner is D and has coordinates (–3, –2).

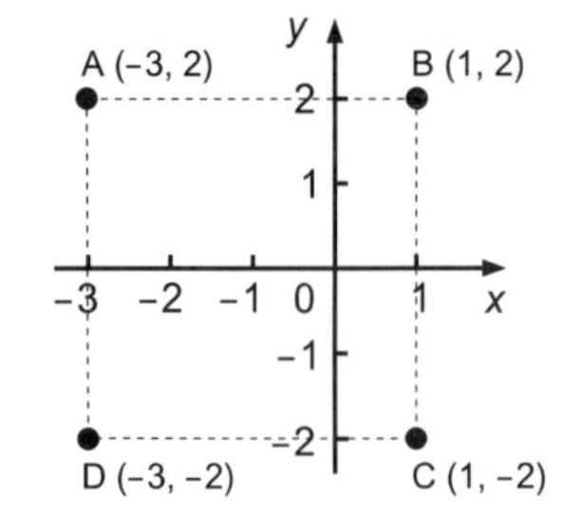

Graphs of Equations

1. Graphs of Equations

Equations can be used to calculate the coordinates of a graph.

Question *Complete the table of coordinates below using the equation $y = 3x^2$.*

x	−2	−1	0	1	2	3
y	12			3		27

Draw the graph of the equation.

The x-coordinates in the table range from $x = -2$ to $x = 3$. Some of the y-coordinates are given; the others must be calculated using the equation $y = 3x^2$

When $x = -1$ $\quad y = 3\times(-1)^2 = 3\times1 = 3$
When $x = 0$ $\quad y = 3\times0^2 = 3\times0 = 0$
When $x = 2$ $\quad y = 3\times2^2 = 3\times4 = 12$

NOTE Use a calculator if you are not very good at mental arithmetic.

The completed table of coordinates is shown below.

x	−2	−1	0	1	2	3
y	12	3	0	3	12	27

The question will include graph paper with labelled axes. Carefully plot the points and join them with a *smooth* curve.

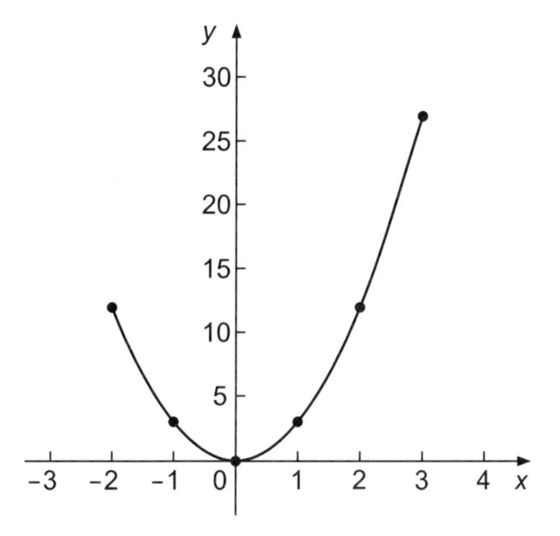

The y-coordinate of each point on the curve can be obtained using the equation of the curve $y = 3x^2$. For example, when $x = 2.5$, $y = 3\times(2.5)^2 = 18.75$. See the dashed line on the graph below.

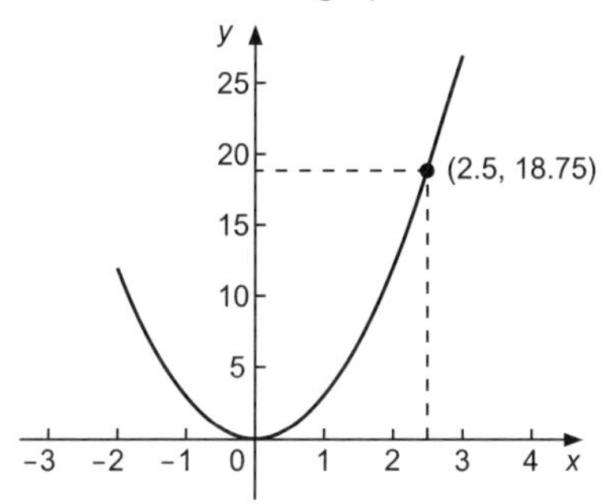

We say that every point on the line **satisfies** the equation $y = 3x^2$. In this case, the point (2.5, 18.75) satisfies the equation $y = 3x^2$.

2. Straight-Line Graphs

You are sometimes expected to make your own table of coordinates, especially for a straight-line graph.

Question *Use the axes provided on the graph paper below to draw the graph of the straight line $y = 2x+2$.*

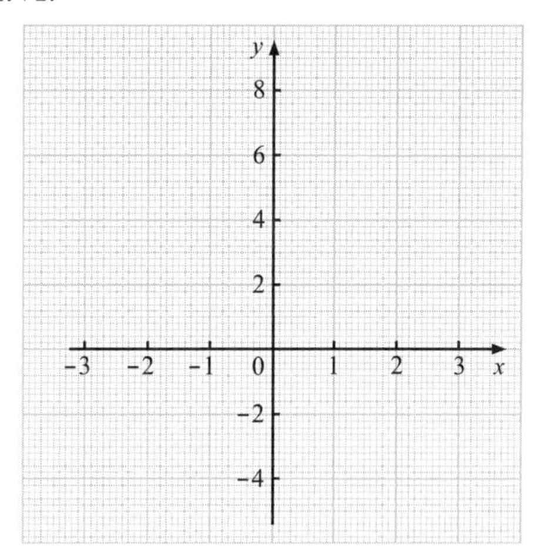

Notice that the x-axis values range from $x = -3$ to $x = 3$. Use the equation to calculate the y-coordinates for these two extreme values of x and for a third value somewhere in between, say $x = 0$.

When $x = -3$ $\quad y = 2\times(-3)+2 = -6+2 = -4$
When $x = 0$ $\quad y = 2\times0+2 = 0+2 = 2$
When $x = 3$ $\quad y = 2\times3+2 = 6+2 = 8$

NOTE Only two points are needed to draw a straight line, but calculating a third point acts as a check, just in case you made a mistake with one of the other points.

You can make a table of these coordinates, but it is not necessary.

x	−3	0	3
y	−4	2	8

Plot the points and join them using a straight line. If they cannot be joined using a straight line, go back and check your calculations.

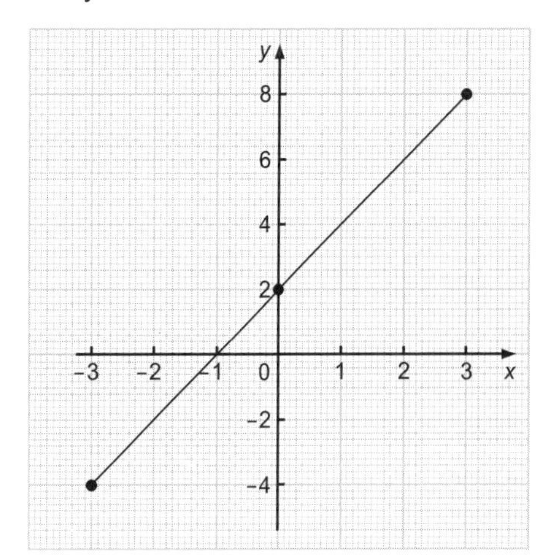

Graphs of Equations (Contd)

3. Using Graphs to Solve Problems

Question *The stopping distance, S m, for a car travelling at a speed of V km/h is given by the formula:*

$$S = 2V + \frac{V^2}{17}$$

Calculate the missing values of S in the table below (to the nearest metre) and plot the graph of S against V. Use your graph to find the speed when the stopping distance is 75 m.

V km/h	5	10	15	20	25	30	35
S m		26		64		113	142

When $V = 5$, $S = 2\times5+\frac{5^2}{17} = 10+\frac{25}{17} = 11.47 \approx 11$

When $V = 15$, $S = 2\times15+\frac{15^2}{17} = 30+\frac{225}{17} = 43.24 \approx 43$

When $V = 25$, $S = 2\times25+\frac{25^2}{17} = 50+\frac{625}{17} = 86.76 \approx 87$

Here is the completed table:

V km/h	5	10	15	20	25	30	35
S m	11	26	43	64	87	113	142

Plot the points and join them with a smooth curve.

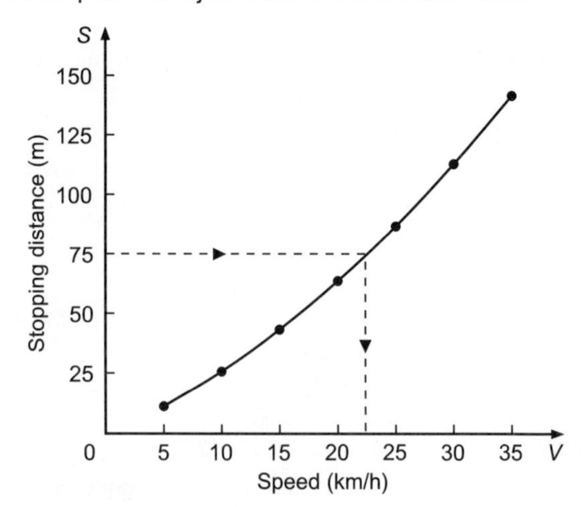

From the graph we can see that $V \approx 22.5$ km/h when $S = 75$ m.

4. Graphs You Should Know

You may be asked to recognise a graph and its equation. Here are a few common examples. Try to remember the general shape of each graph. If you forget, calculate a few values like those in the tables and make a quick sketch.

$y = x^2$

x	-3	-2	-1	0	1	2	3
y	9	4	1	0	1	4	9

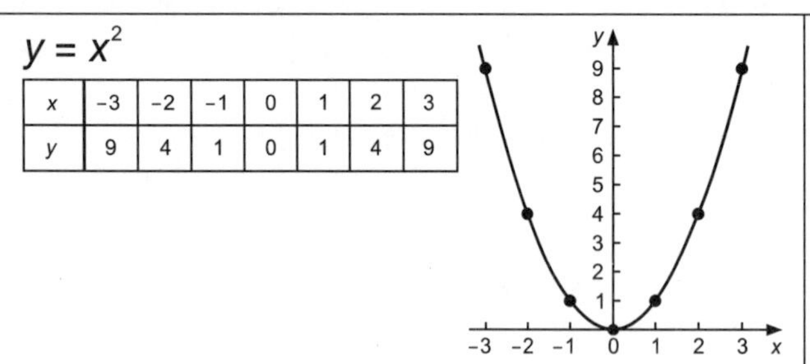

$y = x^3$

x	-2	-1	0	1	2
y	-8	-1	0	1	8

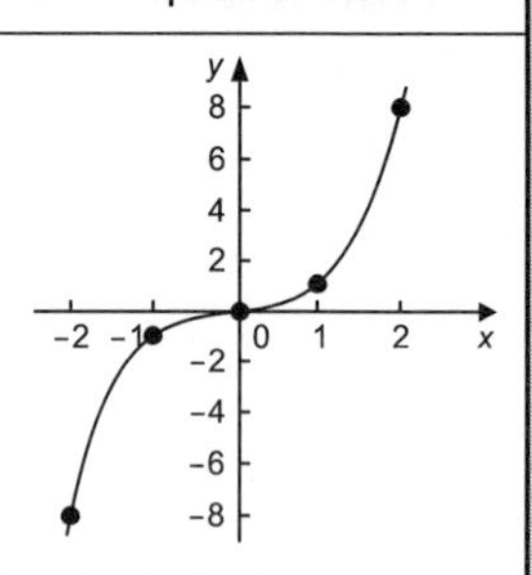

$y = \frac{1}{x}$

x	-1.5	-1	-0.5	0	0.5	1	1.5
y	-0.7	-1	-2	↑	2	1	0.7

$\frac{1}{0}$ cannot be calculated

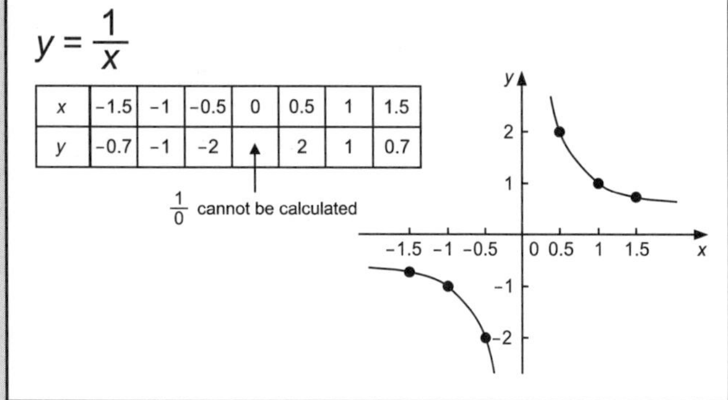

$y = \frac{1}{x^2}$

x	-1.5	-1	-0.5	0	0.5	1	1.5
y	0.4	1	4	↑	4	1	0.4

$\frac{1}{0^2}$ cannot be calculated

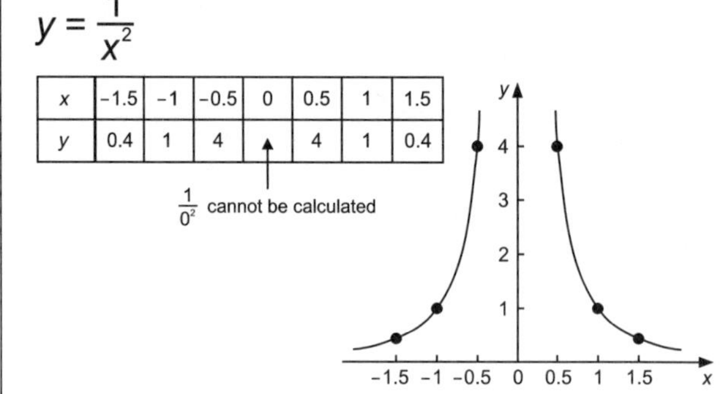

$y = \sqrt{x}$

x	0	1	4	9	16
y	0	1	2	3	4

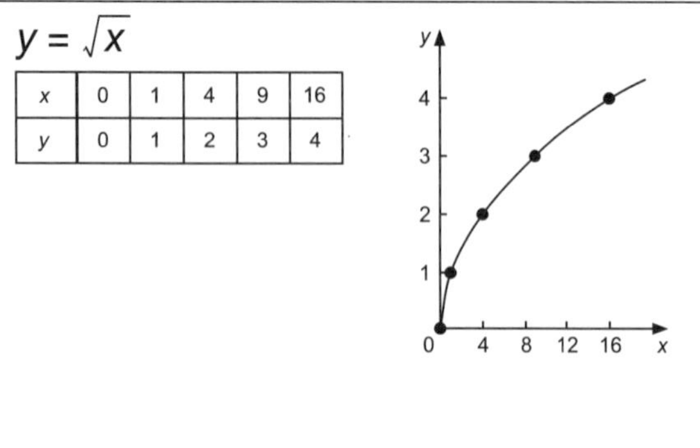

$y = x$

x	-2	-1	0	1	2
y	-2	-1	0	1	2

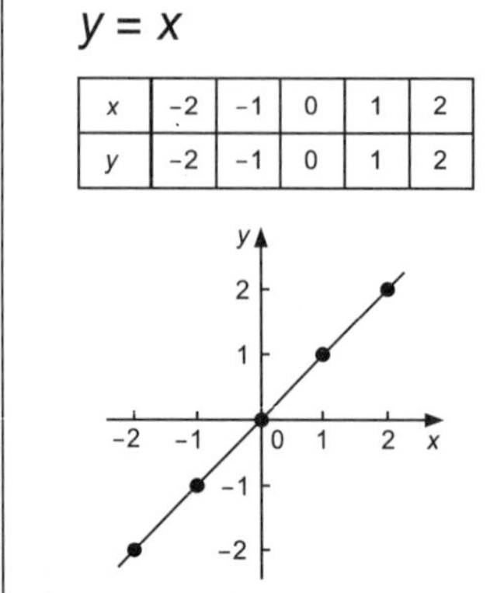

$y = -x$

x	-2	-1	0	1	2
y	2	1	0	-1	-2

Equation of a Straight Line

1. Gradient of a Straight Line

The **gradient** of a straight line is a measure of how steep it is: the bigger the gradient, the steeper the line.

Big gradient / Steep line

Small gradient / Shallow line

To find the gradient of a straight line, first choose any two points on the line (the further apart, the more accurate your answer).

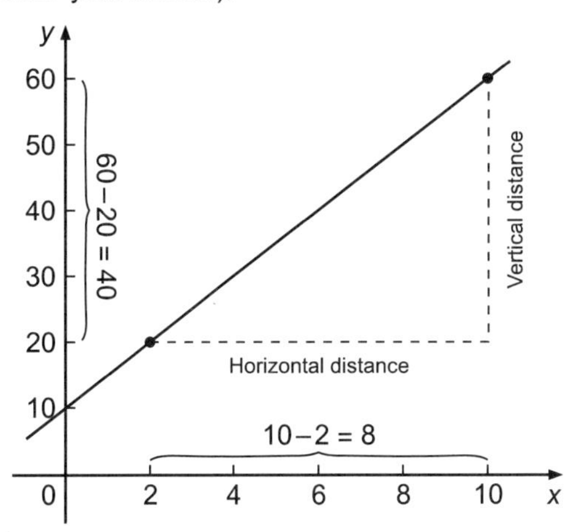

Find the vertical and horizontal distances between the two points:

Vertical distance = 60 − 20 = 40
Horizontal distance = 10 − 2 = 8

Then calculate the gradient using the formula:

$$\text{Gradient} = \frac{\text{Vertical distance}}{\text{Horizontal distance}}$$

For this line, we have:

$$\text{Gradient} = \frac{40}{8} = 5$$

A gradient of 5 means 5 up for every 1 along

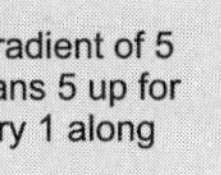

Sign of the Gradient

Gradients can be positive or negative (or 0), depending on the direction of the line.

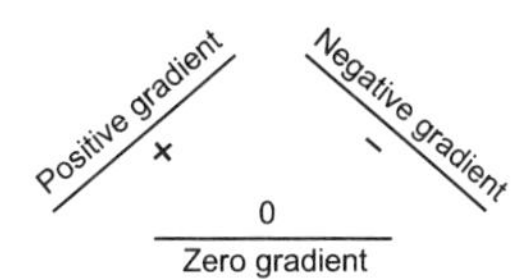

Example

Vertical distance
= 8 − 2 = 6
Horizontal distance
= 4 − 0 = 4

$$\text{Gradient} = -\frac{6}{4} = -1.5$$

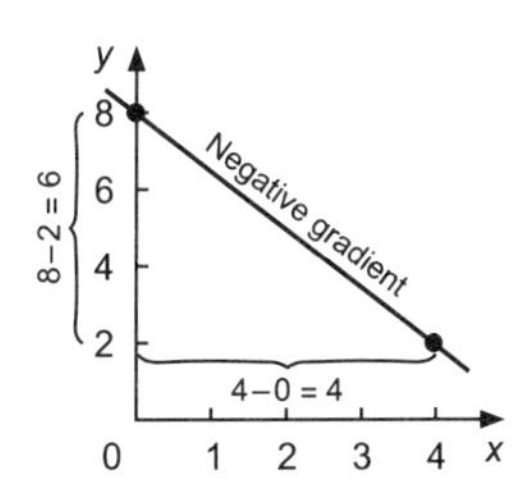

NOTE The horizontal and vertical distances are always *positive* numbers (6 and 4). Put the minus sign before the fraction.

Parallel lines have the same gradient.

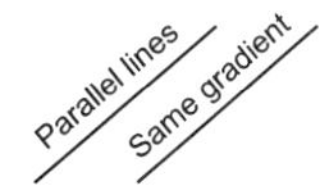

2. Equation of a Straight Line

The equation $y = 5x + 10$ was used to calculate the coordinates in the table below.

x	0	2	4	6	8	10
y	10	20	30	40	50	60

For example, when $x = 4$, $y = 5 \times 4 + 10 = 30$. Plotting these points gives a straight-line graph. This is the same straight line as in Box 1.

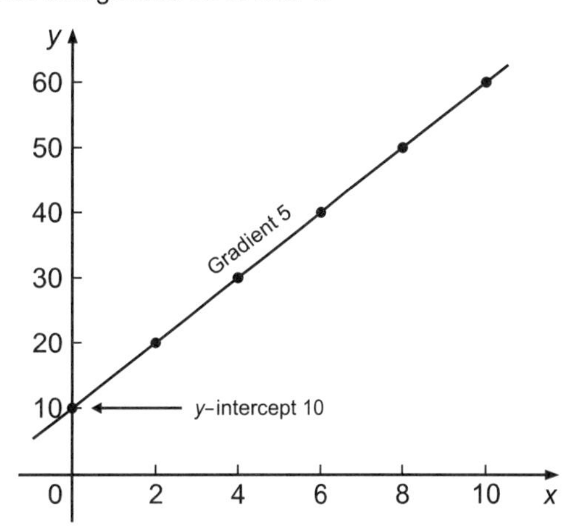

Notice that the line crosses the y-axis at $y = 10$. This is called the ***y*-intercept**.

Also, the gradient of the line is 5 (see Box 1).

These two numbers, 5 and 10, appear in the equation of the straight line (see top of page):

$$y = 5x + 10$$

(5 = Gradient, 10 = y-intercept)

So, the equation of a straight line can be written:
y = (gradient)x + (y-intercept)

This can also be written algebraically as:

$$y = mx + c$$

(m = Gradient, c = y-intercept)

For example, $y = -3x + 30$ is the equation of a straight line whose gradient is −3 and which crosses the y-axis at $y = 30$ (see diagram below).

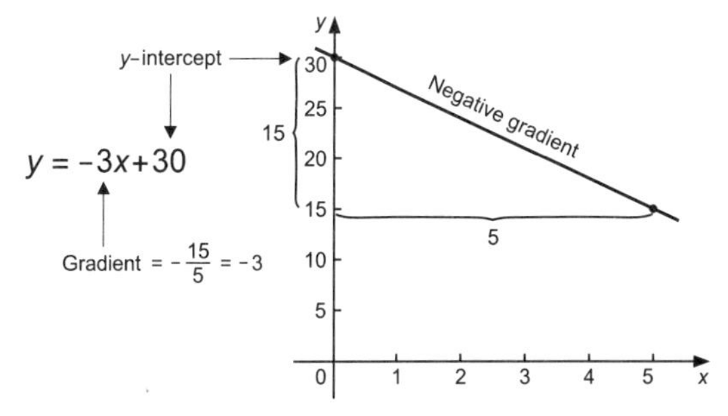

Comparing $y = -3x + 30$ with the general equation of a straight line $y = mx + c$, we can see that the gradient is $m = -3$ and the y-intercept is $c = 30$.

Equation of a Straight Line (Contd)

3. Straight–Line Graphs You Should Know

Here are some graphs whose equations do not look like $y = mx+c$. You should be able to recognise each graph and its equation. You should also be able to draw each graph, given its equation.

$y = 2$

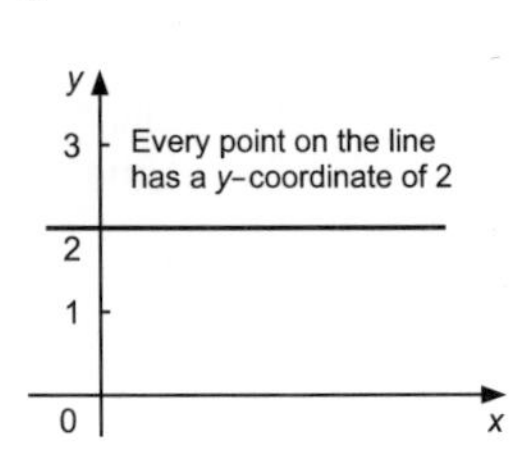

$x = 2$

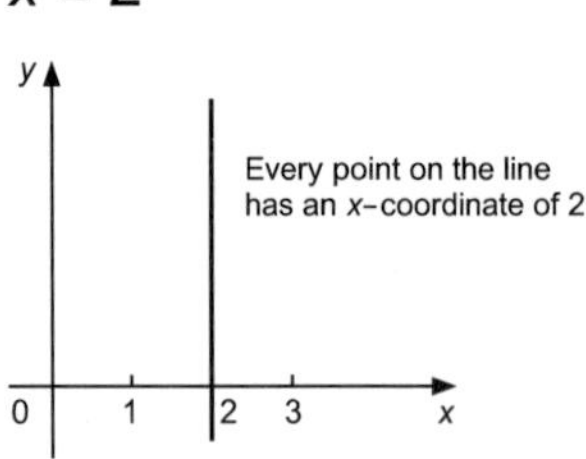

$y = x$

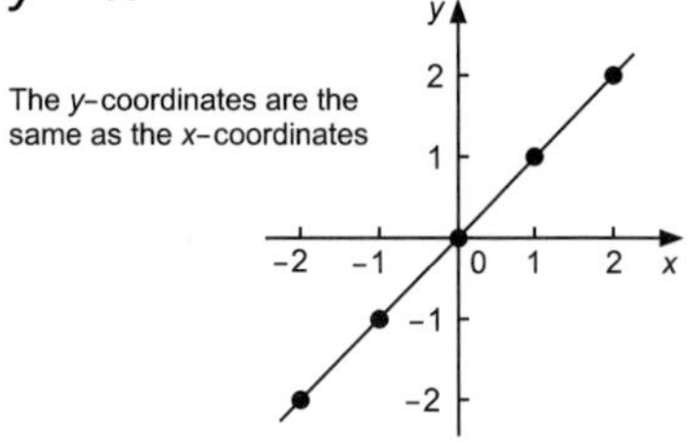

$y = 0$

The x–axis is a straight line with equation $y = 0$. Each point on the line has a y–coordinate of 0

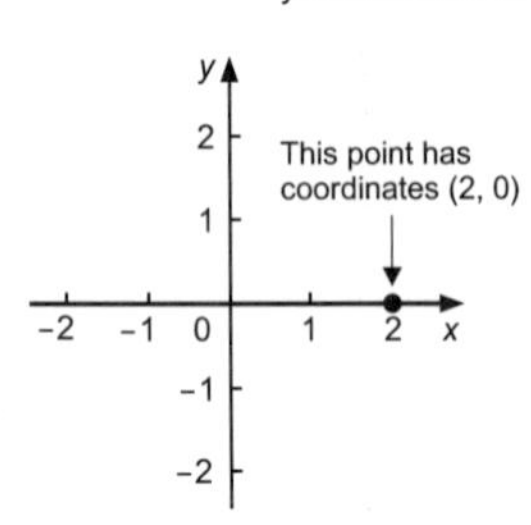

$x = 0$

The y–axis is a straight line with equation $x = 0$. Each point on the line has an x–coordinate of 0

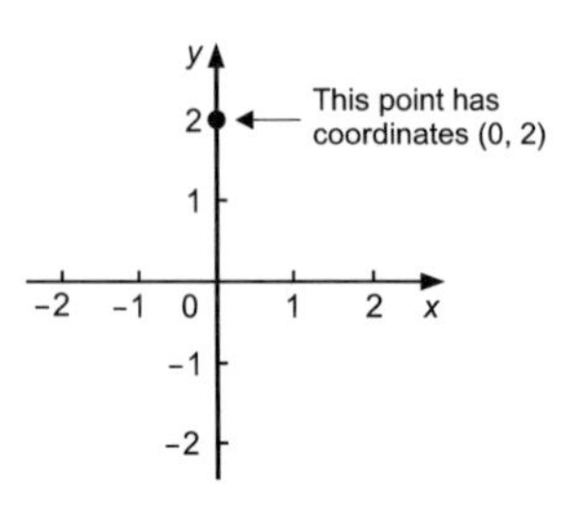

$y = -x$ or $x+y = 0$

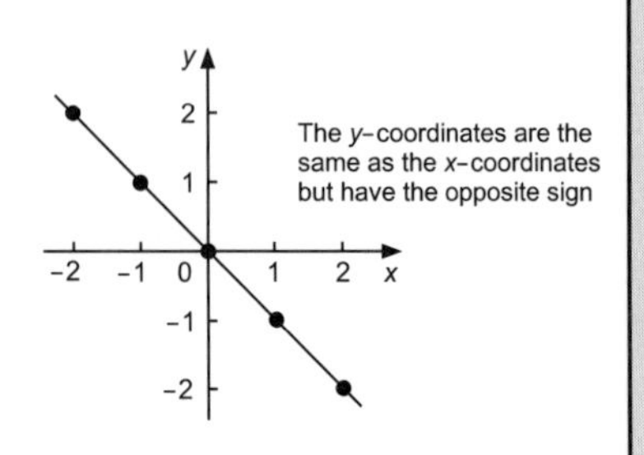

4. Rearranging Equations

Quite often the equation of a straight line is not in the form $y = mx+c$. Rearrange the equation into this form if you need to find the gradient or y–intercept.

Question *Find the gradient and y–intercept of the straight line with equation $x-2y = 6$. Make a sketch of the graph.*

Rearrange the equation into the form $y = mx+c$.

$x-2y = 6$

$\therefore\ x = 6+2y$ — Move $-2y$ to RHS; change to $+2y$

$\therefore\ x-6 = 2y$ — Move $+6$ to LHS; change to -6

$\therefore\ 2y = x-6$ — Turn the equation around

$\therefore\ \frac{2y}{2} = \frac{x}{2} - \frac{6^3}{2}$ — Divide both sides by 2

$\therefore\ y = \frac{1}{2}x-3$ — NOTE $\frac{x}{2}$ is the same as $\frac{1}{2}x$

(Gradient $\frac{1}{2}$, y–intercept -3)

So, the gradient is $\frac{1}{2}$ and the y–intercept is -3.

To make a quick sketch, draw both axes (don't bother about scales). Mark the y–intercept. Since the gradient is positive, draw an upward sloping line through the y–intercept.

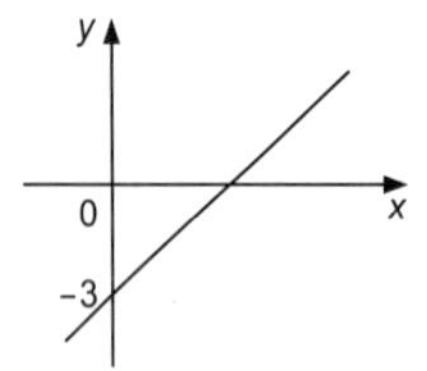

5. Quick Way of Drawing Straight Line Graphs

A quick way to draw a straight–line graph is to join the points where it crosses the x and y axes.

Question *Draw the graph of the straight line with equation $5x+3y = 12$.*

The point where the line crosses the x–axis has a y–coordinate of 0 (see Box 3). So, we can find this x–coordinate by putting $y = 0$ in the equation.

$5x+3\times0 = 12$

$\therefore\ 5x+0 = 12$

$\therefore\ 5x = 12$

$\therefore\ x = \frac{12}{5} = 2.4$

So, the straight line crosses the x–axis at $x = 2.4$ (see graph below).

Similarly, we can find the y–coordinate by putting $x = 0$ in the equation:

$5\times0+3y = 12$

$\therefore\ 0+3y = 12$

$\therefore\ 3y = 12$

$\therefore\ y = 4$

So, the straight line crosses the y–axis at $y = 4$.

Mark these two points on the axes and join them up.

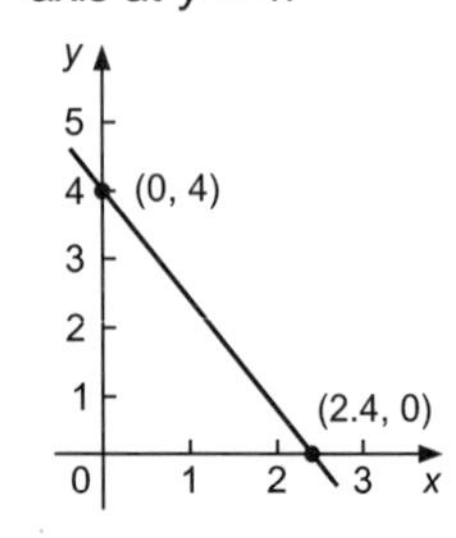

6. Finding the Equation of a Straight Line

Question *The table below shows some temperatures measured both in degrees Fahrenheit and Celsius.*

Celsius (C)	*-10*	*0*	*15*	*40*	*60*
Fahrenheit (F)	*14*	*32*	*59*	*104*	*140*

(a) Draw the graph of F against C.
(b) Find the F-intercept of the straight line.
(c) Find the gradient of the straight line.
(d) Write down the equation of the straight line.
(e) Use your equation to calculate the temperature which is the same measured in degrees Fahrenheit or Celsius.

(a) Carefully plot the points and join them with a straight line.

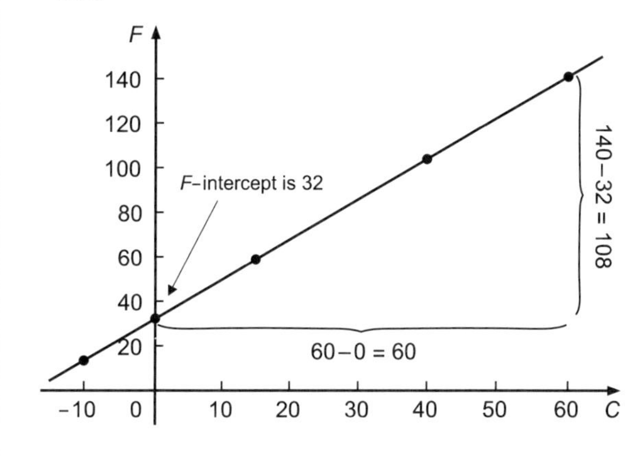

(b) The line crosses the F-axis at $F = 32$

(c) Gradient $= \frac{\text{Vertical distance}}{\text{Horizontal distance}} = \frac{108}{60} = 1.8$

(d) Equation of a straight line is (see Box 2, p57):

$y = (\text{gradient})x + (y\text{-intercept})$

Replace y by F and x by C

$F = (\text{gradient})C + (F\text{-intercept})$

$\therefore\ F = 1.8C+32$

(e) When F is the same as C the equation becomes:

$C = 1.8C+32$

$\therefore\ 0 = 1.8C-C+32$ Move C to RHS; change to $-C$

$\therefore\ 0 = 0.8C+32$ Simplify

$\therefore\ -32 = 0.8C$ Move +32 to LHS; change to −32

$\therefore\ 0.8C = -32$ Turn the equation around

$\therefore\ C = \frac{-32}{0.8} = -40$ Move $0.8\times$ to RHS; change to $\div 0.8$

So, −40 °C is the same as −40 °F.

Rate of Change

1. Rate of Change

Rate of change tells you how much one quantity changes as another, related quantity changes. For example, a car hire firm might hire out a Ford Fiesta at a rate of £40 per day, i.e. the hire charge increases by £40 for each extra day of hire.

A rate of change can be written as an equation. The above rate of £40 per day could be written:

Hire charge for 1 day = £40

This can help to solve problems.

Question *1 litre of water flows from a hosepipe every 12 seconds. What is the rate of flow in litres per minute?*

We must find how much water flows per minute, i.e. in 1 minute.

12 seconds of flow = 1 litre

$\therefore$ 1 second of flow $= \frac{1\text{ litre}}{12} = 0.0833$ litres

$\therefore$ 60 seconds of flow $= 60\times0.0833$ litres = 5 litres

$\therefore$ 1 minute of flow = 5 litres

So, the rate of flow is 5 litres per minute. This can be written briefly as 5ℓ per min or 5ℓ/min.

2. Rate of Change and Gradient

The rate of change of two quantities is the same as the gradient of their graph.

Question *Calculate the gradient of this currency conversion graph. Explain what your answer means?*

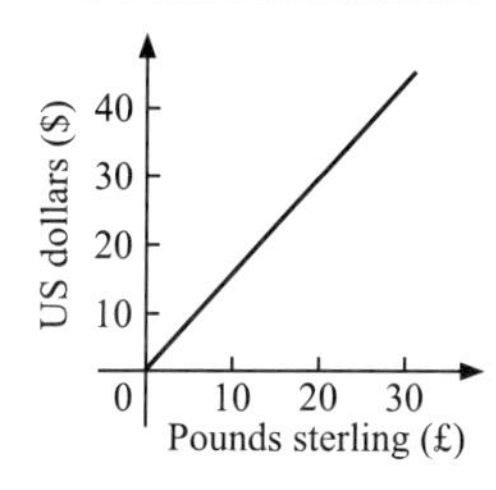

Gradient

$= \frac{\text{Vertical distance}}{\text{Horizontal distance}}$

$= \frac{\$30}{£20}$

$= \frac{\$1.5}{£1}$

Now, $\frac{\$1.5}{£1}$ can be written as \$1.5/£1, or simply \$1.5/£, which is said '\$1.5 per £'. In other words, £1 is equivalent to \$1.5. So, this gradient is the rate of exchange from pounds sterling (£) to US dollars (\$).

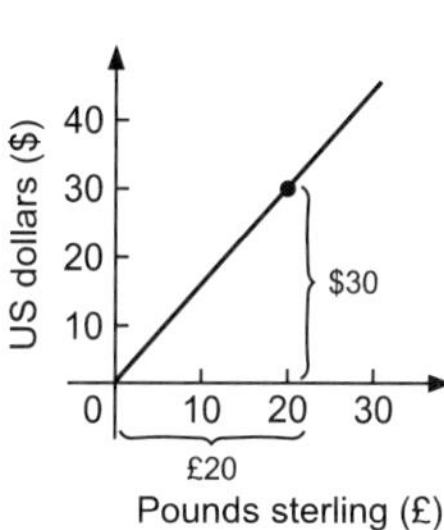

Rate of Change (Contd)

3. Practical Examples of Rate of Change

You may be shown a graph and asked to comment on the rate of change. If the graph is a straight line, it has a constant gradient and so the rate of change is also constant.

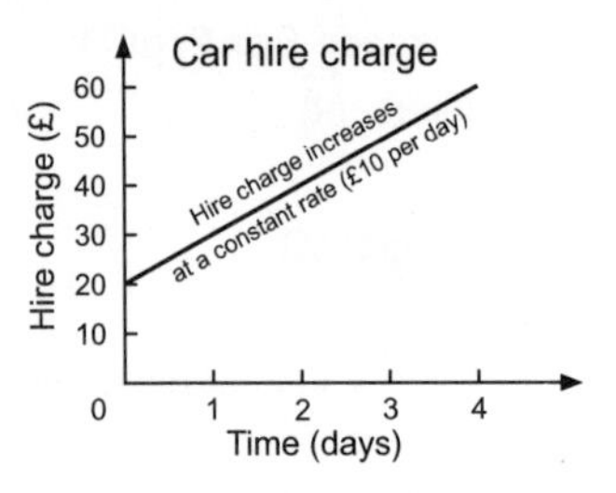

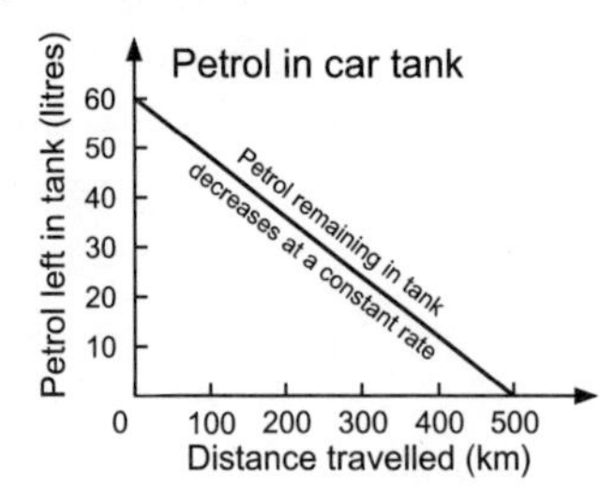

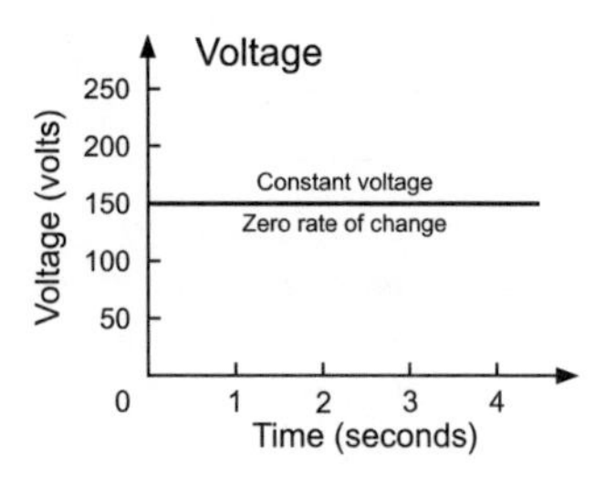

If the graph is curved, the gradient (steepness) changes and so the rate of change also changes: the steeper the line, the faster the rate of change.

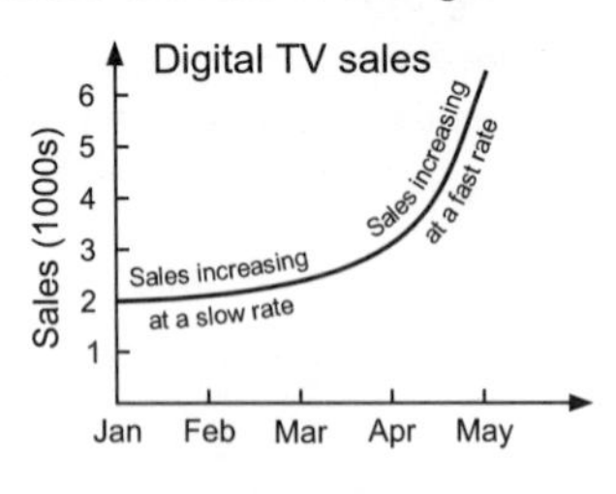

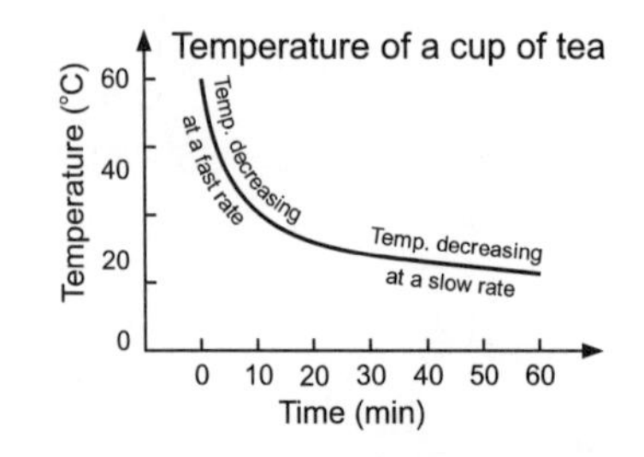

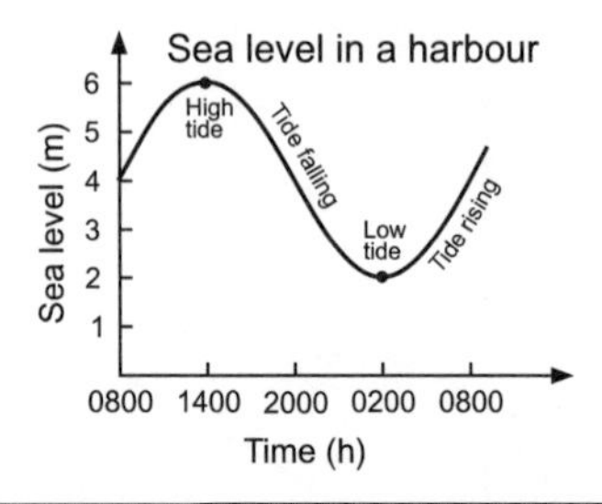

Speed, Distance and Time

1. Time

It is sometimes necessary to convert a period of time into different units. Use the conversion diagram below.

To convert a big unit to a small unit, **multiply**

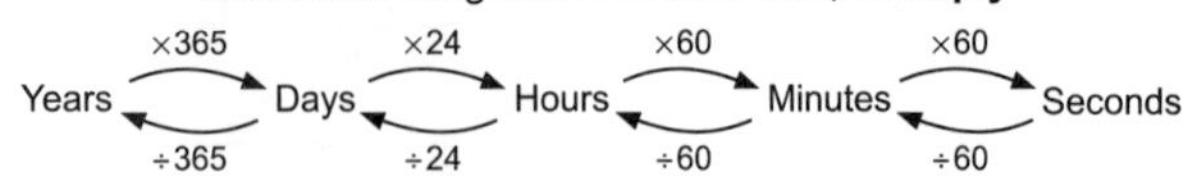

To convert a small unit to a big unit, **divide**

Question *How many minutes are there in a year?*

1 year = 365 days = 365×24 hours
= $365 \times 24 \times 60$ minutes
= 525 600 minutes

Question *Convert 132 minutes to hours.*

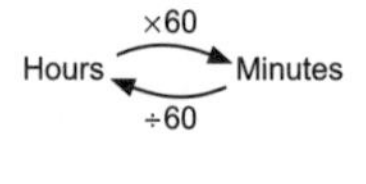

132 minutes = $\frac{132}{60}$ hours = 2.2 hours

0.2 h = 0.2×60 min = 12 min

So, 132 min = 2 h 12 min.

2. Speed

A speed of 5 km/h means that a distance of 5 km is travelled in 1 hour.

Speed (s), distance (d) and time (t) are related by the formula:

$$\text{Speed} = \frac{\text{Distance}}{\text{Time}} \quad \text{or} \quad s = \frac{d}{t}$$

Question *A racing cyclist travelled 65 km in 1 hour 48 minutes. Calculate her speed in km/h.*

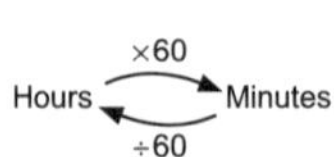

First, convert 48 minutes to hours:
48 minutes = $\frac{48}{60}$ hours = 0.8 hours
So, 1 hour 48 minutes = 1.8 hours

$$\text{Speed} = \frac{\text{Distance}}{\text{Time}} = \frac{65 \text{ km}}{1.8 \text{ h}} = 36.1 \text{ km/h}$$

NOTE It is unlikely that the cyclist kept up a *constant* speed of exactly 36.1 km/h. So we say that his **average speed** was 36.1 km/h for the journey.

Question *Convert 25 km/h to m/s.*

First, convert 25 km to metres:

25 km = 25×1000 = 25 000 m

Then, convert 1 hour to seconds:

1 h = 60×60 = 3600 s

25 km/h means 25 km is travelled in 1 hour and so:

$$\text{Speed} = \frac{\text{Distance}}{\text{Time}} = \frac{25 \text{ km}}{1 \text{ h}} = \frac{25\,000 \text{ m}}{3600 \text{ s}} = 6.94 \text{ m/s}$$

Question *John drives his car at a constant speed of 50 km/h for 18 minutes. How far does he travel?*

In 1 hour John travels 50 km
∴ In 60 minutes John travels 50 km
∴ In 1 minute John travels $\frac{50}{60} = \frac{5}{6}$ km
∴ In 18 minutes John travels $18 \times \frac{5}{6}$ km = 15 km

3. Accuracy When Measuring Speed

Question *Jill ran a distance of 100 m, measured correct to the nearest metre. Her stopwatch showed she took 14.8 seconds, correct to the nearest tenth of a second.*
(a) Write down the longest possible distance she ran.
(b) Write down the shortest possible time she took.
(c) Calculate her maximum possible average speed.

(a) Maximum possible distance run is 100.5 m

(b) Minimum possible time taken is 14.75 s

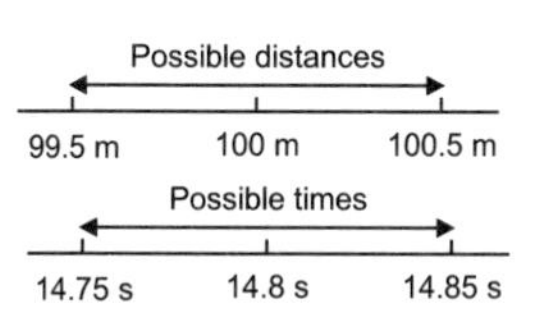

(c) Maximum possible speed $= \dfrac{\text{Maximum possible distance}}{\text{Minimum possible time taken}}$

$= \dfrac{100.5 \text{ m}}{14.75 \text{ s}} = 6.8 \text{ m/s (1 dp)}$

4. Distance–Time Graph

A **distance–time graph** illustrates a journey.The y-axis represents the distance (route) travelled and the x-axis represents time.

Question *Dieter left home at 3.00 pm and cycled along the main road to the park 5 km away. He arrived at 3.30 pm and played football for 1 hour 30 minutes and then cycled home at an average speed of 6 km/h.*
(a) Draw a distance–time graph for his journey.
(b) Which part of the journey did he cycle the faster?
(c) What was his average speed on the outward journey?

(a) Dieter started from home at 3.00 pm, which is where the axes cross. At 3.30 pm he arrived at the park, 5 km away. Mark this point. At 5.00 pm he was still at the park. Mark this point. He cycled home over a distance of 5 km at a speed of 6 km/h. We need to find the time he arrived home.
A speed of 6 km/h means:
6 km = 1 hour = 60 minutes
∴ 1 km = 10 minutes
∴ 5 km = 50 minutes
So, Dieter arrived home at 5.50 pm. Mark this point. Join the points with straight lines.

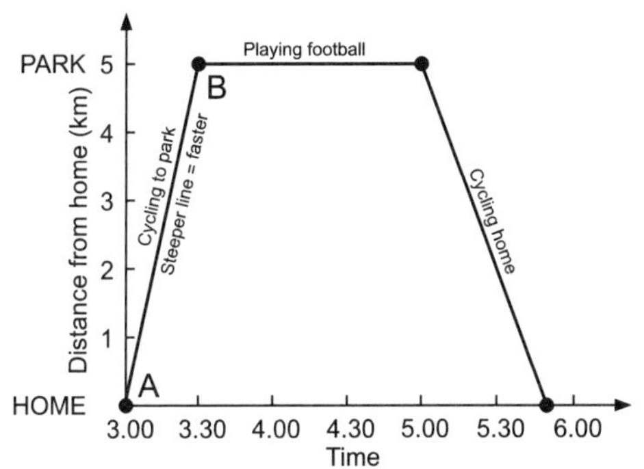

(b) The steeper the line, the greater the speed.

So, Dieter cycled faster from home to the park.

(c) Speed = Gradient of distance–time graph

Speed from home to park = Gradient of line AB

$= \dfrac{\text{Distance travelled}}{\text{Time taken}}$

$= \dfrac{5 \text{ km}}{30 \text{ min}} = \dfrac{5 \text{ km}}{0.5 \text{ h}} = 10 \text{ km/h}$

5. Acceleration

Acceleration is the rate at which speed changes. For example, an acceleration of 5 m/s per second means that the speed increases by 5 m/s every second. An acceleration of 5 m/s per second is written briefly as 5 m/s^2.

Acceleration (a), speed (s) and time (t) are related by the formula:

$$\text{Acceleration} = \frac{\text{Change in speed}}{\text{Time taken}} \quad \text{or} \quad a = \frac{s}{t}$$

Question *A car increases its speed from 15 m/s to 20 m/s in 10 seconds. Calculate the car's acceleration.*

$$\text{Acceleration} = \frac{\text{Change in speed}}{\text{Time taken}} = \frac{20-15}{10} = \frac{5}{10} = 0.5 \text{ m/s}^2$$

6. Speed–Time Graph

Question *A tram travels between two stops. The speed–time graph for the journey is shown below.*
(a) What is the speed of the tram after 8 seconds?
(b) Calculate the acceleration of the tram during the first 10 seconds.
(c) Calculate the distance travelled by the tram when it is travelling at a constant speed.

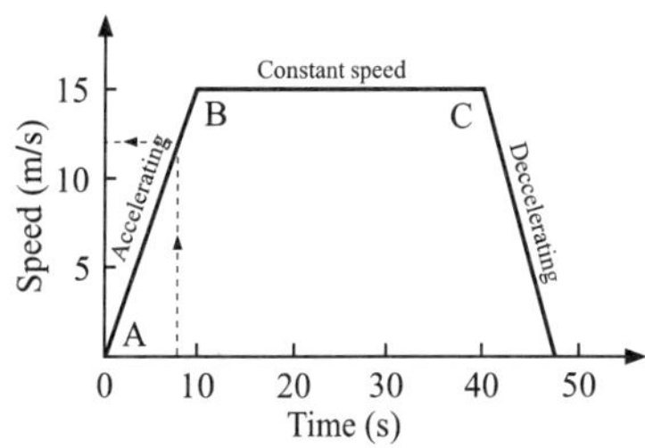

(a) Speed after 8 seconds is 12 m/s (see dashed line).

(b) Acceleration = Gradient of speed–time graph

The tram accelerates from 0 m/s to 15 m/s in 10 seconds. So:

Acceleration = Gradient of AB $= \frac{15-0}{10} = \frac{15}{10} = 1.5 \text{ m/s}^2$

(c) Tram speed is 15 m/s for 30 seconds from B to C. 15 m/s means the tram travels 15 m in 1 second. So, in 30 seconds, tram travels 30×15 m = 450 m.

Tangents and Area Under a Curve H

1. Tangent to a Curve

When a straight line touches a curve at just one point, it is called a **tangent** to the curve.

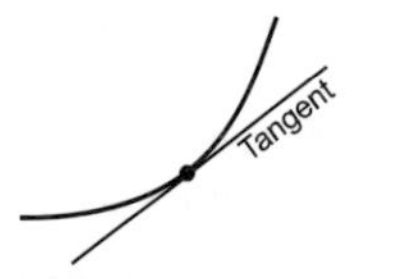

2. Drawing a Tangent to a Curve

To draw a tangent to a curve, first mark the point on the curve where you want the tangent. Gradually move your ruler towards the point, keeping an equal length of curve on either side of the point. When you can only see the point on the curve, draw the tangent.

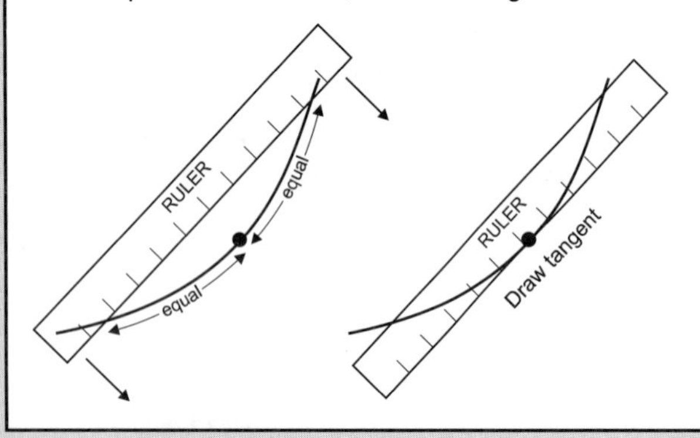

3. Gradient of a Curve

The gradient (steepness) of a curve varies from point to point. So we can only find the gradient at a particular point on a curve

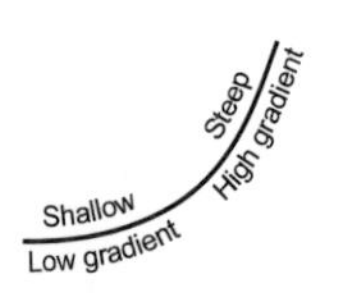

The gradient of a curve at a particular point is the gradient of the tangent to the curve at that point

Question *The distance-time graph shows the first 20 seconds of a car journey.*
(a) Draw the tangent to the curve where t = 15 seconds.
(b) Calculate the gradient of the curve at this point.
(c) What does this gradient represent?

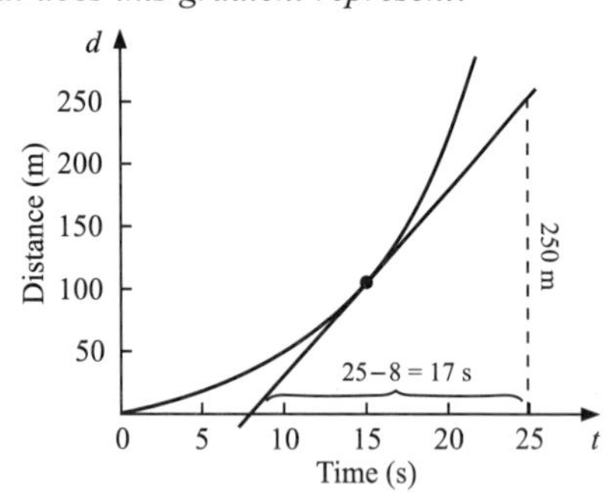

(a) Mark the point on the curve where $x = 15$ and draw the tangent to the curve at this point. Draw the tangent as long as possible.

(b) Calculate the gradient of the tangent. First, choose any two points on the tangent (the further apart, the more accurate your answer). Then:

$$\text{Gradient of curve} = \text{Gradient of tangent} = \frac{250\text{ m}}{17\text{ s}} = 14.7\text{ m/s}$$

(c) From part (b), the gradient represents the speed of the car after the first 15 seconds of its journey.

4. Estimating Areas on Graph Paper

Graph paper is divided into 1 cm squares. The area of a 1 cm square is written 1 cm^2. If you have to estimate the area of a shape drawn on graph paper, it is only necessary to estimate to the nearest quarter of a square.

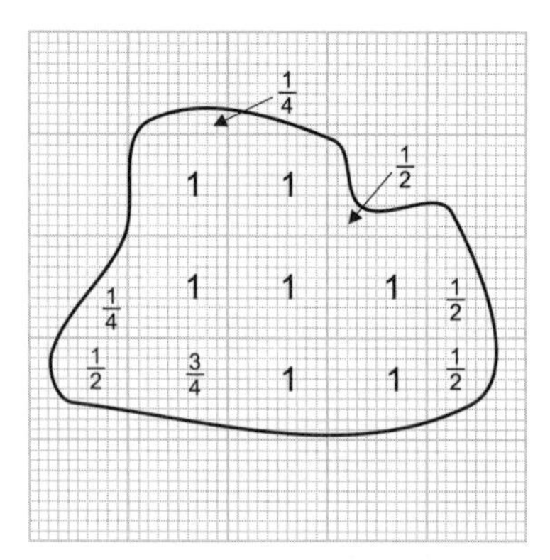

The area of the above shape is approximately:
$7 + \frac{1}{4} + \frac{1}{2} + \frac{1}{4} + \frac{3}{4} + \frac{1}{2} + \frac{1}{2} + \frac{1}{2}$
$= 10.25$ square centimetres $= 10.25$ cm^2

5. Estimating the Area Under a Curve

Question *Estimate the area under this curve.*

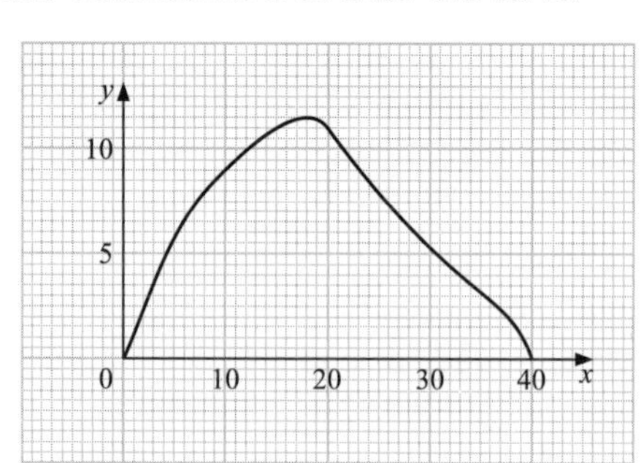

First, use the scales for the x and y axes to find what a 1 cm square *represents.*

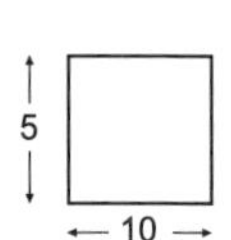

Area = Base×Height
= 10×5 = 50 square units

Now estimate the number of 1 cm squares under the curve (from left to right):

$\frac{3}{4} + \frac{1}{4} + 1 + 1 + \frac{1}{4} + \frac{1}{2} + 1 + \frac{1}{2} = 5.25$

So, area under curve $\approx 5.25 \times 50$ square units
≈ 260 square units

NOTE Sometimes we can calculate the *exact* area under a curve. The area under the curve below is the area of the trapezium ABCD.

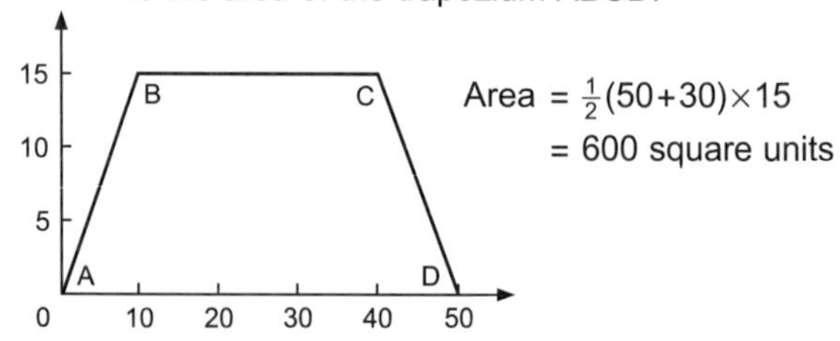

Area $= \frac{1}{2}(50+30) \times 15$
$= 600$ square units

6. Trapezium Rule

Another way of estimating the area under a curve is to use the **trapezium rule**.

Question *The diagram shows the cross-section of an excavated trench. The depth of the trench was measured at 1 metre intervals as shown.*

(a) Use the trapezium rule to estimate the area of the cross-section.

(b) Estimate the volume of earth removed in digging the trench, given that the trench is 20 m long.

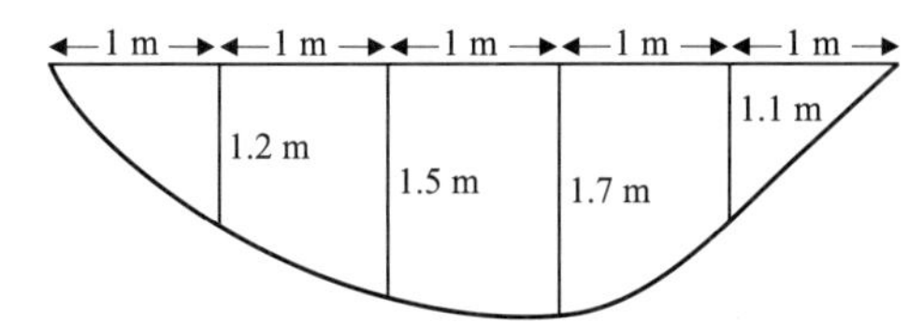

Trapezium Rule

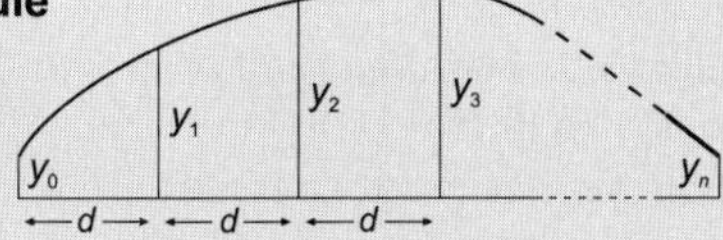

Area under curve $\approx \frac{d}{2}(y_0 + 2y_1 + 2y_2 + ... + y_n)$

(a) d is the interval between measurements. In this case, $d = 1$.

The measurements are labelled y_0, y_1, y_2, ... In this case, $y_0 = 0$, $y_1 = 1.2$, $y_2 = 1.5$, $y_3 = 1.7$, $y_4 = 1.1$ and $y_5 = 0$.

NOTE The left and right edges of the trench have a depth of 0, and so $y_0 = 0$ and $y_5 = 0$

Area $\approx \frac{1}{2}(0+2\times1.2+2\times1.5+2\times1.7+2\times1.1+0)$
$= 0.5\times11 = 5.5 \text{ m}^2$

(b) Volume of trench = Area of cross-section $\times$ Length
$= 5.5\times20 = 110 \text{ m}^3$

7. Area Under a Speed–Time Curve

The area under a speed-time curve is equal to the distance travelled.

Question *A motorcycle travels between two sets of traffic lights. The speed-time graph is shown below.*

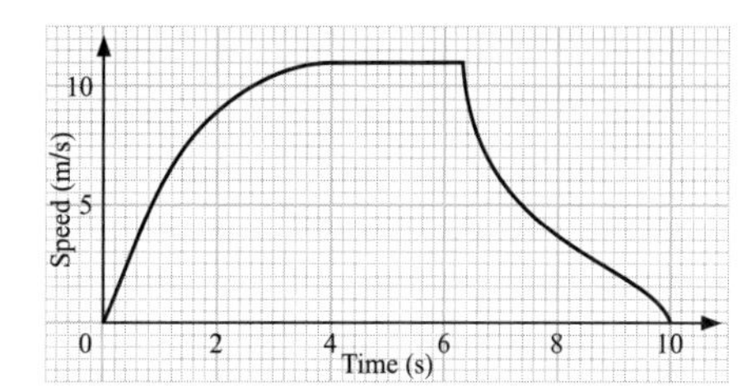

(a) Estimate the acceleration of the motorcycle after 2 seconds.

(b) Estimate the distance between the traffic lights.

(a) Acceleration = Gradient of curve after 2 s
So, draw a tangent to the curve at 2 s:

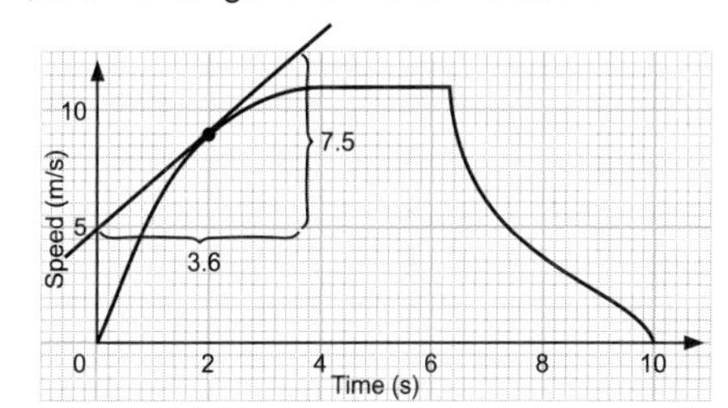

Acceleration = Gradient $\approx \frac{7.5}{3.6} = 2.1 \text{ m/s}^2$

(b) A 1 cm square represents a distance of $2\times5 = 10$ m

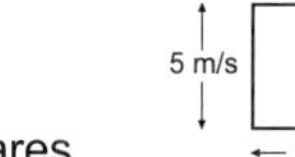

Estimate number of 1 cm squares under curve:

$5 + \frac{3}{4} + \frac{1}{4} + \frac{1}{4} + \frac{1}{2} + \frac{1}{2} = 7.25$

So, distance = $7.25\times10 = 72.5$ m

Graphical Solution of Equations

1. Solving Quadratic Equations Using Graphs

Question *(a) Complete the table below for the equation $y = x^2 - x - 2$.*

x	-3	-2	-1	0	1	2	3
y	10		0		-2	0	

(a) Use your graph to solve the equation $x^2 - x - 2 = 0$.

(b) Use your graph to solve the equation $x^2 - x - 5 = 0$.

(a) When $x = -2$ $y = (-2)^2-(-2)-2 = 4+2-2 = 4$
When $x = 0$ $y = 0^2-0-2 = 0-0-2 = -2$
When $x = 3$ $y = 3^2-3-2 = 9-3-2 = 4$

x	-3	-2	-1	0	1	2	3
y	10	4	0	-2	-2	0	4

Carefully plot these points and join them with a smooth curve.

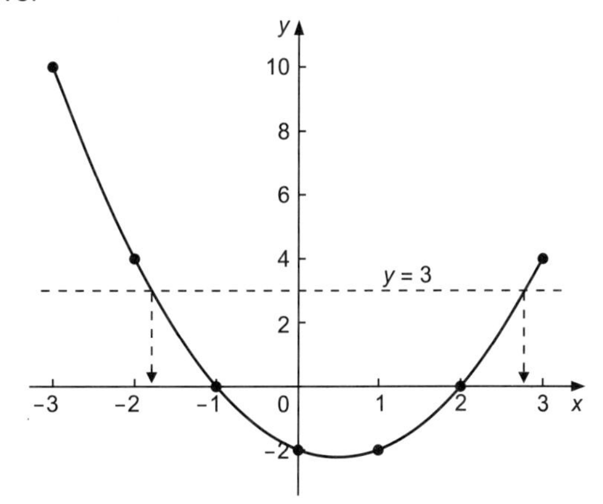

more

Graphical Solution of Equations (Contd)

1. Solving Quadratic Equations Using Graphs (Contd)

(b) The curve crosses the x-axis at two points, where $x = -1$ and $x = 2$. Every point on the x-axis has a y-coordinate of $y = 0$. So if we put $x = -1$ or $x = 2$ in the equation of the curve the answer should be 0.
Check:
When $x = -1$, $y = (-1)^2-(-1)-2 = 1+1-2 = 0$ ✓
When $x = 2$, $y = (2)^2-(2)-2 = 4-2-2 = 0$ ✓
This means that $x = -1$ and $x = 2$ are the solutions of the equation $x^2-x-2 = 0$.

(c) Since we must use the graph of $y = x^2-x-2$ to solve the equation $x^2-x-5 = 0$, we need to change the LHS to x^2-x-2:

$x^2-x-5 = 0$
$\therefore\ x^2-x-2-3 = 0$ Split -5 into $-2-3$
$\therefore\ x^2-x-2 = 3$

So now we have to find the values of x which make $x^2-x-2 = 3$. On the graph, $y = x^2-x-2$ and so we are looking for the values of x where $y = 3$. Draw the line $y = 3$ on the graph and read off the two values of x where it crosses the curve (see dashed lines). From the graph, we can see that $x \approx -1.8$ and $x \approx 2.8$. These are the required solutions of the equation $x^2-x-5 = 0$.

2. Solving Simultaneous Equations

Question *Complete the tables of values below for the equations $y = x+3$ and $2y+x = 9$. Hence, solve the simultaneous equations $y = x+3$ and $2y+x = 9$.*

$y = x+3$

x	−2	0	3
y	1		

$2y+x = 9$

x	−2	0	3
y			3

For $y = x+3$:
When $x = 0$, $y = 0+3 = 3$
When $x = 3$, $y = 3+3 = 6$

x	−2	0	3
y	1	3	6

For $2y+x = 9$:
When $x = -2$ $2y-2 = 9$
$\therefore\ 2y = 11\ \therefore\ y = 5.5$
When $x = 3$ $2y+3 = 9$
$\therefore\ 2y = 6\ \therefore\ y = 3$

x	−2	0	3
y	5.5	4.5	3

Plot the points and join them with straight lines:

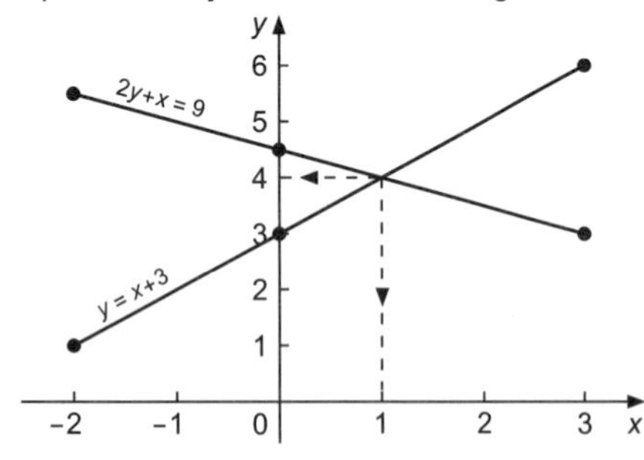

Read the x and y coordinates of the point of intersection of the lines: $x \approx 1$ and $y \approx 4$.

Check these values are the solution of the equations.

For $y = x+3$: $4 = 1+3$ ✓
For $2y+x = 9$: $2\times4+1 = 9$ ✓

3. More Difficult Simultaneous Equations

Question *The graph of $y = x^3-6x^2+9x+4$ has been drawn below.*

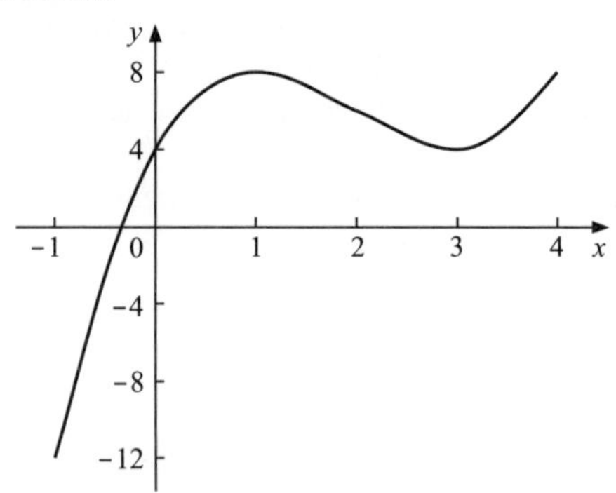

(a) Draw the graph of the straight line $y = 4x-4$ using the same axes.
(b) Find the x-coordinates of the points of intersection of the two graphs.
(c) Show that the answers to part (b) are the solutions of the equation $x^3-6x^2+5x+8 = 0$.

(a) Make a table of values for the equation $y = 4x-4$:
When $x = -1$ $y = 4\times(-1)-4 = -4-4 = -8$
When $x = 1$ $y = 4\times1-4 = 4-4 = 0$
When $x = 3$ $y = 4\times3-4 = 12-4 = 8$

x	−1	1	3
y	−8	0	8

Carefully plot the points using the same axes as for the graph above. Join the points with a straight line.

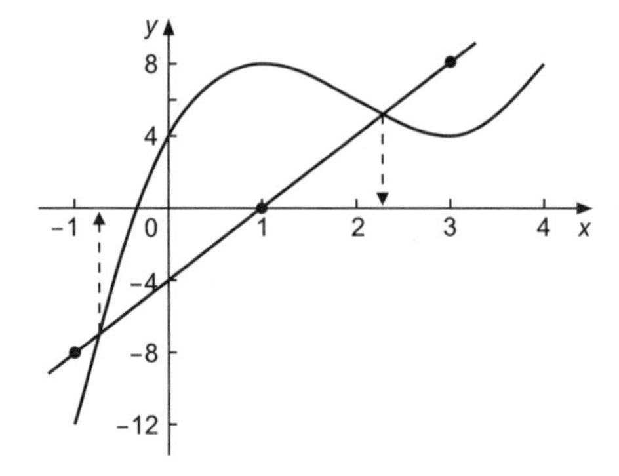

(b) Read off the x-coordinates of the points of intersection of the straight line and curve: $x \approx -0.7$ and $x \approx 2.3$.

(c) Since the points of intersection lie on *both* lines, either equation can be used to calculate their y-coordinates: $y = x^3-6x^2+9x+4$ or $y = 4x-4$. They both give the same y-coordinates for the x-coordinates found in part (b). So, for these particular x-coordinates:

$x^3-6x^2+9x+4 = 4x-4$
$\therefore\ x^3-6x^2+9x+4-4x+4 = 0$
$\therefore\ x^3-6x^2+9x-4x+4+4 = 0$
$\therefore\ x^3-6x^2+5x+8 = 0$

Thus, $x = -0.7$ and $x = 2.3$ are the approximate solutions of this equation.

Graphical Solution of Inequalities

1. Graphs of Simple Inequalities

Inequalities can be used to describe regions on graph paper. For example, the inequality $x < 4$ tells us that the x-coordinates of all points in the region are less than 4.

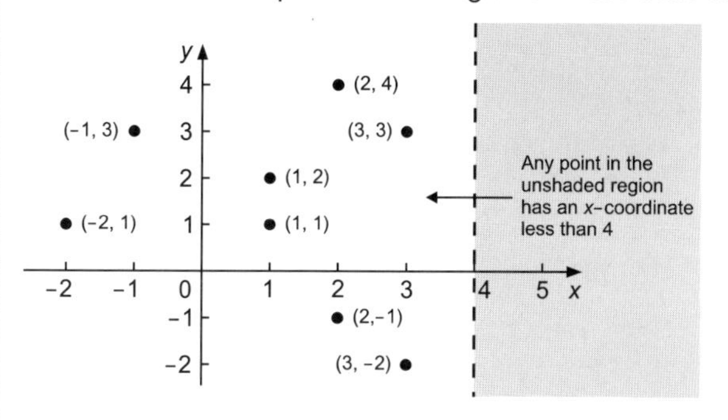

Points on the dashed line have x-coordinates equal to 4 and so are **not** included in the region $x < 4$. We say that the points in the unshaded region **satisfy** the inequality $x < 4$.

Similarly, $y \leqslant 3$ defines the region of points whose y-coordinates are less than or equal to 3. The points on the line $y = 3$ *are* included in the region.

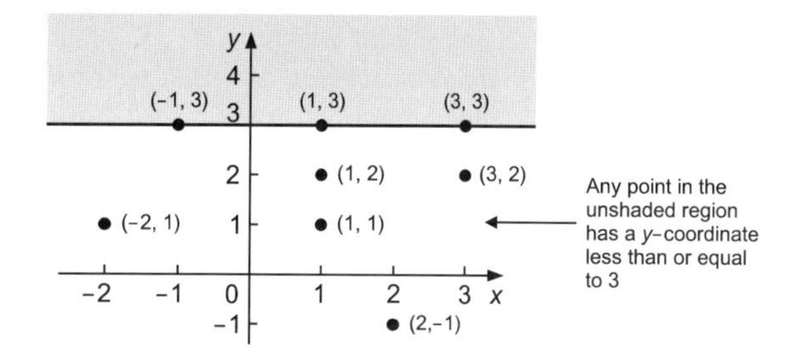

2. Straight Lines and Inequalities

A straight line divides the graph paper into two regions. For example, the straight line with equation $y = 2x+3$ divides the graph paper into regions A and B below:

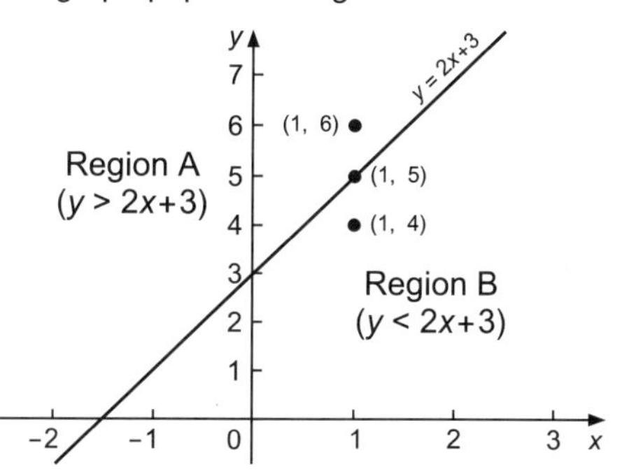

The coordinates of points lying *on the line* satisfy the equation $y = 2x+3$, e.g. for the point (1, 5) we have $x = 1$, $y = 2\times1+3 = 5$ ✓ See graph.

The coordinates of points lying in region A satisfy the inequality $y > 2x+3$, e.g. for the point (1, 6) we have $6 > 2\times1+3 = 5$ ✓ See graph.

The coordinates of points lying on the opposite side of the line in region B satisfy the inequality $y < 2x+3$, e.g. for the point (1, 4) we have $4 < 2\times1+3 = 5$ ✓ See graph.

Question *Mark the region R satisfying the inequality $2x+y \geqslant 20$.*

First, replace the $\geqslant$ with = and draw the straight line $2x+y = 20$. Make a table of values using three points.

When $x = 0$ $\quad 2\times(0)+y = 20 \quad \therefore 0+y = 20 \quad \therefore y = 20$
When $x = 6$ $\quad 2\times6+y = 20 \quad \therefore 12+y = 20 \quad \therefore y = 8$
When $x = 10$ $\quad 2\times10+y = 20 \quad \therefore 20+y = 20 \quad \therefore y = 0$

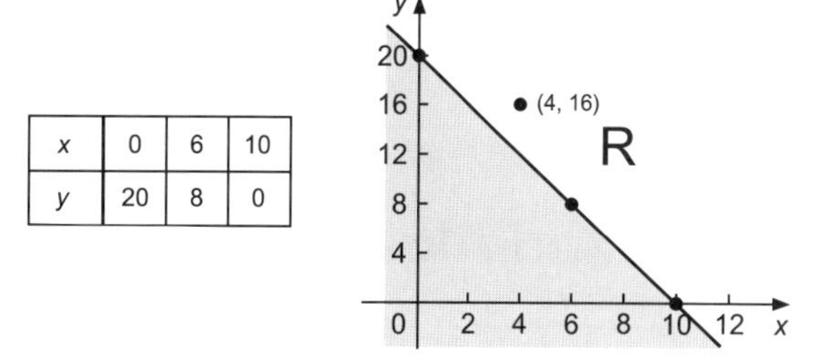

x	0	6	10
y	20	8	0

Choose any point that is ***not*** on the line, e.g. (4, 16) and check whether its coordinates satisfy the inequality:

$2x+y \geqslant 20$ becomes $2\times4+16 \geqslant 20$, which is true.

Label this side of the line R. Shade the unwanted side.

NOTE If we had chosen a point on the other side, say (4, 8), the inequality would not have been satisfied: $2x+y \geqslant 20$ becomes $2\times4+8 \geqslant 20$, which is not true. We would shade the other side.

3. Simultaneous Inequalities

Question *Use shading to indicate the region satisfying the inequalities*

$$y < 2 \qquad x+y > 4 \qquad x < 3$$

Each inequality describes a region of points. The points in the overlap of these regions satisfy all three inequalities at once (simultaneously).

Replace < and > with = to change the inequalities into equations and draw the lines $y = 2$, $x+y = 4$ and $x = 3$ on graph paper (use dashed lines).

To find the region described by the inequality $x+y > 4$, choose any point ***not*** on the line $x+y = 4$, e.g. (2, 1).

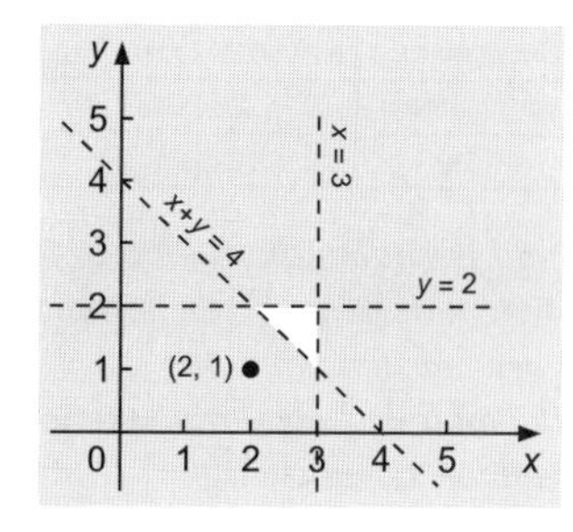

Check to see whether this point satisfies the inequality: $x+y > 4$ becomes $2+1 > 4$, which is not true. So, the other side of the line satisfies the inequality.

Shade the unwanted regions.

Graphical Solution of Inequalities

4. Solving Problems Using Inequalities

Question *At each performance of a school play the audience had to satisfy the following conditions:*

(i) no more than 250 children

(ii) a maximum size of audience of 300

(iii) at least twice as many children as adults

(a) If there were x children and y adults, write down three inequalities that x and y must satisfy.

(b) Use shading to indicate the region on graph paper that satisfies all three inequalities.

(c) Use your graph to find the maximum number of adults at a performance.

(d) If tickets cost £3 for children and £4 for adults, find the maximum possible income

(a) (i) Number of children (x) less than or equal to 250 gives the inequality $x \leqslant 250$.

(ii) Audience = Children + Adults = $x+y$
The audience is less than or equal to 300 and so $x+y \leqslant 300$.

(iii) The number of children (x) is greater than or equal to twice the number of adults ($2y$), which gives the inequality $x \geqslant 2y$.

(b) Draw the lines $x = 250$, $x+y = 300$ and $x = 2y$ and shade the unwanted regions. The points in the unshaded region satisfy all three inequalities.

(c) The number of adults is represented by the vertical axis and so the greatest possible number of adults corresponds to the highest point in the unshaded region, i.e. A (200, 100).

This point represents an audience of 200 children and 100 adults. So, the greatest possible number of adults is 100.

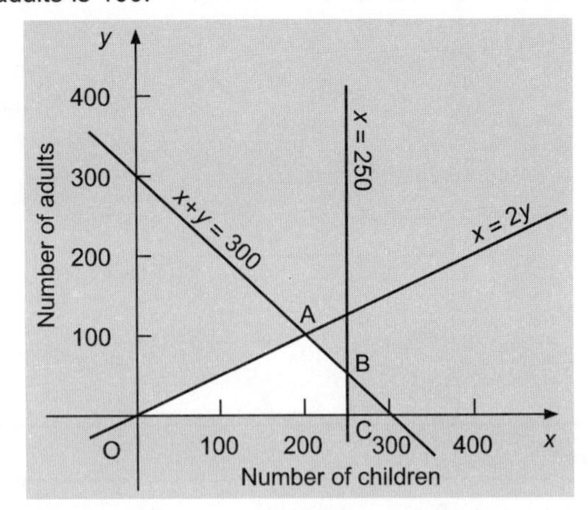

(d) The total income from x children's tickets at £3 and y adults' tickets at £4 is £$(3x+4y)$. We must find the point in the unshaded region which maximises this income. This will be one of the corner points.

For A (200, 100), $x = 200$ and $y = 100$, giving an income of £$(3\times200+4\times100)$ = £1000

For B (250, 50), $x = 250$ and $y = 50$, giving an income of £$(3\times250+4\times50)$ = £950

For C(250, 0), $x = 250$ and $y = 0$, giving an income of £$(3\times250+4\times0)$ = £750

So, the maximum possible income is £1000.

Graphs and Algebraic Laws

1. Algebraic Laws

An **algebraic law** is a formula connecting several quantities. For example, the law connecting voltage (V), resistance (R) and current (I) in an electrical circuit is given by the formula $V = IR$.

Simple algebraic laws are sometimes verified by drawing a graph of two quantities in the formula.

Question *A group of science students measured the time, t seconds, taken for a ball to fall to the ground from various heights, h metres, and recorded their results in the table below.*

Time, t (seconds)	0.65	0.85	1.00	1.10	1.20
Height, h (metres)	1	2	3	4	5
$\sqrt{h}$	1				

Their teacher told them that the relationship between the height, h, and time, t, is given by the formula $t = a\sqrt{h}+b$, where a and b are constant numbers.

(a) Complete the table by calculating the values of $\sqrt{h}$.

(b) Plot the graph of t against $\sqrt{h}$.

(c) Use your graph to estimate the values of a and b.

(a) Square root the values of h in the table.

Time, t (seconds)	0.65	0.85	1.0	1.1	1.2
Height, h (metres)	1	2	3	4	5
$\sqrt{h}$	1	1.4	1.7	2	2.2

(b) Carefully plot t against $\sqrt{h}$. This means that t is represented by the vertical axis.

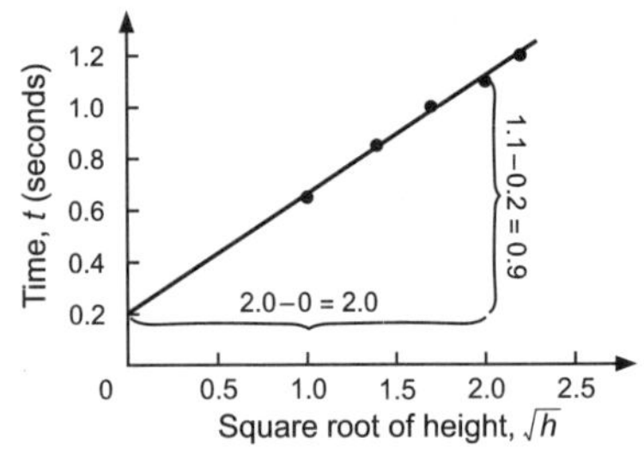

(c) Notice that you get a straight line. Compare the formula $t = a\sqrt{h}+b$ with the equation of a straight line:

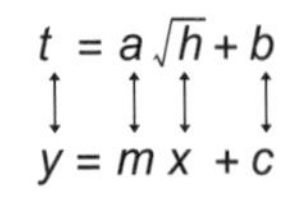

a corresponds to the gradient and b the y-intercept.

From the graph, a = gradient = $\frac{1.1-0.2}{2.0-0} = \frac{0.9}{2} = 0.45$

And b = y-intercept = 0.2

The formula connecting h and t is: $t = 0.45\sqrt{h}+0.2$

2. Exponential Growth

H

A quantity **grows exponentially** if it is repeatedly multiplied by a number greater than 1.

Question *A single cell is placed in a dish. The number of cells in the dish doubles every 5 hours.*
(a) Complete the table below.
(b) Plot a graph of the number of cells, n, against time, t
(c) Write down an algebraic formula connecting n and t.

Time, t (hours)	0	5	10	15	20	25	30
Number of cells, n	1						

(a) After $t = 0$ hours, number of cells = $n = 1$
After $t = 5$ hours, number of cells = $n = 2\times1 = 2$
After $t = 10$ hours, number of cells = $n = 2\times2 = 4$
After $t = 15$ hours, number of cells = $n = 2\times4 = 8$
etc.

Time, t (hours)	0	5	10	15	20	25	30
Number of cells, n	1	2	4	8	16	32	64

(b) Carefully plot these points and join them with a smooth curve.

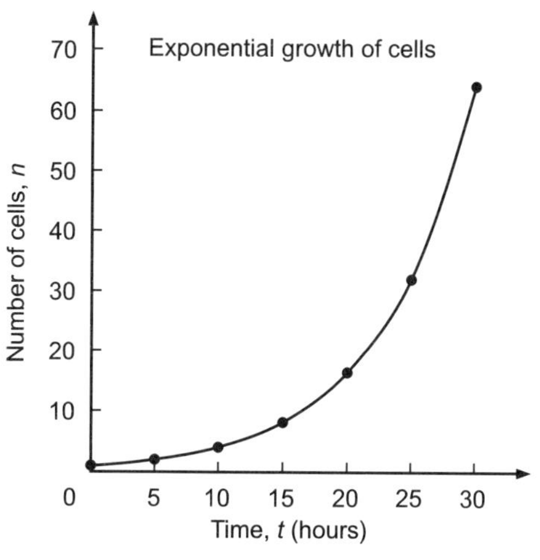

(c) The numbers of cells in the table are powers of 2.

Time (t hours)	0	5	10	15	20	25	30
Number of cells (n)	1	2	4	8	16	32	64
	2^0	2^1	2^2	2^2	2^3	2^4	2^5

Notice that the indices of these powers can be found by dividing the number of hours by 5. For example, $5\div5 = 1$, $10\div5 = 2$, $15\div5 = 3$.

So, the rule connecting the number of cells and time is:

$$\text{Number of cells} = 2^{\text{Time}\div5}$$

which can be written algebraically as:

$$n = 2^{\frac{t}{5}}$$

3. Exponential Decay

H

A quantity **decays exponentially** if it is repeatedly multiplied by a number less than 1.

Question *The graph below shows how the value of a piece of machinery decreases over the years. The value, £V, of the machinery after t years is given by the formula $V = p(q^t)$, where p and q are constant numbers.*
(a) Use the graph to estimate the values of p and q.
(b) Estimate the value of the machinery when it is 10 years old.

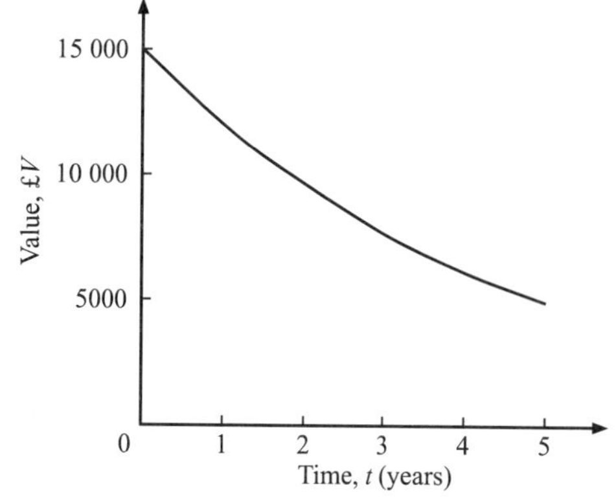

(a) We can use the graph to find pairs of values of V and t.

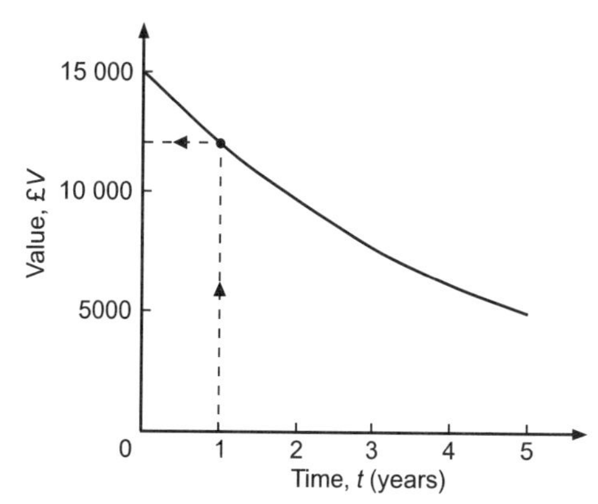

When $t = 0$, $V = 15\,000$
When $t = 1$, $V = 12\,000$

We can now substitute these pairs of values into the formula $V = p(q^t)$.
Substituting $t = 0$, $V = 15\,000$ gives:

$15\,000 = p(q^0)$
$\therefore 15\,000 = p\times1$ Because $q^0 = 1$
$\therefore p = 15\,000$

So we now know the formula is $V = 15\,000(q^t)$.
Substituting $t = 1$, $V = 12\,000$ gives:

$12\,000 = 15\,000(q^1)$
$\therefore 12\,000 = 15\,000\times q$
$\therefore 15\,000q = 12\,000$
$\therefore q = \frac{12\,000}{15\,000} = 0.8$

So the formula is $V = 15\,000(0.8^t)$.

(b) When $t = 10$, $V = 15\,000(0.8^{10}) \approx 1611$

The machinery will have a value of approximately £1611 when it is 10 years old.

Functions and Graphs

1. Functions

A **function** is a rule that changes one number into another. For example, the rule 'add 2' is a function. Functions are often represented by the letters f, g, F, and G. Let's represent the function 'add 2' by the letter f. Then, f is the rule that adds 2 to a given number:

f changes 3 into 3+2
f changes 4 into 4+2
f changes 5 into 5+2

Generally, f changes x into $x+2$, which can be written briefly as $f : x \rightarrow x+2$
or simply $f(x) = x+2$

Question *Given that* $f(x) = x^2-2x$, *calculate the values of (a)* $f(5)$ *and (b)* $f(-2)$.

(a) Replacing x by 5 in the function $f(x) = x^2-2x$ gives:

$f(5) = 5^2-2\times5 = 25-10 = 15$

NOTE $f(5)$ is called the **function value** when $x = 5$.

(b) $f(-2) = (-2)^2-2\times(-2) = 4+4 = 8$

The function $f(x) = x+2$ can also be illustrated using a **mapping diagram**:

$x \rightarrow x+2$
$1 \rightarrow 1+2$
$2 \rightarrow 2+2$
$3 \rightarrow 3+2$

2. Graph of a Function

You can use a function to calculate the y-coordinates of a graph.

Question *Plot the graph of* $y = f(x)$, *where* $f(x) = x^2+2x$ *for the values* $-3 \leqslant x \leqslant 3$.

$y = f(x)$ means that the y-coordinates are calculated using the function $f(x)$. In this case, $f(x)$ is the function x^2+2x. So this question is another way of asking you to plot the graph of the equation $y = x^2+2x$.

The inequality $-3 \leqslant x \leqslant 3$ tells you that the values of x range from $x = -3$ to $x = 3$.

Complete the table of values and carefully plot the points, joining them with a smooth curve.

$f(-3) = (-3)^2+2(-3) = 9-6 = 3$
$f(-2) = (-2)^2+2(-2) = 4-4 = 0$ etc.

x	-3	-2	-1	0	1	2	3
f(x)	3	0	-1	0	3	8	15

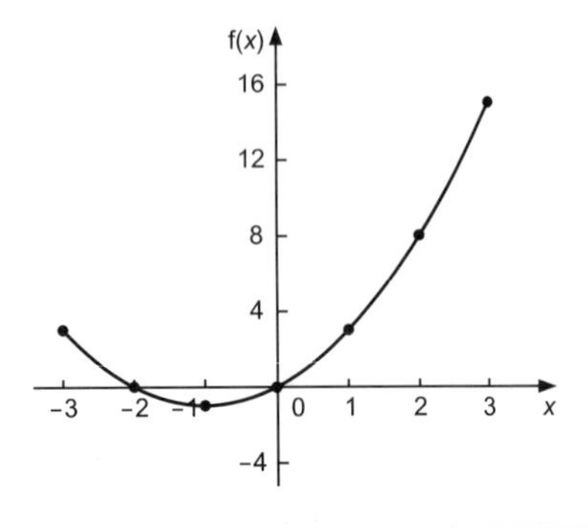

3. Related Functions

H

Consider the function $f(x) = \frac{1}{x}$.

If we replace x by $x+1$ in both sides of the equation, we get the **related function** $f(x+1) = \frac{1}{x+1}$.

Here are some more functions related to $f(x)$. Each of these functions is obtained by modifying both sides of the original function $f(x) = \frac{1}{x}$.

$f(x) = \frac{1}{x}$	Original function
$f(2x) = \frac{1}{2x}$	Replace x by $2x$
$f(x)+2 = \frac{1}{x}+2$	Add 2 to both sides
$f(-x) = \frac{1}{-x}$	Replace x by $-x$

4. Graphs of Related Functions

H

In Box 2 we drew the graph of the function $f(x) = x^2+2x$.

If we modify the function, the graph is also modified. Here are some of the ways the function $f(x) = x^2+2x$ and its graph can be modified. These changes can be applied to all functions.

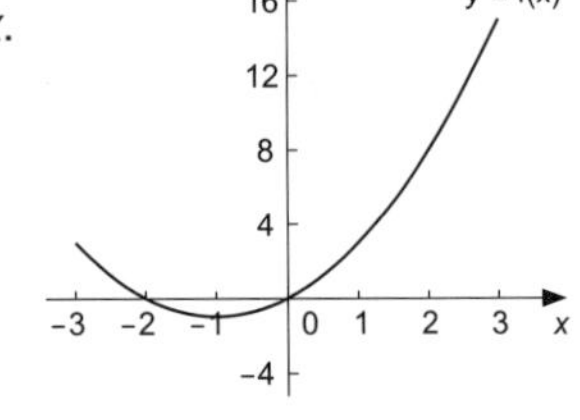

The original graph of $f(x)$ is shown as a dashed line.

Translation in the y–direction

Changing $f(x)$ to $f(x)+6$ moves the curve up 6. We say that the curve $y = f(x)$ has been translated +6 in the y-direction.

Subtracting 6 would move the curve 6 downwards.

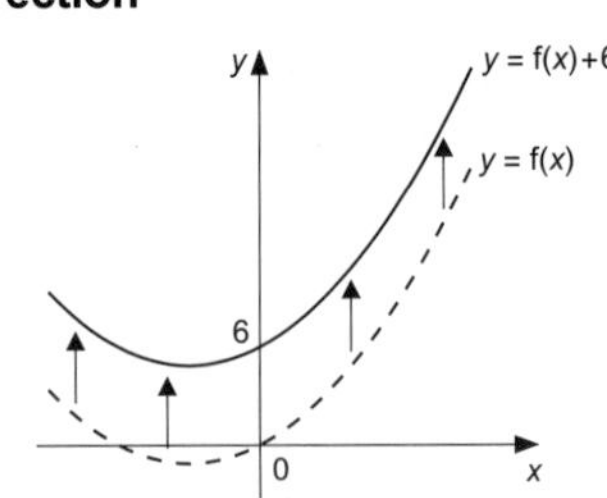

Translation in the x–direction

Changing $f(x)$ to $f(x-2)$ moves the curve 2 to the right in the x-direction. We say that the curve $y = f(x)$ has been translated +2 in the x-direction.

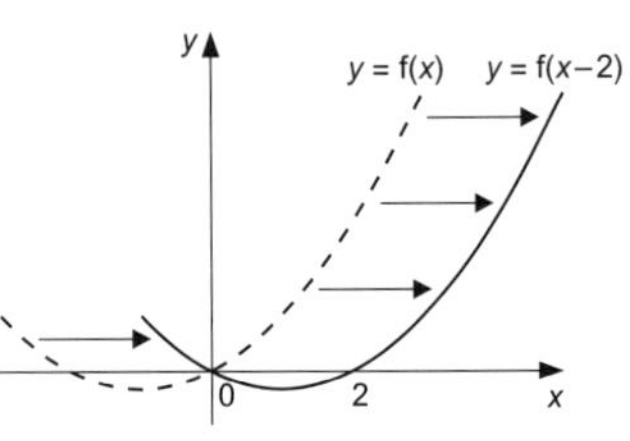

Changing $f(x)$ to $f(x+2)$ would move the curve 2 to the left. Don't get these mixed up

Reflection in the x–axis

Changing $f(x)$ to $-f(x)$ reflects the curve in the x-axis.

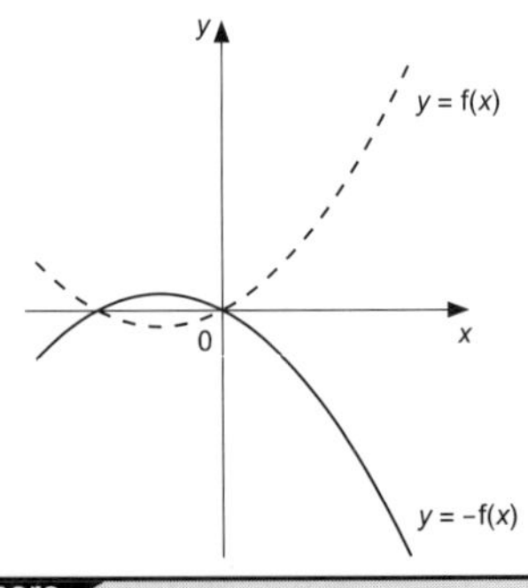

more

4. Graphs of Related Functions (Contd)

Reflection in the *y*–axis

Changing f(*x*) to f(–*x*) reflects the curve in the *y*-axis.

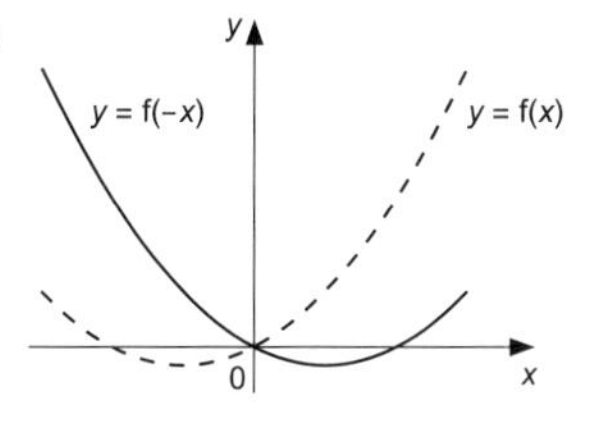

Stretching in the *y*–direction

Changing f(*x*) to 2f(*x*) stretches the curve by a factor of 2 in the *y*-direction: the distance from the *x*-axis of every point on the curve is doubled. This makes the curve steeper.

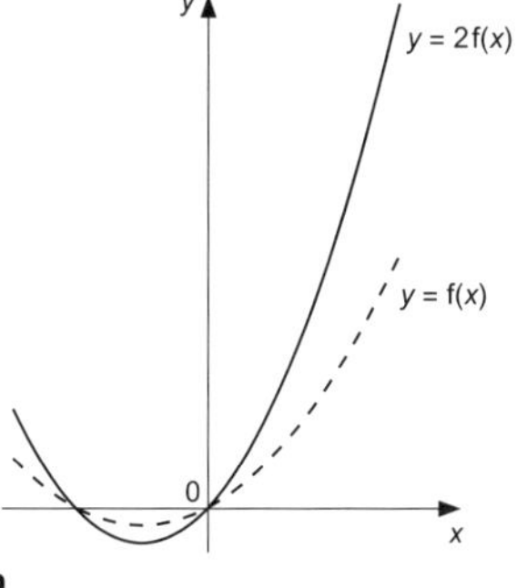

Stretching in the *x*–direction

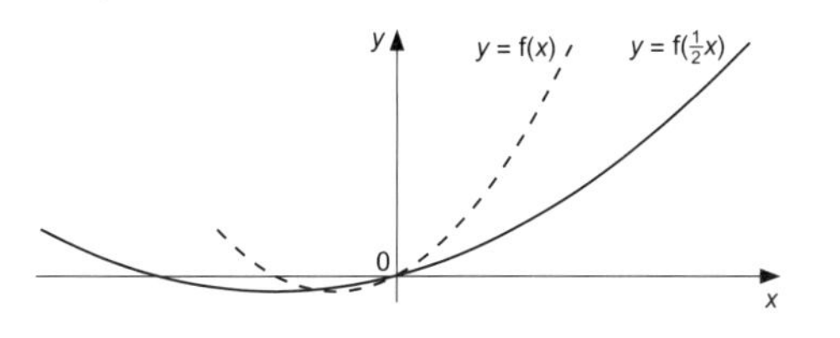

Changing f(*x*) to f($\frac{1}{2}x$) stretches the curve by a factor of 2 in the *x*-direction: the distance from the *y*-axis of every point on the curve is doubled. This makes the curve less steep.

Reciprocal of a function

Replacing f(*x*) by $\frac{1}{f(x)}$ changes large *y*-coordinates into small *y*-coordinates and vice-versa. If the original graph of f(*x*) crosses the *x*-axis, the graph of $\frac{1}{f(x)}$ breaks at this point. See example below for more details.

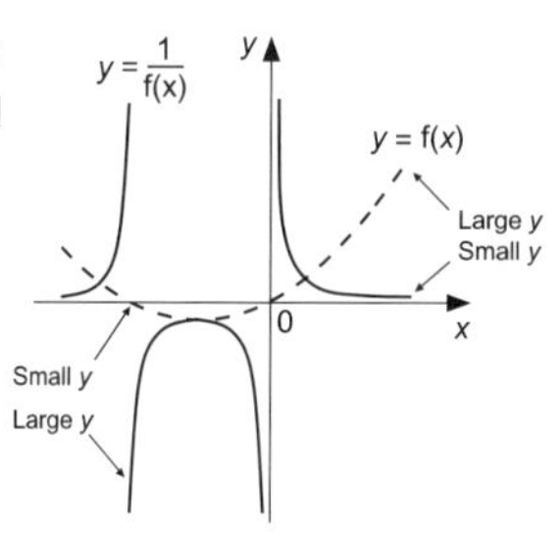

When you forget how to draw a related graph ....

Another way of sketching graphs of related functions is to calculate a few *y*-coordinates, though this is usually more time consuming.

Question *The graph of the function* $f(x) = \frac{1}{x}$ *is shown opposite. Sketch the graph of the function* $f(x+0.5)$.

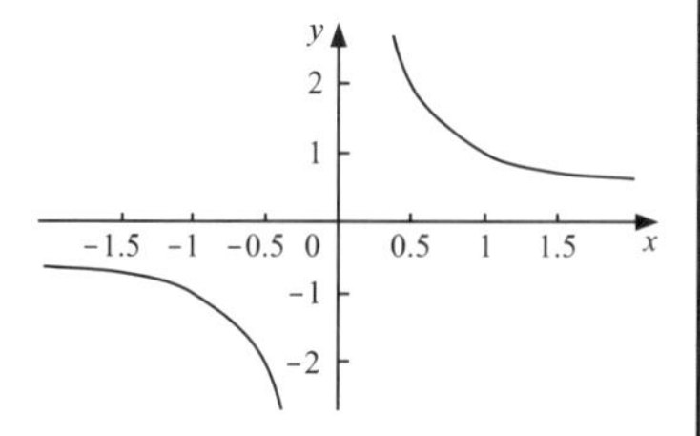

$f(x+0.5) = \frac{1}{x+0.5}$. Make a table of values.

When $x = -1.5$: $f(x+0.5) = \frac{1}{-1.5+0.5} = -1$, etc.

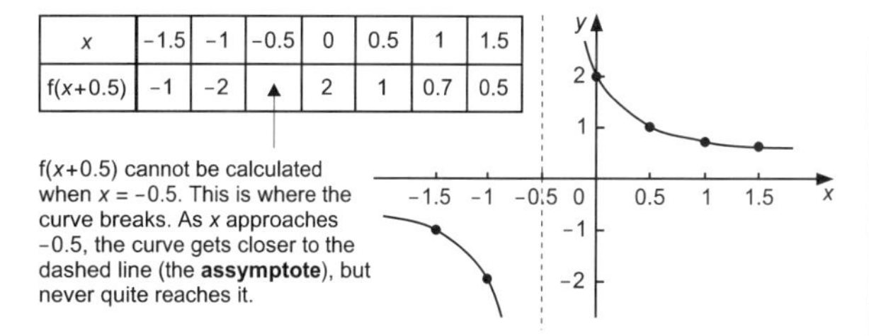

x	–1.5	–1	–0.5	0	0.5	1	1.5
f(*x*+0.5)	–1	–2	▲	2	1	0.7	0.5

Three–dimensional Coordinates

The position of a point on a flat surface can be described using a pair of *x* and *y* coordinates, e.g. the point (3, 2). The *x* and *y* axes lie on the flat surface of the page.

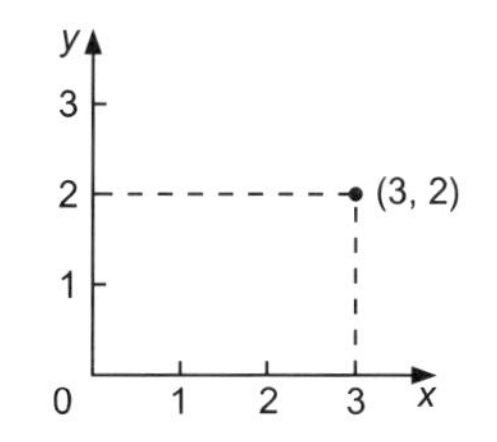

A point in 3-D space needs an extra *z*-coordinate to describe its position, e.g. the point (3, 2, 4). Think of the *x* and *y* axes as lying on the page with the *z*-axis coming towards you at right angles.

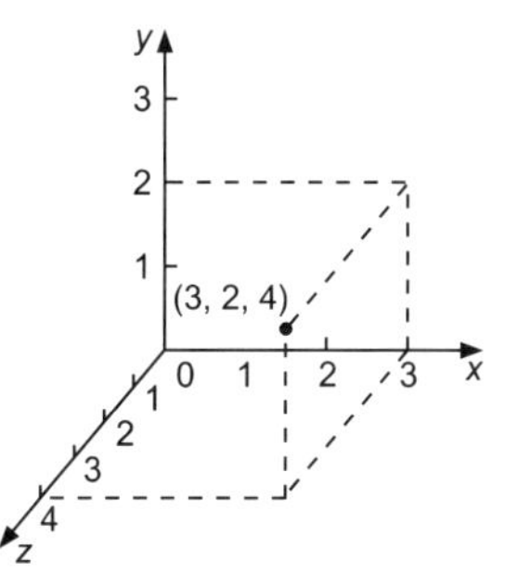

Question *The cuboid OABCDEFG is drawn using 3-D axes. Point P is the midpoint of edge DE. Find the coordinates of P.*

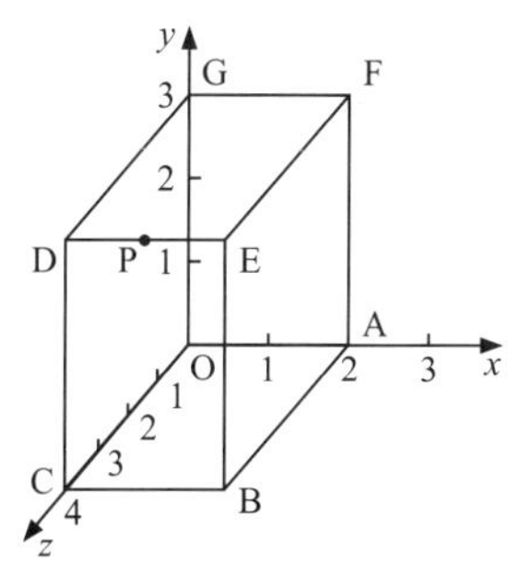

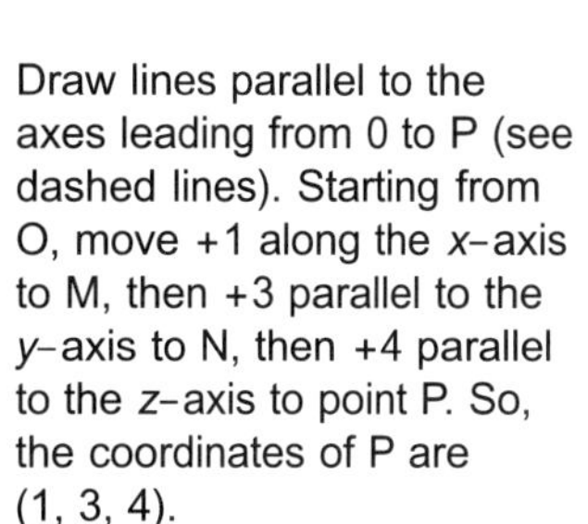

Draw lines parallel to the axes leading from 0 to P (see dashed lines). Starting from O, move +1 along the *x*-axis to M, then +3 parallel to the *y*-axis to N, then +4 parallel to the *z*-axis to point P. So, the coordinates of P are (1, 3, 4).

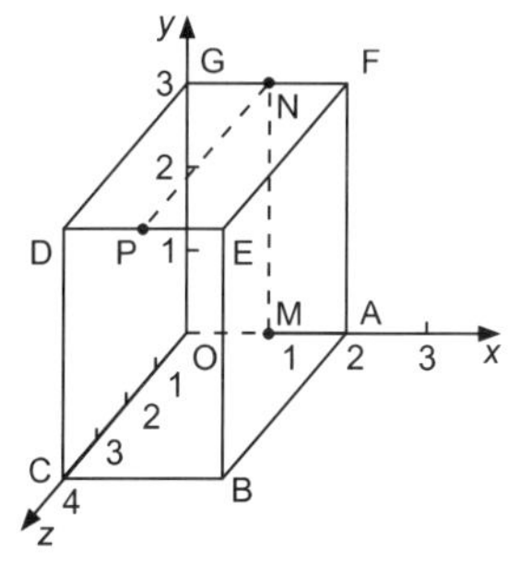

Perimeters

The **perimeter** of a shape is the total length of its outside edges.

Question *Calculate the perimeter of this rectangular door, giving your answer in metres.*

First, convert 80 cm to m:
80 cm = 80÷100 m = 0.8 m

Then perimeter of door
= 0.8+0.8+2+2 = 5.6 m
(opposite edges of a rectangle are equal)

Sometimes you have to calculate missing lengths of sides, as in the following question.

Question *Calculate the perimeter of this shape, giving your answer in centimetres.*

Convert 1.2 m to cm:
1.2 m = 1.2×100 cm = 120 cm

Then calculate missing sides:
EF = HG = 70−20 = 50 cm
GF = 120−30−30 = 60 cm

Perimeter = 70+120+70+30+50+60+50+30 = 480 cm

Question *The fence around the sheep pen is a tenth of the length of the fence around the field. Calculate the width of the sheep pen.*

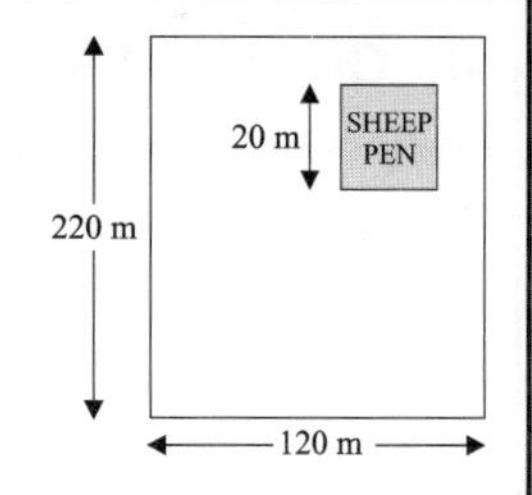

Perimeter of field = 120+220+120+220 = 680 m

So, perimeter of sheep pen = $\frac{1}{10}$ of 680 m = 68 m

The total length of the two given sides of the sheep pen is 20+20 = 40 m

The remaining two sides have a total length of 68−40 = 28 m

So, width of sheep pen = 28÷2 = 14 m

Area

1. Units of Area

The basic unit of area is the square metre (m^2). 1 m^2 is the area of a square with 1 m sides.

Similarly, 1 cm^2 is the area of a square with 1 cm sides.

And 1 mm^2 is the area of a square with 1 mm sides.

Question *Convert 3.2 m^2 to cm^2.*

For converting **length** we used the diagram below (see Box 6, p28):

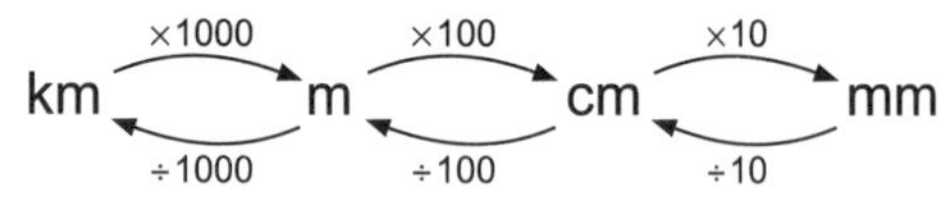

For converting **area**, square the numbers on the diagram:

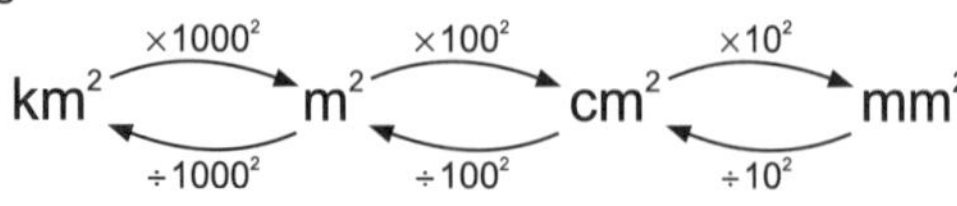

So, 3.2 m^2 = 3.2×100^2 cm^2 = 32 000 cm^2

Question *Convert 15mm^2 to cm^2.*

15 mm^2 = 15÷10^2 cm^2 = 0.15 cm^2

2. Area of a Rectangle

Area of a rectangle
= Base × Height

Question *Calculate the area of the photograph in cm^2.*

First, convert the lengths to cm. This is easier than converting the answer to cm^2 later on.

100 mm = 100÷10 cm = 10 cm
150 mm = 150÷10 cm = 15 cm

So, Area = Base × Height = 10 cm×15 cm = 150 cm^2

Question *Calculate the area of the shaded frame of the photograph.*

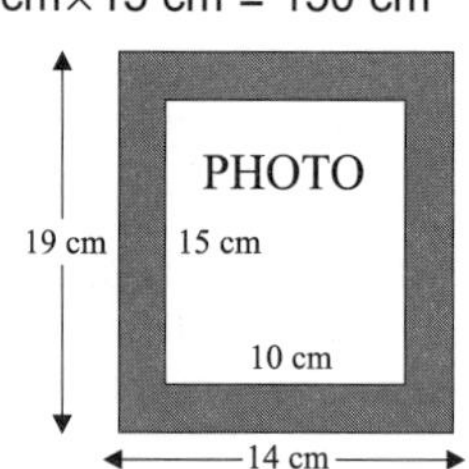

Area of frame = Area of outer rectangle − Area of inner rectangle
= 14×19 − 10×15
= 266−150
= 116 cm^2

3. Area of a Square

A **square** is a rectangle with equal sides.

Area of a square $=$ Side $\times$ Side
$= (\text{Side})^2$

Question *The square and rectangle have the same area. Calculate the side of the square.*

Let x be the length of the side of the square

Area of rectangle $=$ Base$\times$Height $= 20\times10 = 200$ mm^2

Area of square $= (\text{Side})^2 = x^2$

These areas are equal, so: $x^2 = 200$ mm^2

$\therefore x = \sqrt{200} = 14.1$ mm

4. Tiling Problem

Question *Harry covered a wall using 15 cm square tiles, as shown in the diagram below. Some tiles needed cutting in half.*

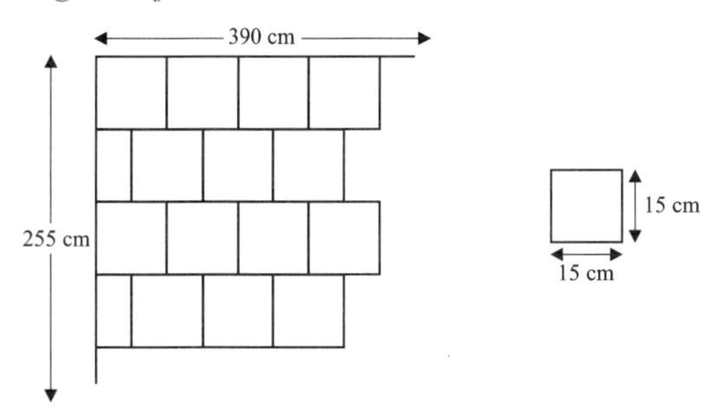

(a) How many tiles are there in the top row?
(b) How many rows are there?
(c) How many tiles did Harry use to cover the wall?
(d) How many tiles did he cut in half?
(e) If a box of tiles covers an area of 0.45 m^2, how many boxes did Harry need to buy?

(a) No. of tiles in top row $= 390\div15 = 26$

(b) No. of rows $= 255\div15 = 17$

(c) No. of tiles $=$ No. of rows $\times$ No. of tiles per row
$= 17\times26 = 442$

(d) Since 15 cm divides exactly into 390 cm, rows that begin with a whole tile must also end in one. Rows that begin with a half tile must also end in one; there are 8 such rows and so Harry needed to cut 8 tiles in half.

(e) Convert measurements of the wall to m:

390 cm $= 390\div100 = 3.9$ m
255 cm $= 255\div100 = 2.55$ m

Wall area $=$ Base$\times$Height $= 3.9\times2.55 = 9.945$ m^2

No. of boxes needed $= 9.945\div0.45 = 22.1 \approx 23$

5. Area of a Triangle

The area of a triangle is given by the formula:

Area $= \frac{1}{2}$ Base $\times$ Height

The height used must be perpendicular to the base.

Question *Calculate the area of this triangle.*

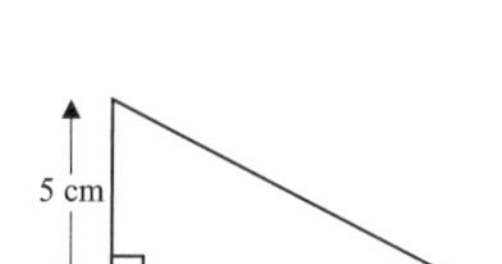

Since the 5 cm side is perpendicular to the 12 cm side we can take 12 cm as the base and 5cm as the perpendicular height

Area $= \frac{1}{2}$ Base $\times$ Height $= 0.5\times12$ cm$\times5$ cm $= 30$ cm^2

Question *The window shown in the diagram has square pane of side 30 cm and a triangular pane. The overall height of the window is 50 cm. Calculate the area, in cm^2, of the window. Convert your answer to m^2.*

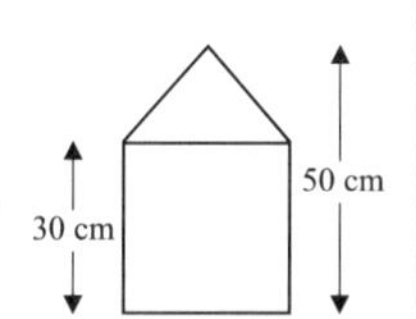

Height of triangle $= 50$ cm-30 cm $= 20$ cm

Base of triangle $=$ Base of square $= 30$ cm

Area of window $=$ Area of square $+$ Area of triangle
$= 30\times30 + \frac{1}{2}\times30\times20$
$= 900 + 0.5\times30\times20$
$= 900+300$
$= 1200$ cm^2

1200 cm$^2 = 1200\div100^2$ m^2
$= 1200\div10\,000$ m^2
$= 0.12$ m^2

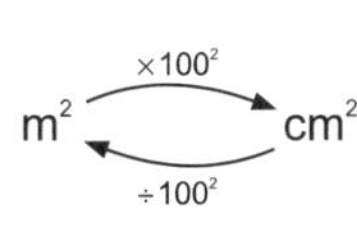

6. Area of a Trapezium

The area of a trapezium is given by the formula:

Area $= \frac{1}{2}(a+b)h$

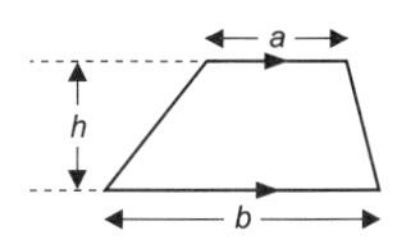

In words, the area of a trapezium is half the sum of the parallel sides times the perpendicular distance between them.

Question *Calculate the area, in mm^2, of the scalpel blade shown in the diagram . Convert your answer to cm^2.*

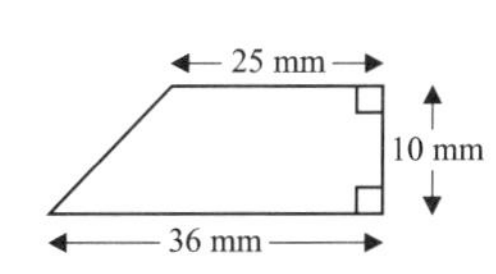

The 25 mm and 36 mm sides are parallel because they are both at right angles to the 10 mm side. The perpendicular distance between them is 10 mm.

Area $= \frac{1}{2}(a+b)h$
$= 0.5(25+36)10 = 0.5\times61\times10 = 305$ mm^2

305 mm$^2 = 305\div10^2$ cm^2
$= 305\div100$ cm^2
$= 3.05$ cm^2

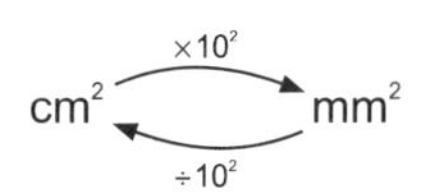

Area (Contd)

7. Area of a Parallelogram

The area of a parallelogram is given by the formula:

Area = Base × Height

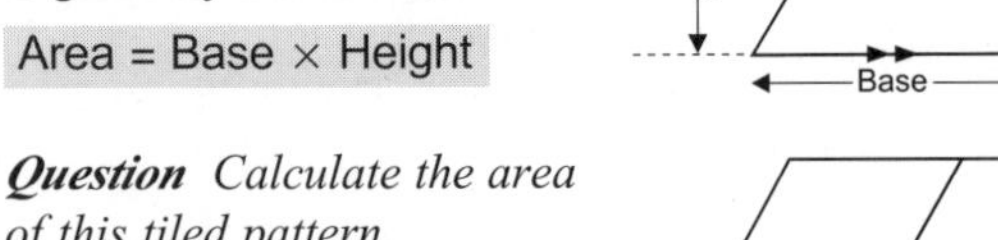

Question *Calculate the area of this tiled pattern.*

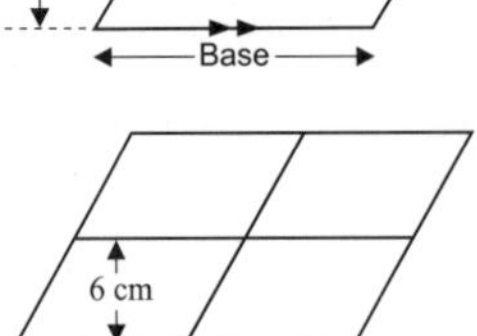

Area of 1 tile
= Base×Height
= 12 cm×6 cm = 72 cm^2

Area of 4 tiles = 4×72 = 288 cm^2

8. Area of a Circle

The area of a circle is given by the formula:

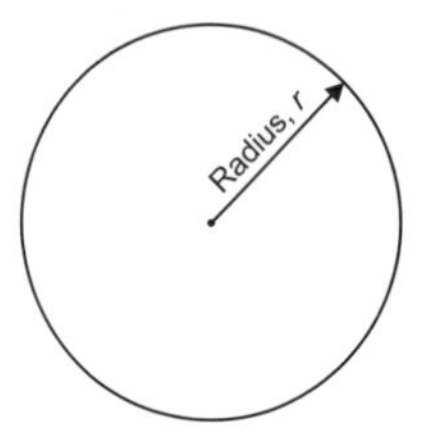

Area = $\pi \times (\text{Radius})^2$

or, using algebra:

Area = πr^2

Circumference = $2\pi r$

Question *Calculate the area of the top of this can of paté.*

PATÉ

12 cm

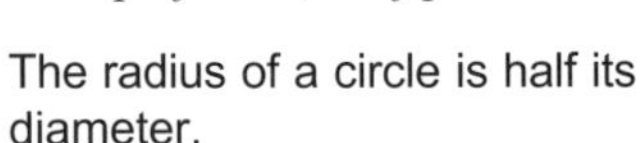

The radius of a circle is half its diameter.

Radius of circular can top = 12 cm÷2 = 6 cm

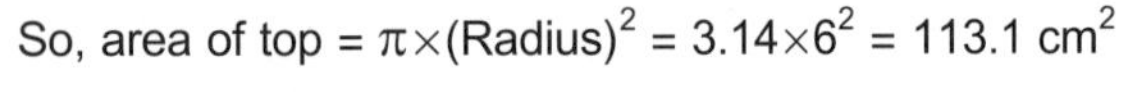

So, area of top = $\pi \times (\text{Radius})^2 = 3.14 \times 6^2 = 113.1$ cm^2

9. Sector of a Circle

A **sector** is a fraction of a circle, bounded by two radii and an arc.

The area of a sector and the length of arc are given by the formulas:

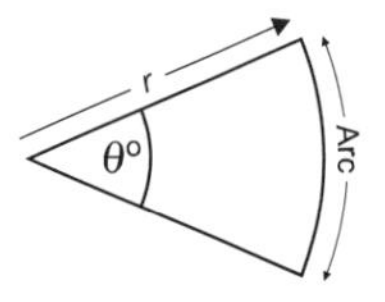

Area of sector = $\frac{\theta}{360}$ × Area of circle = $\frac{\theta}{360} \times \pi r^2$

Length of arc = $\frac{\theta}{360}$ × Circumference = $\frac{\theta}{360} \times 2\pi r$

Question *The beam from a lighthouse sweeps through an angle of 40° and can be seen from a distance of 4 km. Calculate the area from which the lighthouse can be seen.*

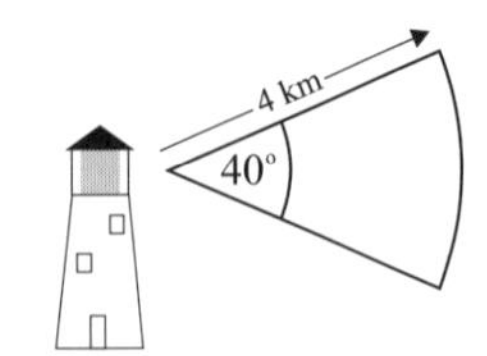

Area of sector = $\frac{\theta}{360} \times \pi r^2 = \frac{40}{360} \times \pi \times 4^2 = 5.59$ km^2

10. Segment of a circle

The diagram shows a **segment** of a circle.

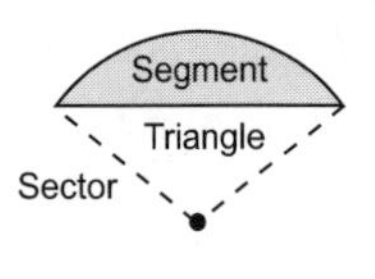

Area of segment = Area of sector − Area of triangle

Question *The diagram shows the end view of a barn. Calculate the area of this end.*

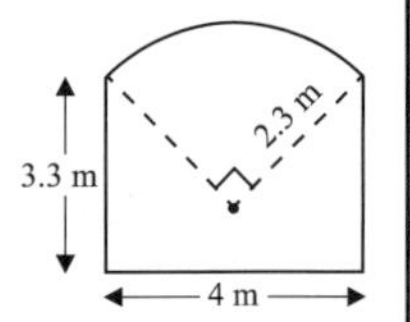

Draw a horizontal line to make a segment and a triangle.

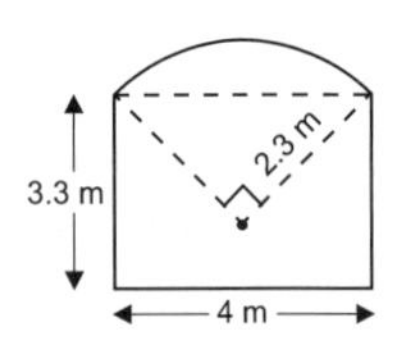

Area of barn = Area of rectangle + Area of segment

Area of rectangle = 3.3×4 = 13.2 m^2

Area of segment = Area of sector − Area of triangle

$= \frac{\theta}{360} \times \pi r^2 - \frac{1}{2} \times \text{Base} \times \text{Height}$

$= \frac{90}{360} \times \pi (2.3)^2 - \frac{1}{2} \times 2.3 \times 2.3$

$= 90 \div 360 \times \pi \times 2.3^2 - 0.5 \times 2.3 \times 2.3$

= 4.155−2.645

= 1.51 m^2

So, area of barn end = 13.2+1.51 = 14.71 m^2

11. Concentric Circles

Concentric circles have the same centre.

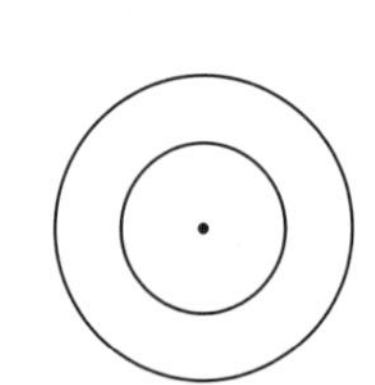

Question *Calculate the shaded area of this archery target. What percentage of the target is shaded?*

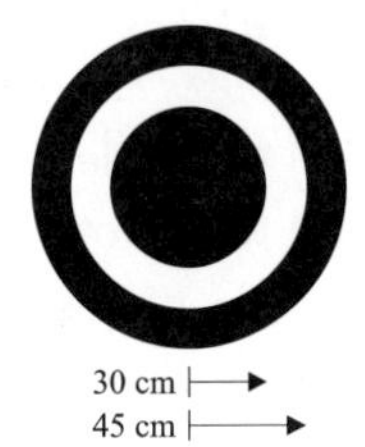

30 cm
45 cm
60 cm

Shaded area = Inner circle + Outer ring

Area of inner circle = $\pi r^2 = \pi \times 30^2 = 2827.4$ cm^2

Area of ring = Area of 60 cm circle − Area of 45 cm circle

$= \pi \times 60^2 - \pi \times 45^2$

= 11 309.7−6361.7

= 4948.0 cm^2

So, shaded area = 2827.4+4948.0 = 7775.4 cm^2

Total area of target = Area of 60 cm circle

= 11309.7 cm^2 (from above)

So, % area shaded = $\frac{7775.4}{11309.7} \times 100 = 68.7\%$

Surface Area

1. Surface Area of a Cuboid

A **cuboid** is a block or box with six rectangular faces. Its surface area is the sum of the areas of its six rectangular faces.

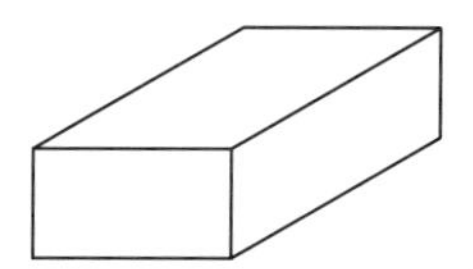

Question *(a) Calculate the surface area of this wooden block.*

(b) A can of red paint can cover an area of 2.2 m². How many blocks could be given a single coat of paint?

TOP, SIDE, FRONT, 8 cm, 12 cm, 25 cm

(a) Area of front face = $8 \times 12 = 96$ cm²
Area of side face = $25 \times 8 = 200$ cm²
Area of top face = $12 \times 25 = 300$ cm²

Total surface area = $2 \times 96 + 2 \times 200 + 2 \times 300$
= 1192 cm²   Opposite faces have equal area

(b) First, convert 2.2 m² to cm²:
2.2 m² = 2.2×100^2 cm² = 22 000 cm²
No. of bricks = $22\,000 \div 1192 = 18.46$
≈ 18 complete blocks

2. Surface Area of a Sphere

H

The surface area of a sphere is given by the formula.

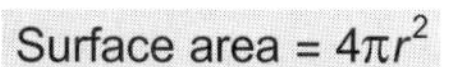

Surface area = $4\pi r^2$

You will be given this formula in the question or on the formula sheet of the question paper.

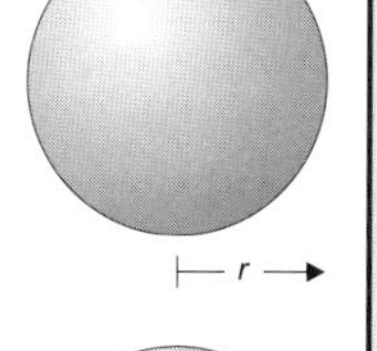

A **hemisphere** is half a sphere, and so its surface area is $2\pi r^2$.

Question *A child made a party hat by gluing a plastic hemisphere onto a cardboard circular ring.*
(a) Calculate the surface area of the hemisphere.
(b) Calculate the surface area of the top of the hat.

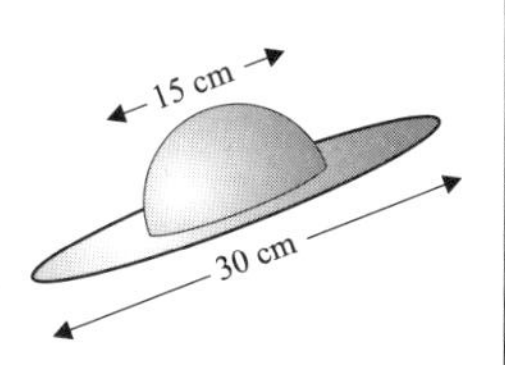

(a) Radius of hemisphere = 15 cm ÷ 2 = 7.5 cm
Surface area of hemisphere = $2\pi r^2 = 2 \times \pi \times 7.5^2$
= 353.4 cm²

(b) Area of ring = Large circle − Small circle
= $\pi \times 15^2 - \pi \times 7.5^2$
= 530.1 cm²

So, total surface area of hat
= 353.4 + 530.1 = 883.5 cm²

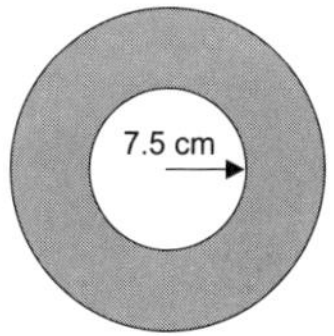

3. Surface Area of a Cylinder

A solid cylinder has two circular ends and a curved wall. The area of the curved wall is given by the formula:

Area of curved wall = $2\pi rh$

You will be given this formula in the question or on the formula sheet of the question paper.

r, Circle, Curved wall, h, Circle

Question *A rectangular sheet of paper is rolled up to form the curved wall of the cylinder shown in the diagram. You may assume that there are no overlapping edges.*
(a) Calculate the area of the wall of the cylinder.
(b) Calculate the length of the sheet of paper.

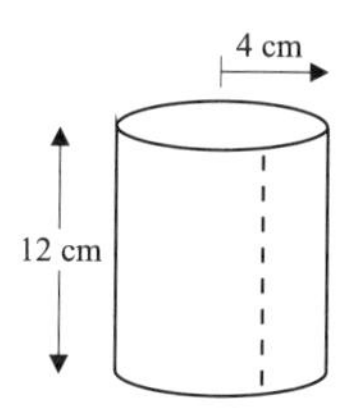

(a) Area of wall = $2\pi rh = 2 \times \pi \times 4 \times 12 = 301.6$ cm²

(b) If the cylinder is unrolled, the top circle becomes the top edge of the sheet of paper.

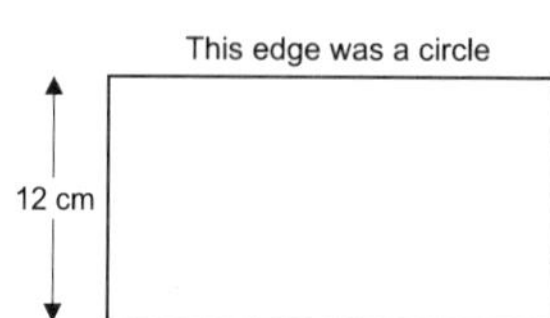

So, length of paper = Circumference of circle
= $2\pi r$
= $2 \times \pi \times 4 = 25.1$ cm

Question **H** *The diagram shows a wedge of cheese cut from a cylindrical block.*
(a) Calculate the area of the sector OAD.
(b) Calculate the total surface area of the wedge.

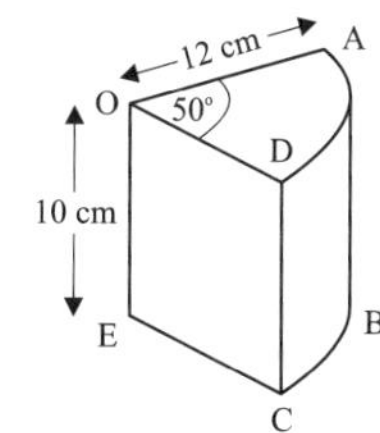

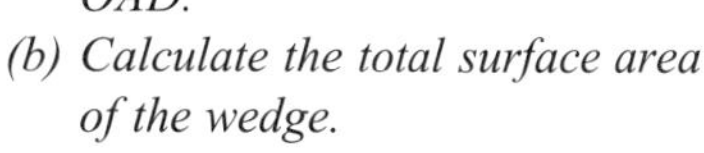

(a) Area of sector = $\frac{50}{360}$ of Area of circle
(see Box 9, p72)
= $\frac{50}{360} \times \pi \times 12^2$
= $50 \div 360 \times \pi \times 12^2$
= 62.83 cm²

(b) Area of rectangular side ODCE = $10 \times 12 = 120$ cm²
Area of curved side = $\frac{50}{360}$ of Wall of cylinder
= $\frac{50}{360} \times 2\pi rh$
= $\frac{50}{360} \times 2 \times \pi \times 12 \times 10$
= 104.7 cm²

Total surface area
= 2 Rectangles + 2 Sectors + Curved side
= $2 \times 120 + 2 \times 62.83 + 104.7$
= 470.4 cm²

Question *A pot of paint just covers 20 wooden spheres with a single coat. Wooden cylinders are manufactured whose radius and height are both equal to the radius of the spheres. How many cylinders can be coated with the pot of paint?*

Surface area of a sphere = $4\pi r^2$

Cylinders have radius r and height r. So:
Surface area of a cylinder = $2\pi r \times r + 2\pi r^2 = 4\pi r^2$

This is the same as the surface area of a sphere. So, the same number of cylinders can be painted, i.e. 20.

Surface Area (Contd)

4. Surface Area of a Cone

H

A cone has a circular base and a curved wall. The area of the curved wall is given by the formula:

Area of curved wall = πrl

where l is the slant height of the cone (see diagram). You will be given this formula in the question or on the formula sheet of the question paper.

Question *A conical oil can has a base of radius 3 cm and a slant height of 12 cm. Calculate its total surface area.*

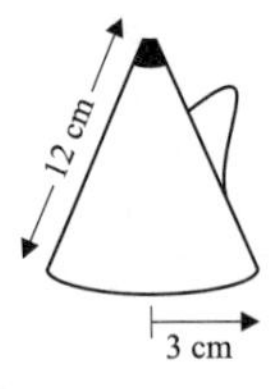

Area of circular base = $\pi r^2 = \pi \times 3^2 = 28.3$ cm^2

Area of wall = $\pi rl = \pi \times 3 \times 12 = 113.1$ cm^2

So, total surface area = $28.3 + 113.1 = 141.4$ cm^2

5. Surface Area of a Pyramid

A square pyramid has a square base.

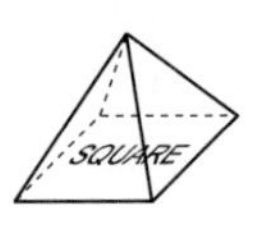

A triangular pyramid has a triangular base.

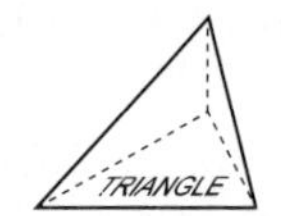

The surface area of a pyramid is the sum of the areas of its faces.

Question *A student cut out this cardboard shape and folded it up to make a square pyramid. Calculate the total surface area of the outside of the pyramid.*

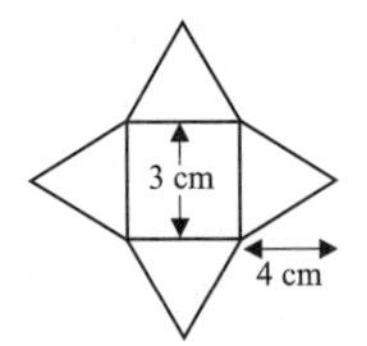

Area of square base = $3 \times 3 = 9$ cm^2

Area of triangular face $= \frac{1}{2}$ Base $\times$ Height
$= 0.5 \times 3 \times 4$
$= 6$ cm^2

Total surface area = Base + 4 Triangular faces
$= 9 + 4 \times 6$
$= 33$ cm^2

Volume

1. Units of Volume

The basic unit of volume is the **cubic metre** (m^3).

1 m^3 is the volume of a cube with 1 m sides.

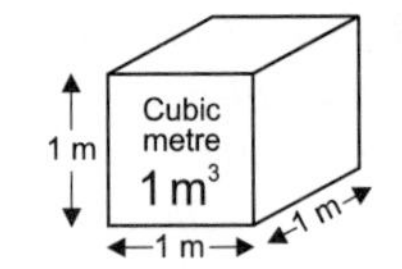

Similarly, 1 cm^3 is the volume of a cube with 1 cm sides.

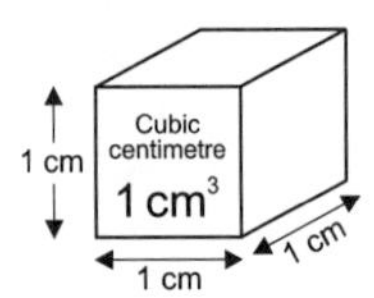

And 1 mm^3 is the volume of a cube with 1 mm sides.

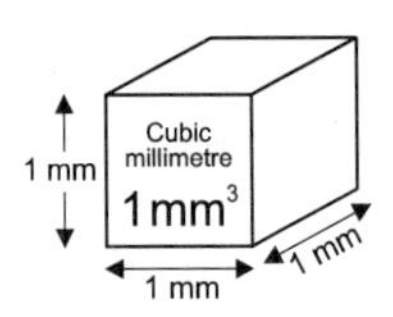

Question *Convert 3125 cm^3 to m^3.*

For converting **length** we used the diagram below (see Box 6, p28).

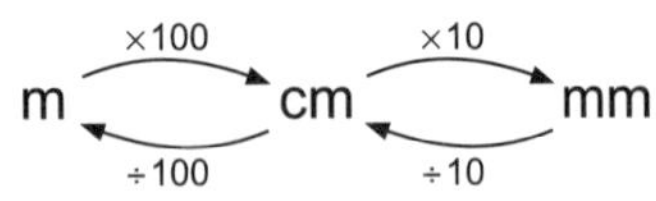

For converting **volume**, cube the numbers on the above diagram:

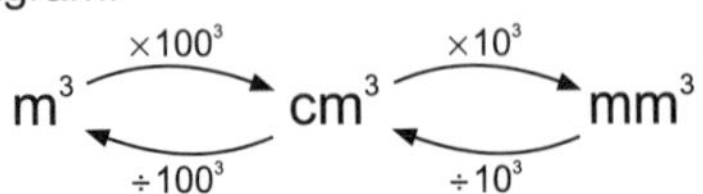

So, 3125 cm^3 = $3125 \div 100^3$ m^3 = $3125 \div 1\,000\,000$ m^3
= 0.003 125 m^3

2. Volume of a Cuboid

Volume of a cuboid
= Length $\times$ Breadth $\times$ Height
= lbh

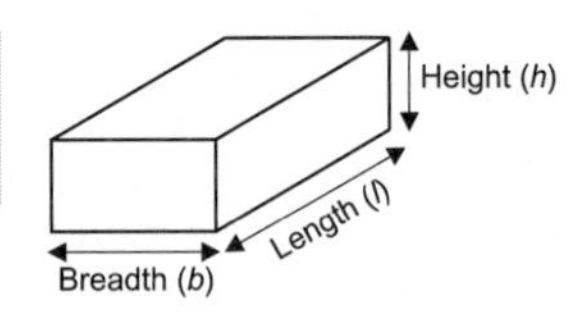

Question *The diagram below shows a concrete platform used for the presentation of medals.*
(a) Calculate the volume of concrete, in cm^3.
(b) What is the volume in m^3?

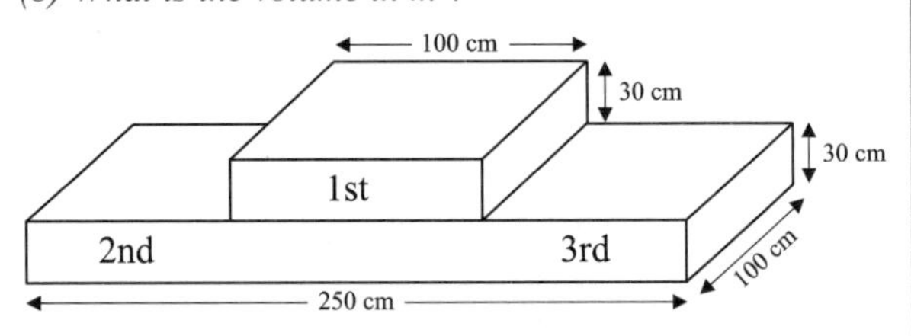

(a) The platform can be split into two cuboids.

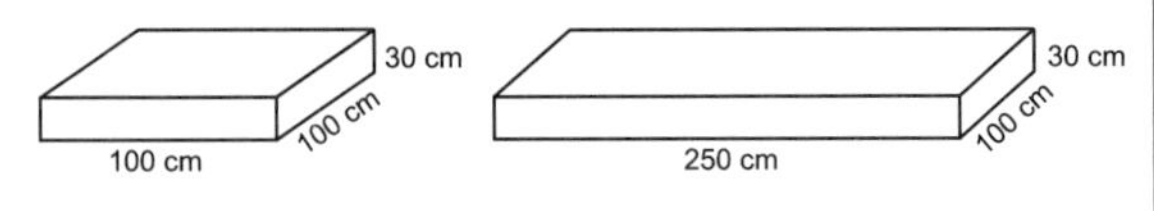

Volume
= lbh
= $100 \times 100 \times 30$
= 300 000 cm^3

Volume
= lbh
= $250 \times 100 \times 30$
= 750 000 cm^3

So, volume of platform = 300 000 + 750 000
= 1 050 000 cm^3

(b) 1 050 000 cm^3 = $1\,050\,000 \div 100^3$ m^3
= $1\,050\,000 \div 1\,000\,000$ m^3
= 1.05 m^3

Volume

3. Problems Involving Cuboids

Question *A cube of gold of side 2.5 cm is rolled into a thin rectangular sheet of width 10 cm and length 2 m.*
(a) Calculate the volume of gold, in mm^3.
(b) Calculate the thickness of the rectangular sheet, correct to the nearest 0.01 mm.

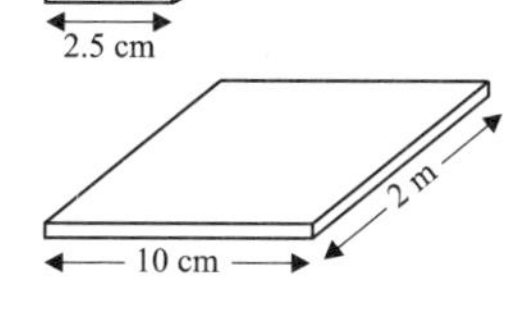

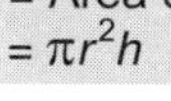

(a) A **cube** is a cuboid whose sides are equal.

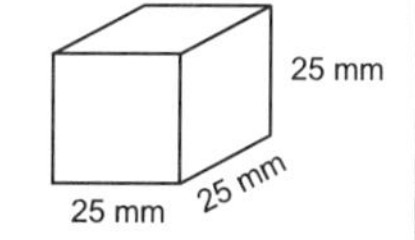

First, convert 2.5 cm to mm:
2.5 cm = 2.5×10 mm = 25 mm

Volume of cube = lbh = 25×25×25 = 15 625 mm^3

(b) The rectangular sheet is also a cuboid.

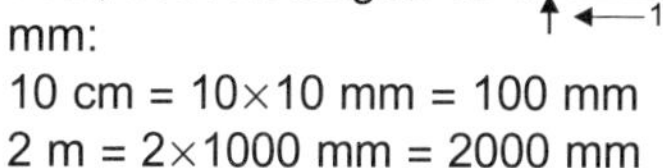

First, convert lengths to mm:
10 cm = 10×10 mm = 100 mm
2 m = 2×1000 mm = 2000 mm

Although we do not know the height, h, we can still substitute the length and breadth into the formula:

Volume of sheet = lbh = 100×2000×h
= 200 000h mm^3

Now, this is the same volume as the cube. So:
200 000h = 15 625

$\therefore\ h = \frac{15\,625}{200\,000} = 0.078\,125 \approx 0.08$ mm

4. Volume of a Prism

A **prism** is a solid whose cross-section is the same throughout its length.

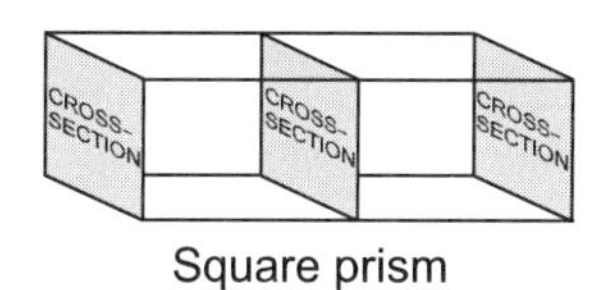

Square prism

Triangular prism

Volume of a prism
= Area of cross-section × Length

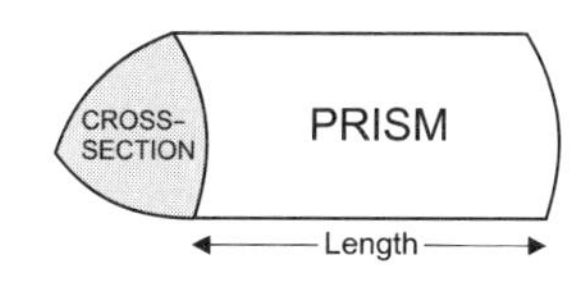

Question *The diagram shows a paint trough in the shape of a prism.*
(a) Calculate the area of the cross-section.
(b) Calculate the volume of the trough.

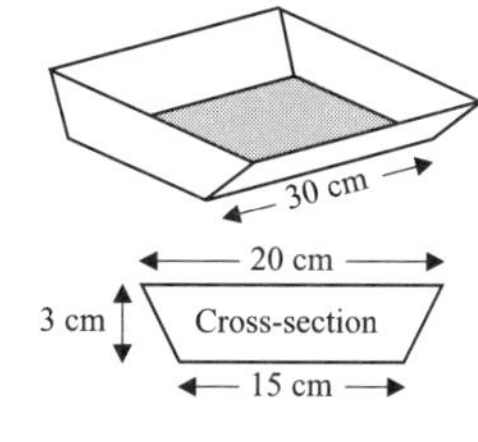

(a) The cross-section is in the shape of a trapezium.
Area of cross-section
= Area of trapezium
$= \frac{1}{2}(a+b)h = \frac{1}{2}\times(15+20)3 = 0.5\times35\times3 = 52.5$ cm^2

(b) Volume of trough = Area of cross-section×Length
= 52.5×30 = 1575 cm^3

5. Volume of a Cylinder

Volume of a cylinder
= Area of circular base × Height
= $\pi r^2 h$

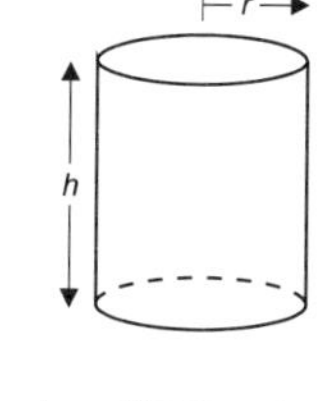

Question *A company drinks machine accepts tokens made in the shape of a cylinder, as shown in the diagram.*
(a) Calculate the volume of a token, in mm^3.
(b) A cylindrical hole is drilled in the middle of each, reducing its volume to 400 mm^3. Calculate the radius of the hole.

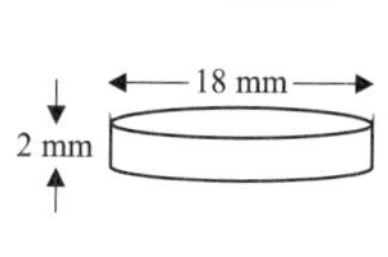

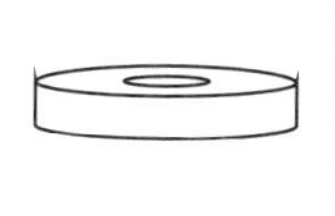

(a) Volume of cylinder = $\pi r^2 h = \pi\times9^2\times2 = 508.9$ mm^3

(b) If the new volume is to be 400 mm^3 then:
Volume of hole = 508.9−400 = 108.9 mm^3

The hole is a cylinder with height 2 mm and unknown radius, r. So, using the formula, we have:

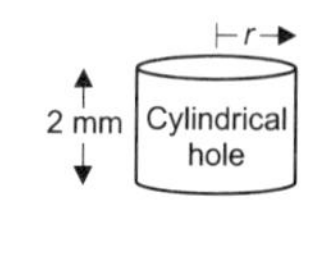

Volume of hole = $\pi r^2 h = \pi\times r^2\times2$
$= 2\pi r^2$

So, $2\pi r^2 = 108.9$
$\therefore\ r^2 = \frac{108.9}{2\pi} = 17.3$
$\therefore\ r = \sqrt{17.3} = 4.2$ mm (1 dp)

Question *Calculate the volume of this loaf of bread to the nearest 100 cm^3. The cross-section has a semicircular top.*

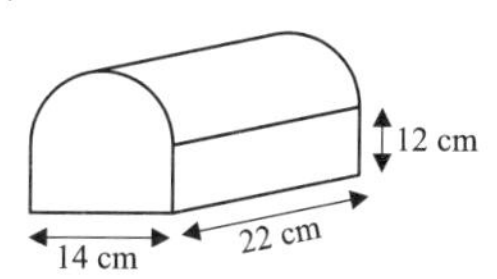

Prism method

Radius of circle = 7 cm

Cross-section
= Rectangle + Semi-circle
$= bh + \frac{1}{2}$ of πr^2
$= 14\times12 + 0.5\times\pi\times7^2$
$= 245.0$ cm^3

Volume of loaf = Area of cross-section × Length
= 245.0×22
≈ 5400 cm^3 (to nearest 100 cm^3)

Cylinder method

Radius of circle = 7 cm

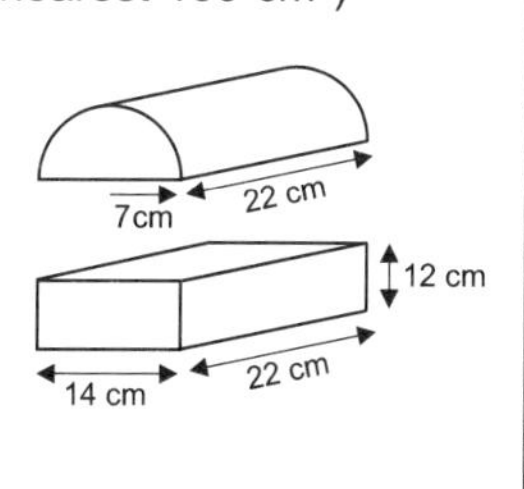

Volume of loaf
= Volume of cuboid + Volume of half cylinder

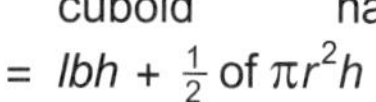

$= lbh + \frac{1}{2}$ of $\pi r^2 h$

$= 22\times14\times12 + 0.5\times\pi\times7^2\times22$
$= 5389.3$ cm^3
≈ 5400 cm^3 (to nearest 100 cm^3)

Volume (Contd)

6. Volume of a Sphere

H

Volume of a sphere = $\frac{4}{3}\pi r^3$

You will be given this formula in the question or on the formula sheet of the question paper.

A **hemisphere** is half a sphere, and so its volume is $\frac{2}{3}\pi r^3$.

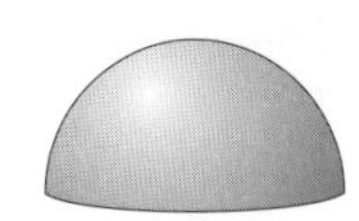

Question *A spherical glass ball of radius 5 cm is placed in a tank of water and is completely covered by the water.*

(a) Calculate the volume of the glass ball.

(b) Calculate the rise in water level.

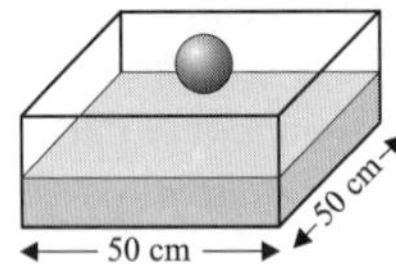

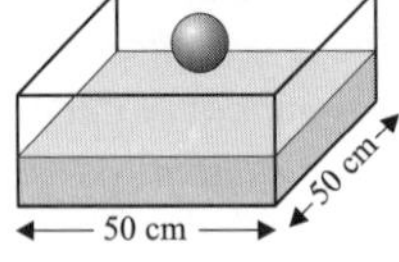

(a) Volume of sphere = $\frac{4}{3}\pi r^3 = \frac{4}{3}\times\pi\times5^3$

$= 4\div3\times\pi\times5^3$

$= 523.6\ \text{cm}^3$

4 ÷ 3 × π × 5 x^y 3 = 523.598776

(b) When the ball is immersed, the water level rises. The water that rises is the dark shaded cuboid in the diagram and has the same volume as the sphere.

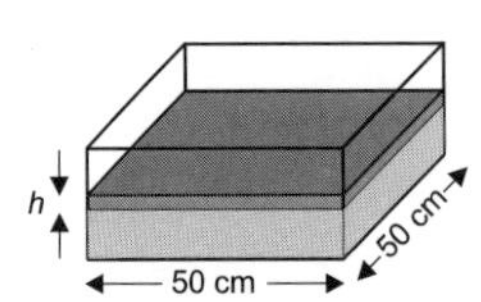

Volume of cuboid = $lbh = 50\times50\times h = 2500h\ \text{cm}^3$

Now, volume of cuboid = Volume of sphere

So, $2500h = 523.6$

$\therefore\ h = \frac{523.6}{2500} = 0.21$ cm

The water level rises 0.21 cm.

7. Volume of a Cone

Volume of cone = $\frac{1}{3}\pi r^2 h$

where h is the vertical height of the cone (see diagram). You will be given this formula in the question or on the formula sheet of the question paper.

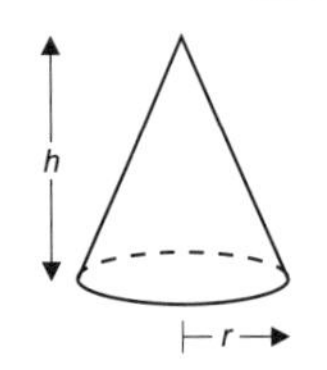

Question *The diagram shows a conical paper drinking cup.*

(a) Calculate the maximum volume of water the cup can hold.

(b) How many cups can be filled from a tank containing 25 litres?

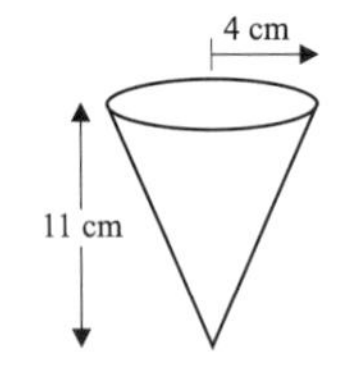

(a) Volume of cup = $\frac{1}{3}\pi r^2 h = \frac{1}{3}\times\pi\times4^2\times11 = 184.3\ \text{cm}^3$

(a) 1 litre = 1000 cm^3

25 litres = $25\times1000\ \text{cm}^3$ = 25 000 cm^3

Number of cups = $\frac{25\,000}{184.3} = 135.6$

So, 135 cups can be filled from the tank.

8. Volume of a Pyramid

H

Volume of a pyramid
= $\frac{1}{3}\times$ Area of base $\times$ Height

NOTE The height must be perpendicular to the base

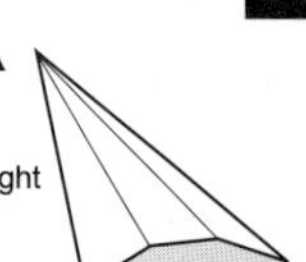

Question *A wax candle is made in the shape of a pyramid with a square base. The candle burns down a distance of 6 cm.*

(a) Calculate the volume of wax that has melted.

(b) Calculate the volume of wax remaining.

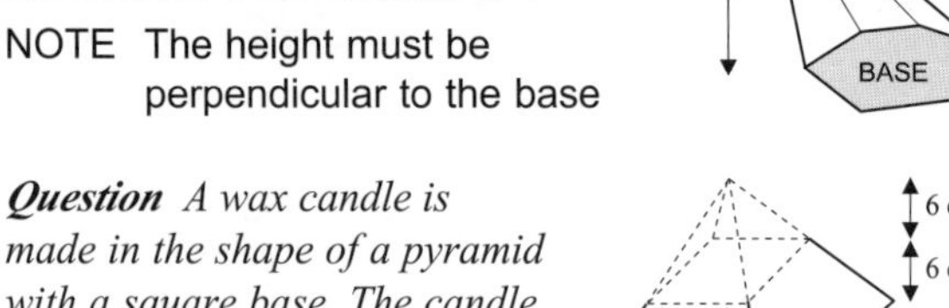

(a) Volume of melted wax

= Volume of small pyramid

$= \frac{1}{3}\times\text{Base}\times\text{Height}$

$= \frac{1}{3}\times2.5\times2.5\times6$

$= 12.5\ \text{cm}^3$

(b) Volume of large pyramid

$= \frac{1}{3}\times\text{Base}\times\text{Height}$

$= \frac{1}{3}\times5\times5\times12$

$= 100\ \text{cm}^3$

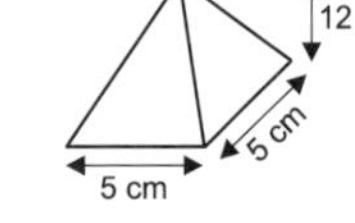

Wax remaining = $100 - 12.5 = 87.5\ \text{cm}^3$

9. Density

The **density** of a substance tells you its mass per unit volume. For example, cork has a density of 0.25 g/cm^3, which means that 1 cm^3 of cork has a mass of 0.25 g.

Question *An ice-making machine can produce cylindrical blocks of ice with radius 7 cm and of any length.*

(a) Calculate the volume of a block of ice 20 cm long.

(b) Given that the density of ice is 0.9 g/cm^3, calculate the weight this block.

(c) Calculate the length of a block of ice weighing 4 kg.

(a) Volume of block = $\pi r^2 h = \pi\times7^2\times20 = 3078.8\ \text{cm}^3$

(b) 1 cm^3 of ice weighs 0.9 g

So, 3078.8 cm^3 weighs 3078.8×0.9 g = 2771 g

(c) Weight of block of ice = 4 kg = 4×1000 g = 4000 g

Now, 0.9 g of ice has a volume of 1 cm^3

$\therefore$ 1 g has a volume of $\frac{1}{0.9} = 1.\dot{1}\ \text{cm}^3$

$\therefore$ Volume of 4000 g = $4000\times1.\dot{1}\ \text{cm}^3 = 4444.\dot{4}\ \text{cm}^3$

Store this in the memory of your calculator.

So, volume of block of ice = $4444.\dot{4}\ \text{cm}^3$.

Using the formula for the volume of a cylinder:

Volume of block of ice = $\pi r^2 h = \pi\times7^2\times h\ \text{cm}^3$

So, $\pi\times7^2\times h = 4444.\dot{4}$

$\therefore\ h = \frac{4444.4}{\pi\times7^2} = 28.9$ cm

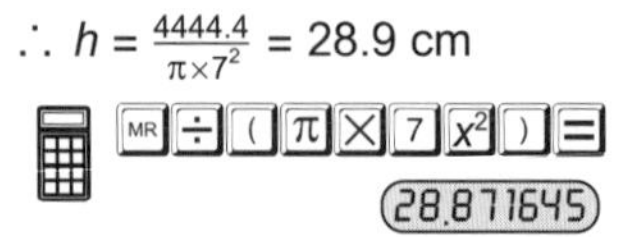

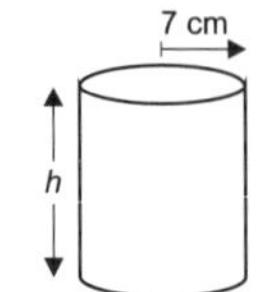

Dimensions and Formulas

Length (1 dimension)

When you use a formula to calculate a length, the answer is in metres, m (or in cm, mm, km).

For example, the perimeter of a rectangle is given by the formula:

Perimeter = $2(l+b)$

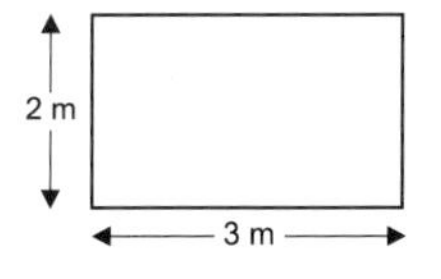

For this rectangle, l = 3 m and b = 2 m. So:

Perimeter = 2(3 m + 2 m) = 2×5 m = 10 m

Area (2 dimensions)

When you use a formula to calculate an area (length×length), the answer is in square metres, m^2 (or in cm^2, mm^2, km^2).

For example, the total surface area of a cylinder is given by the formula:

Area = $2\pi r(r+h)$

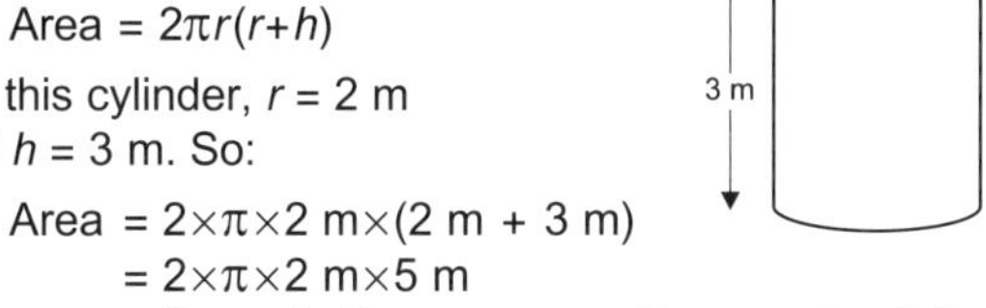

For this cylinder, r = 2 m and h = 3 m. So:

Area = $2\times\pi\times2$ m×(2 m + 3 m)
= $2\times\pi\times2$ m×5 m
= $2\times\pi\times2\times5$ m×m Rearranging letters
= 62.8 m^2

Volume (3 dimensions)

When you use a formula to calculate a volume (length×length×length), the answer is usually in cubic metres, m^3 (or in cm^3, mm^3).

For example, the volume of a cuboid is given by the formula:

Volume = lbh

For this cuboid, l = 3 m, b = 1 m and h = 2 m. So:

Volume = 3 m × 1 m × 2 m = 3×1×2 m^3 = 6 m^3

Question *The diagram shows a deodorant stick in the shape of a prism. The following formulas can be used in connection with this prism:*

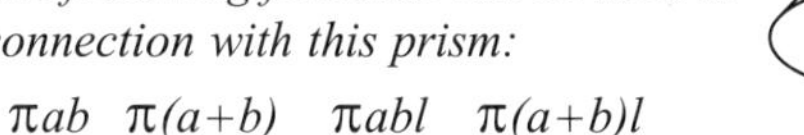

πab $\pi(a+b)$ πabl $\pi(a+b)l$

Which of these formulas represent area?

Replace each letter by m, the unit for length.

πab becomes πmm = π m^2	Area
$\pi(a+b)$ becomes π(m+m) = $\pi\times2$ m = 2π m	Length
πabl becomes πmmm = π m^3	Volume
$\pi(a+b)l$ becomes π(m+m)m = $\pi\times2$ m×m = 2π m^2	Area

So, the formulas πab and $\pi(a+b)l$ represent areas.

Similar Shapes and Solids

1. Enlargement and Scale Factors

Statue B is an enlarged replica of statue A. The lengths of statue A have been multiplied by 2 to obtain the lengths of statue B. We say that statue A has been enlarged by a **scale factor** of 2.

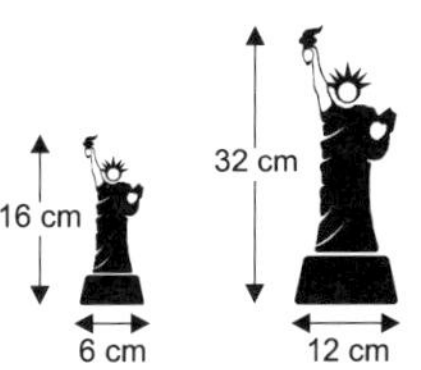

The scale factor can be calculated by dividing any two corresponding lengths of the statues. For example, using their widths gives: 12÷6 = 2.

Another way of describing the relationship between the lengths of the statues is to use the ratio of their lengths. The widths of the statues are in the ratio 6 : 12 or, equivalently, 1 : 2.

A	:	B
6 cm	:	12 cm
1	:	2

Alternatively, we could use the heights of the statues. The heights of the statues are in the ratio 16 : 32 or, equivalently, 1 : 2.

A	:	B
16 cm	:	32 cm
1	:	2

2. Similar Shapes and Solids

Two shapes or solids are said to be **similar** if one is an enlargement of the other. So, the statues in Box 1 are similar solids.

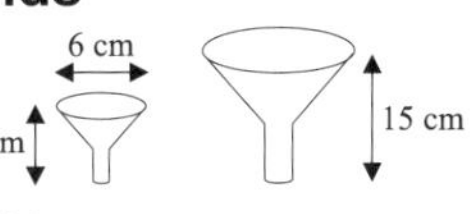

Question *These two funnels are similar in shape. Calculate the width of the larger funnel.*

The funnels are similar and so one is an enlargement of the other. The scale factor of the enlargement can be found by dividing the heights of the funnels:

Scale factor = 15÷8 = 1.875

Width of larger funnel = 1.875 ×Width of smaller funnel
= 1.875×6 = 11.25 cm

Question *A4 and A5 sizes of paper are similar in shape. Calculate the width of an A5 sheet.*

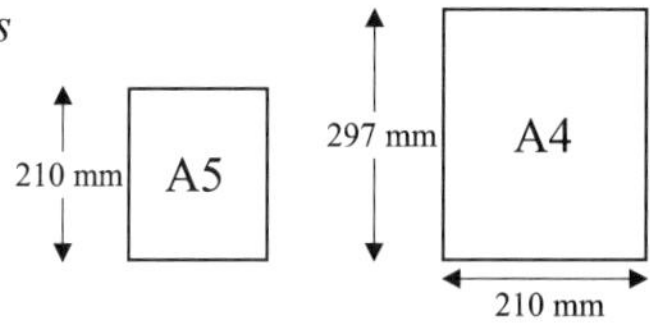

The A4 sheet is an enlargement of the A5 sheet. Use their heights to find the scale factor:

Scale factor = 297÷210 = 1.41

So, width of A4 sheet = 1.41 × Width of A5 sheet

We know that the width of an A4 sheet is 210 mm. So,

So, 210 = 1.41 × Width of A5 sheet

∴ Width of A5 sheet = 210÷1.41 ≈ 148 mm

Similar Shapes and Solids (Contd)

3. Areas of Similar Shapes and Solids

Rectangles A and B are similar. The lengths of B are 3 times the lengths of A. So, the lengths of A have been enlarged by a scale factor of 3.

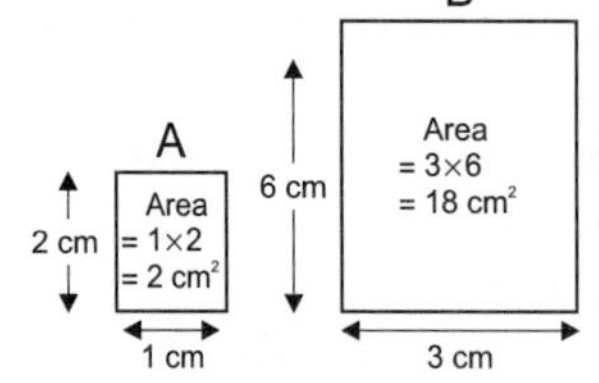

Notice that the **area** of B is 9 times the area of A. So, the area of A has been enlarged by a scale factor of **9**, which is the square of the length scale factor 3.

Scale factor for area = (Scale factor for length)^2

Question *These two cans of soup have a simlar shape. The area of the smaller label is 85 cm^2. Calculate the area of the larger label.*

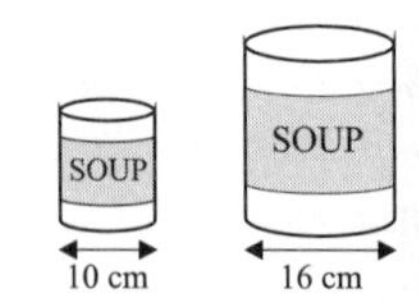

Scale factor for length = $\frac{16}{10}$ = 1.6

So, scale factor for area = 1.6^2 = 2.56

So, area of larger label = 2.56 × Area of smaller label
= 2.56×85 cm^2
= 217.6 cm^2

4. Volumes of Similar Shapes and Solids

Cuboids A and B are similar. The lengths of B are twice the lengths of A. So, the lengths of A have been enlarged by a scale factor of 2.

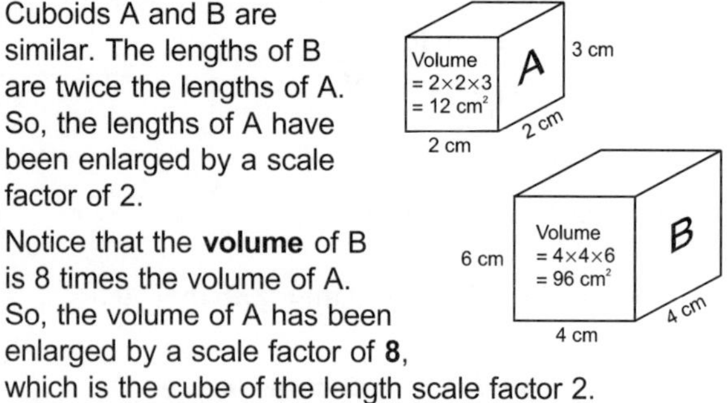

Notice that the **volume** of B is 8 times the volume of A. So, the volume of A has been enlarged by a scale factor of **8**, which is the cube of the length scale factor 2.

Scale factor for volume = (Scale factor for length)^3

Question *Brian has built a scale model of an oil tanker, using a scale of 1:72. The real oil tanker can carry 25 000 m^3 of oil. How many cm^3 of oil can the model tanker carry?*

Scale factor for length = 72

So, scale factor for volume = 72^3 = 373 248

∴ Volume of tanker = 373 248 × Volume of model

∴ 25 000 m^3 = 373 248 × Volume of model tanker

∴ Volume of model tanker = $\frac{25\,000}{373\,248}$ = 0.067 m^3

And 0.067 m^3 = 0.067×100^3 cm^3 = 67 000 cm^3

5. Length, Area and Volume of Similar Shapes and Solids

Question *These two hot-air balloons have a similar shape. The surface area of Sky is 800 m^2 and the surface area of Ascender is 1000 m^2. When fully inflated, the volume of air in Ascender is 2700 m^3. Calculate the volume of air in Sky, correct to the nearest 100 m^3.*

Scale factor for areas = $\frac{1000}{800}$ = 1.25

So, scale factor for length = $\sqrt{1.25}$ = 1.1180

So, scale factor for volume = 1.1180^3 = 1.3975

So, volume of air in Sky = 2700÷1.3975 ≈ 1900 m^3

Angles and Parallel Lines

1. 360° in a Circle

There are 360° in a circle.

Question *Find the angle x.*

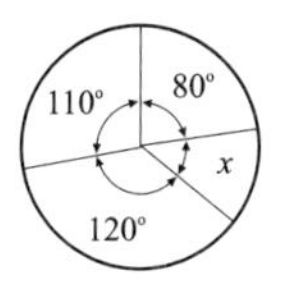

Total angle = 360°

$\therefore\ x+80°+110°+120° = 360°$

$\therefore\ x = 360°-80°-110°-120°$

$\therefore\ x = 50°$

2. Names of Angles

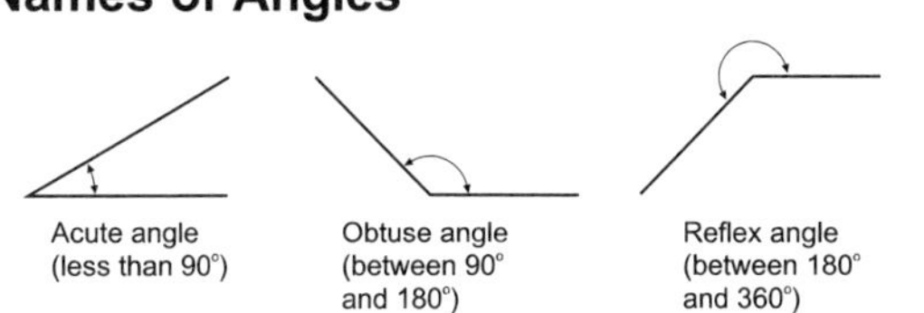

Question *Mark the acute angle(s) in this shape.*

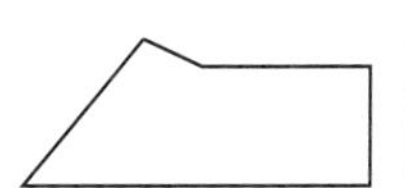

Acute angles are *less* than 90° and so the right angles have not been marked. There is only one acute angle in this shape.

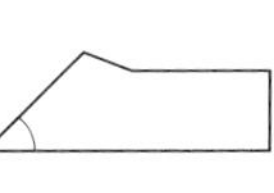

Right Angle

An angle of 90° is called a **right angle** and is indicated by a small square (see diagram).

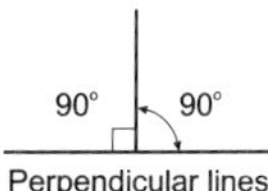

Perpendicular lines

Lines that meet at right angles are called **perpendicular** lines. For example, horizontal and vertical lines are perpendicular.

Question *Find the angle marked x.*

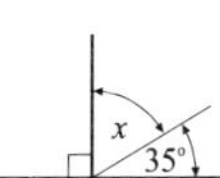

$x+35° = 90°$

$\therefore\ x = 90°-35° = 55°$

3. Describing an Angle

There are various ways of referring to an angle in a diagram.

The 50° angle in this triangle is called angle ABC, because it lies between the sides AB and BC. Other ways of writing angle ABC are: $A\hat{B}C$, $\hat{B}$ or simply B.

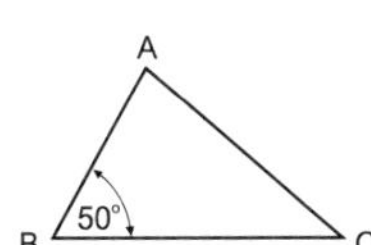

4. Angle of a Straight Line

The angle of a straight line is 180°.

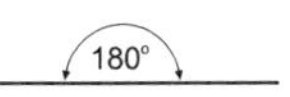

Question *Calculate the angle x.*

$\therefore\ x+120° = 180°$

$\therefore\ x = 180°-120° = 60°$

5. Opposite Angles

Opposite angles are equal.

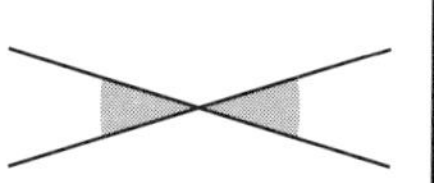

Question *Calculate the angles x and y.*

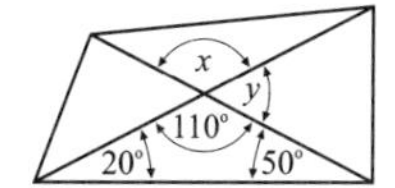

$x = 110°$ Opposite angles

$\therefore\ y = 180°-110° = 70°$ Angle of a straight line

6. Parallel Lines

Parallel lines have the same direction, indicated by arrows.

A straight line crossing parallel lines meets them at the same angle.

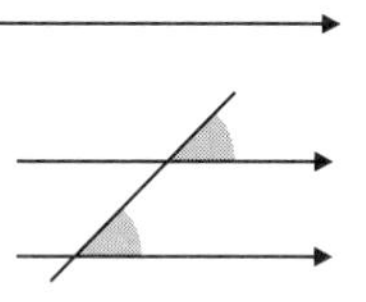

Question *Find angles a, b and c.*

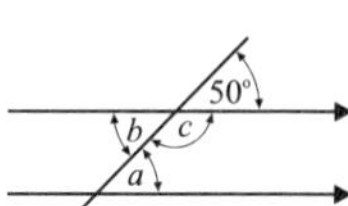

$a = 50°$ Parallel lines

$\therefore\ b = 50°$ Opposite angles

$\therefore\ c = 180°-50° = 130°$ Angle of a straight line

Alternate (Z) angles are equal.

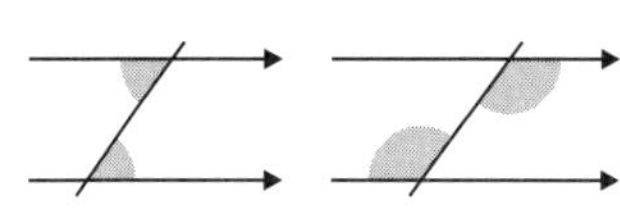

Question *Calculate angles x and y*

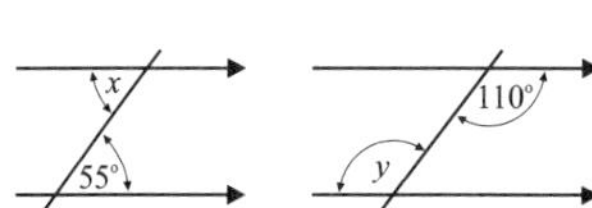

$x = 55°$ Alternate angles

$y = 110°$ Alternate angles

Interior angles add up to 180°.

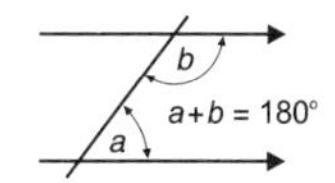

Question *Calculate the angle x.*

$x+120° = 180°$

$\therefore\ x = 180°-120° = 60°$

Question *The diagram shows the side elevation of a lean-to shed. Find the angle marked x.*

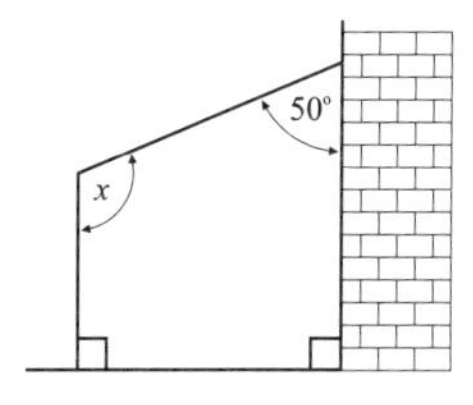

The walls are parallel because they are both vertical (at right angles to the ground). So, x and 50° are interior angles:

$\therefore\ x+50° = 180°$

$\therefore\ x = 180°-50° = 130°$

Triangles

1. Angles of a Triangle

The interior angles of a triangle add up to 180°.

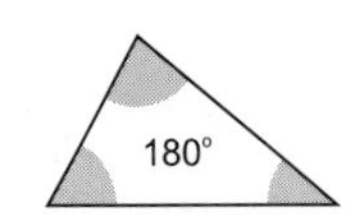

Question *Find the angle x.*

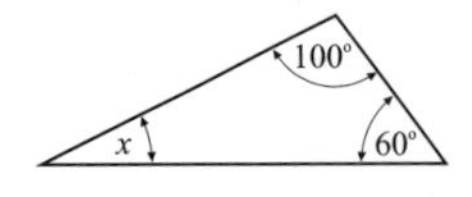

Sum of angles = 180°

$\therefore\ x + 60° + 100° = 180°$

$\therefore\ x = 180° - 60° - 100°$

$\therefore\ x = 20°$

2. Right–angled Triangles

A right–angled triangle contains a 90° angle, indicated by a small square.

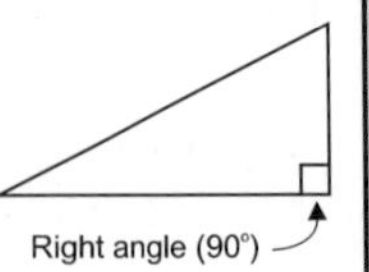

Question *Find the angle x.*

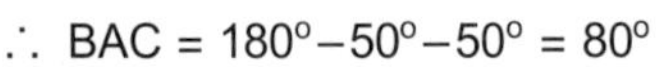

$x + 30° + 90° = 180°$

$\therefore\ x = 180° - 90° - 30°$

$= 90° - 30°$
$= 60°$

This shows that we only need to subtract 30° from 90° to find x

Question *Calculate angles a, b, c and d in this roof structure.*

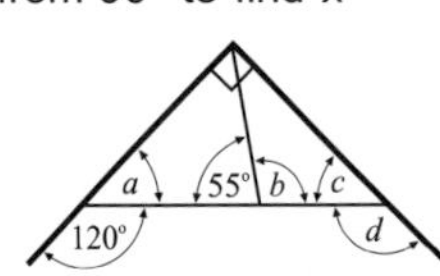

$a = 180° - 120° = 60°$	Angle of a straight line
$b = 180° - 55° = 125°$	Angle of a straight line
$c = 90° - a = 90° - 60° = 30°$	Angles of a triangle
$d = 180° - c = 180° - 30° = 150°$	Angle of a straight line

NOTE As soon as you find an angle, put it on the diagram and see how it can help you find the next angle.

3. Equilateral Triangle

An **equilateral triangle** has all its sides equal. The interior angles of an equilateral triangle are all 60°

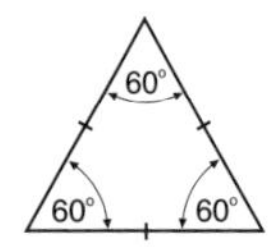

Question *12 identical matches were used to make this pattern.*
(a) State the size of angle GAB, giving a reason for your answer.
(b) Calculate angle ABC.

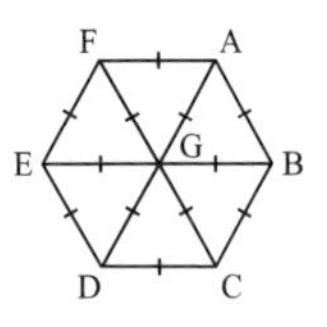

(a) GAB = 60°
Equilateral triangle

(b) ABC = ABG+GBC
= 60°+60°
= 120°

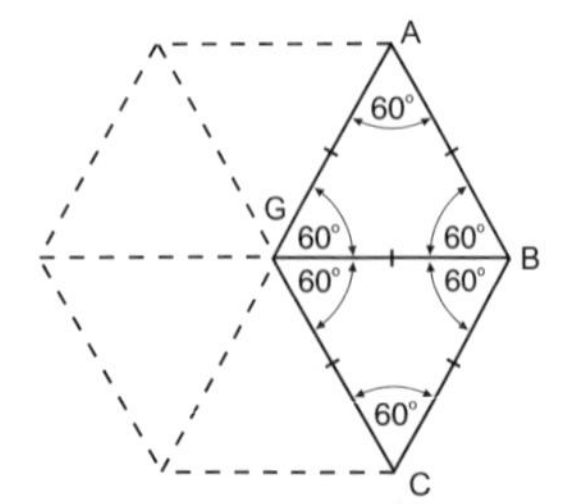

4. Isosceles Triangle

An **isosceles triangle** has two sides the same length (indicated here by dashes). Its two **base angles** are equal. Isosceles triangles are very common in questions involving angles.

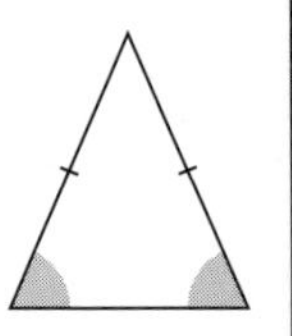

Question *ABC is an isosceles triangle with AB = AC and angle ABC = 50° Calculate angle BAC.*

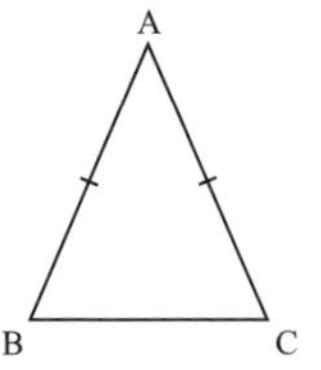

Mark angle ABC = 50° on the diagram.

Then, ACB = 50°

Base angles are equal

So, BAC+50°+50° = 180°

Angles of a triangle add up to 180°

$\therefore$ BAC = 180°–50°–50° = 80°

Question
(a) Calculate the size of angle ACD.
(b) If triangle ABC is also isosceles, what are the two possible values of angle ABC.

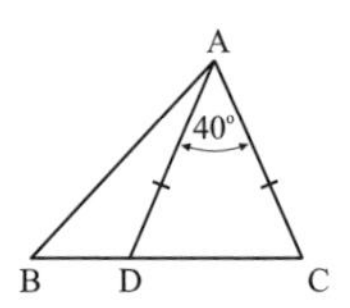

(a) The angles of triangle ADC add up to 180°. We know that angle DAC is 40°, which leaves 180°–40° = 140° for the two base angles ADC and ACD. Since the base angles are equal, then ACD = 140°÷2 = 70°.

(b) Triangle ABC can be isosceles in the two ways shown below.

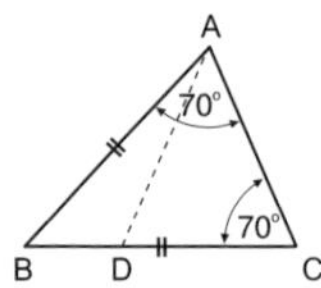

ACB and CAB are equal base angles and so CAB = 70°

ABC = 180°–70°–70°
= 40°

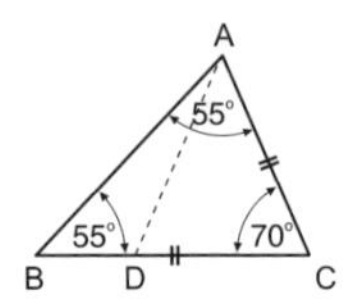

ABC and CAB are equal base angles that add up to 180°–70° = 110°

So, ABC = 110°÷2 = 55°

Question *A garden trellis is made in the form of a rectangle. Given that AB = BC, calculate the size of angle ABF.*

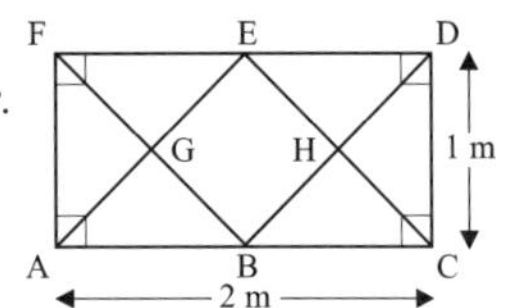

Since AB = BC and AC = 2 m, then AB = 1 m and AF = 1 m also. So, triangle FAB is isosceles (see diagrams).

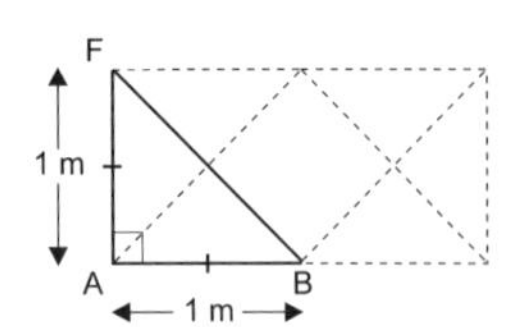

The base angles AFB and ABF add up to 90° (because 180°–90° = 90°).

So, ABF = 90°÷2 = 45°

5. Pythagoras' Theorem

The longest side of a right-angled triangle is opposite the right angle and is called the **hypotenuse**.

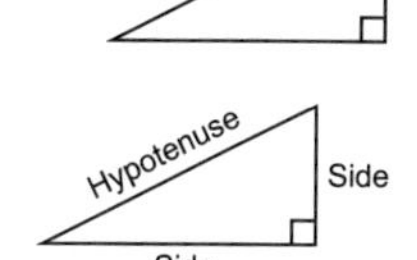

Pythagoras' theorem says that the square of the hypotenuse is equal to the sum of the squares of the other two sides:

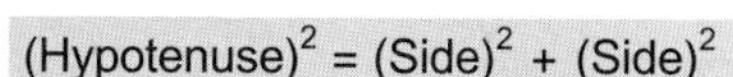

$(\text{Hypotenuse})^2 = (\text{Side})^2 + (\text{Side})^2$

This equation can be written algebraically as: $a^2 = b^2 + c^2$

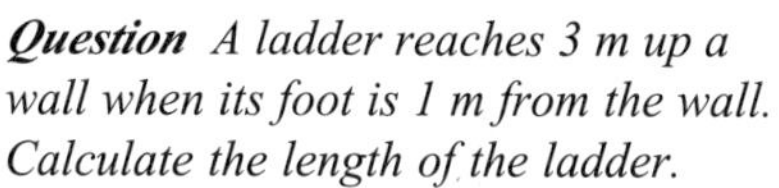

Question *A ladder reaches 3 m up a wall when its foot is 1 m from the wall. Calculate the length of the ladder.*

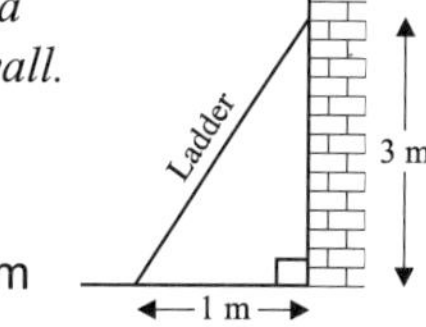

$(\text{Ladder})^2 = 1^2+3^2 = 1+9 = 10$

So, length of ladder = $\sqrt{10} = 3.16$ m

Question *A 50 cm television screen means that it is 50 cm from corner to corner. How tall is this screen?*

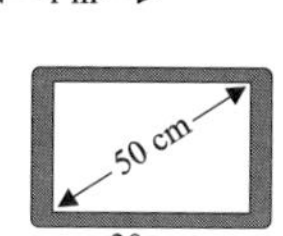

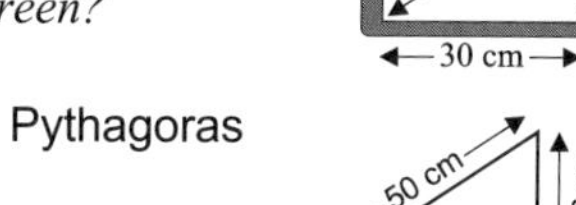

$50^2 = (\text{Height})^2+30^2$ Pythagoras

$\therefore (\text{Height})^2 + 30^2 = 50^2$

$\therefore (\text{Height})^2 = 50^2-30^2$

$= 2500-900 = 1600$

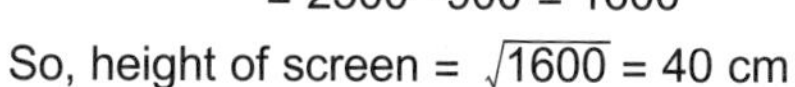

So, height of screen = $\sqrt{1600} = 40$ cm

Question *Calculate the area of this isosceles triangle.*

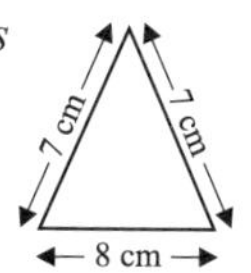

An isosceles triangle can be divided into two identical right-angled triangles

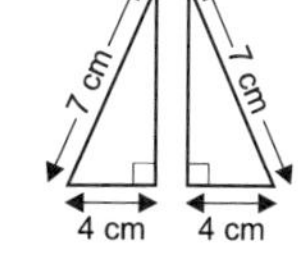

$7^2 = (\text{Height})^2 + 4^2$ Pythagoras

$\therefore (\text{Height})^2 + 4^2 = 7^2$

$\therefore (\text{Height})^2 = 7^2-4^2 = 49-16 = 33$

So, height of triangle = $\sqrt{33} = 5.74$ cm

Area of triangle = $\frac{1}{2}\times$ Base $\times$ Height

$= 0.5\times8\times5.74 = 23.0 \text{ cm}^2$

6. Similar Triangles

Triangles are **similar** if they have the same angles. This means they have the same shape.

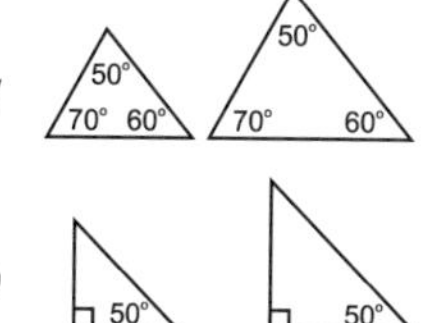

The third angle of each of these triangles must be the same and so the triangles are similar.

Question *Write down the two triangles that are similar.*

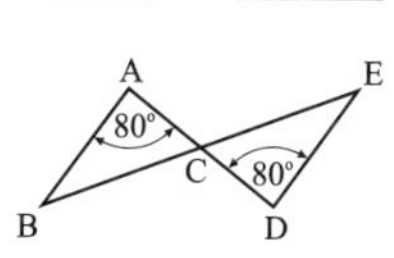

Angle ACB = Angle DCE   Opposite angles

So, angles ABC and CED must also be equal.

So, triangle CAB is similar to triangle CDE.

NOTE Make sure that the letters of one triangle correspond to the letters of the other, e.g. angle A is the same as angle D.

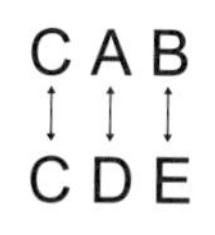

If two triangles are similar, then one is an enlargement of the other, and vice-versa.

Question *The diagram shows a playground slide.*
(a) Which two triangles are similar?
(b) Calculate the height of the support AB.

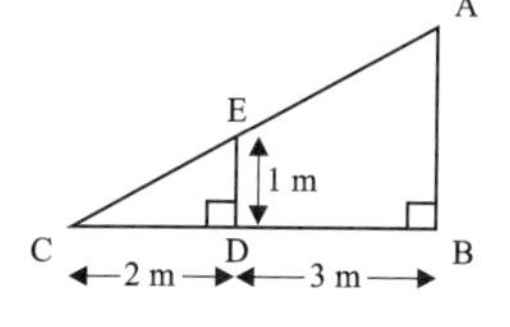

(a) Triangles ACB and ECD are similar because they have angles C and 90° in common.

(b) So, triangle ACB is an enlargement of triangle ECD.

Draw and label the two triangles separately so that you can see them more clearly.

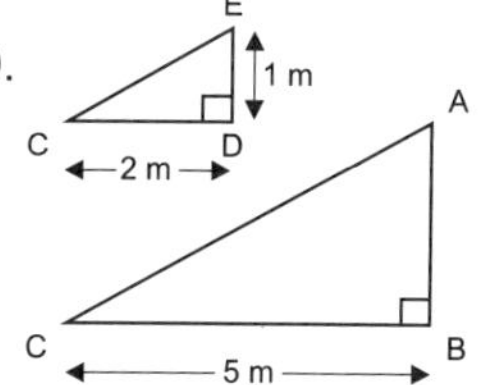

Scale factor of enlargement = $\frac{5}{2} = 2.5$

So, all lengths of triangle ACB are 2.5 times the corresponding lengths of triangle ECD

So, AB = 2.5×ED = 2.5×1 m = 2.5 m

7. Congruent Triangles

Triangles are **congruent** if they are identical. This means they have the same sides and angles.

You may be asked to explain why two particular triangles are congruent. The three possibilities are shown below.

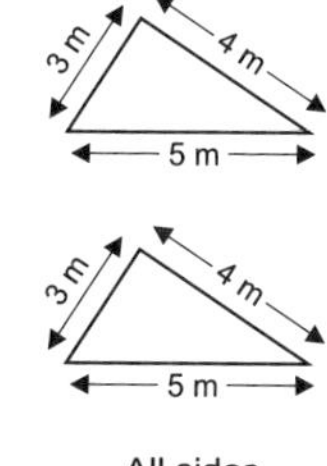

All sides equal

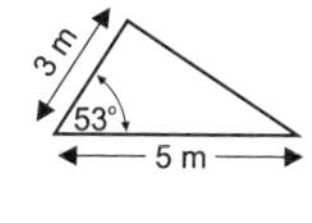

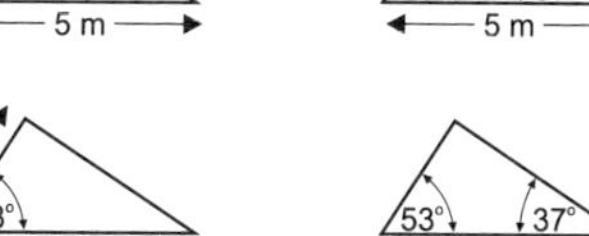

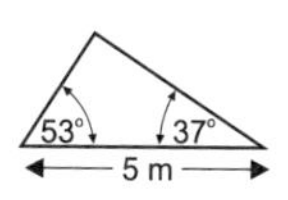

Two sides and included angle equal

One side and two matching angles equal

Question *Explain why triangles ABE and CDE are congruent.*

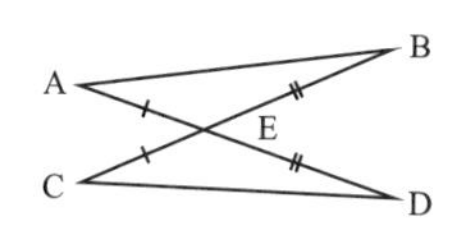

Angle AEB = Angle CED   Opposite angles

So, triangles ABE and CDE are congruent because two sides and their included angle are equal (CE = AE, ED = EB and angle AEB = angle CED).

Question *Explain why triangle ADB is **not** congruent to triangle DCB.*

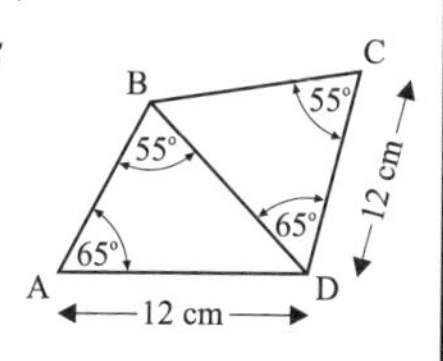

Angle ADB = 180°−65°−55° = 60° which is not the same as angle DCB. So, although the sides AD and DC are equal, the matching angles are not.

Quadrilaterals

1. Quadilaterals

A **quadrilateral** is a shape which has four sides.

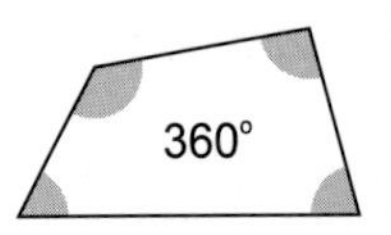

The angles of a quadrilateral add up to 360°.

Question *Find the angle marked x.*

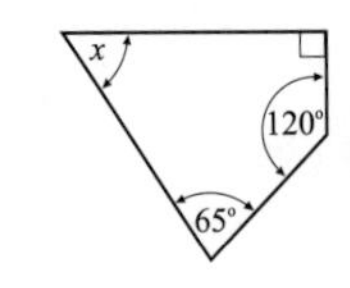

Sum of angles = 360°

$\therefore x+90°+120°+65° = 360°$

$\therefore x = 360°-90°-120°-65°$

$\therefore x = 85°$

2. Rectangle

A **rectangle** has four right angles and equal opposite sides.

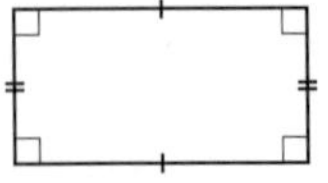

The diagonals are equal and cut each other in half (**bisect** each other).

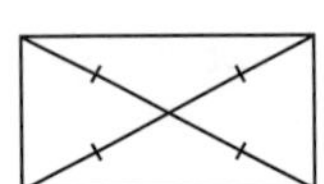

Opposite sides are parallel.

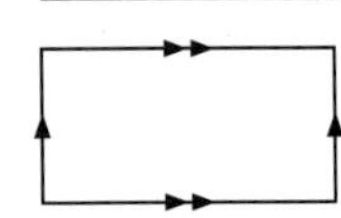

Question *Find the length of the diagonal bar of this rectangular gate.*

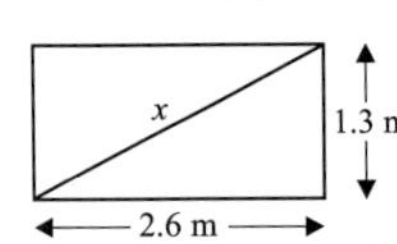

Using Pythagoras' theorem:

$x^2 = 1.3^2+2.6^2 = 8.45$

$\therefore x = \sqrt{8.45} = 2.9$ m

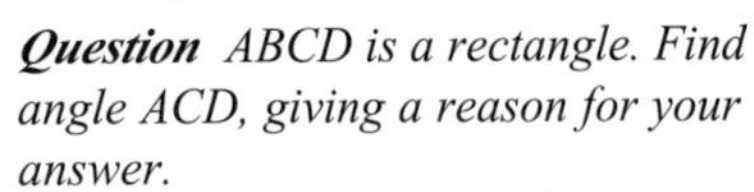
Question *ABCD is a rectangle. Find angle ACD, giving a reason for your answer.*

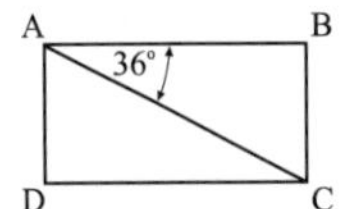

AB and CD are parallel. So:
ACD = 36° Alternate angles
(See Box 6, p79)

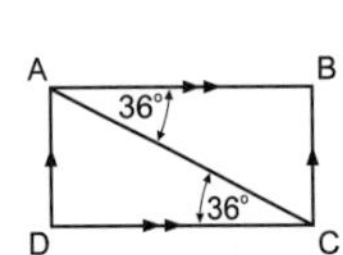

3. Square

A **square** is a rectangle with four equal sides.

The diagonals are equal and cross at right angles (90°). They cut the corner angles in half.

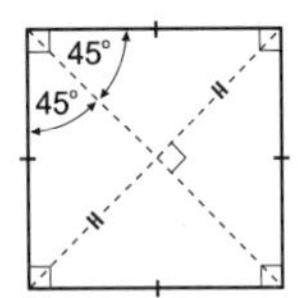

Question *The diagonal of a square boxing ring is 8.5 m. What is the length of its sides, to the nearest m?*

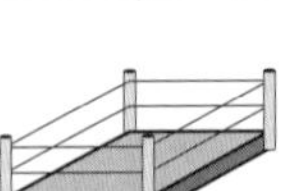

Let x be the length of its sides.

Using Pythagoras' theorem:

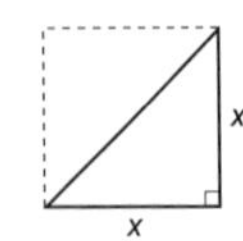

$x^2+x^2 = 8.5^2$

$\therefore 2x^2 = 72.25$

$\therefore x^2 = 72.25 \div 2$

$\therefore x^2 = 36.13$

$\therefore x = \sqrt{36.13} \approx 6$ m

4. Rhombus

A **rhombus** is like a square that has been pushed over.

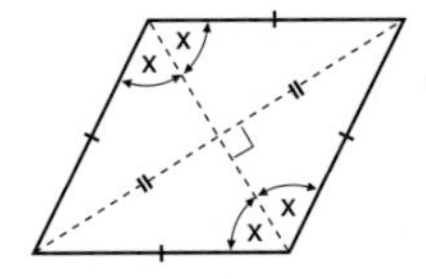

Opposite sides are parallel and equal.

Opposite angles are equal.

The diagonals bisect each other and cross at 90°.

Question *PQRS is a rhombus. Find angle PQS, giving a reason for your answer.*

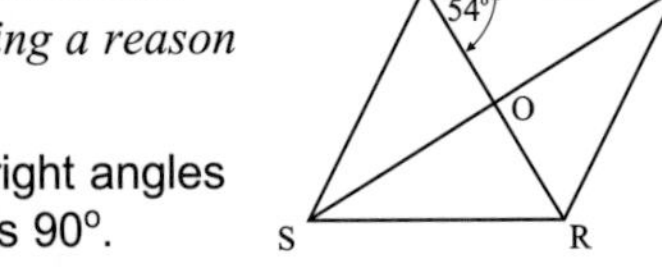

Diagonals cross at right angles and so angle POQ is 90°.

So, PQO = 180°−54°−90° = 36°

5. Parallelogram

A **parallelogram** is like a rectangle that has been pushed over.

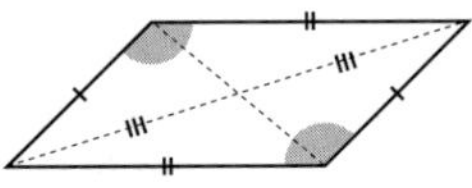

Opposite sides are parallel and equal.

Opposite angles are equal.

The diagonals bisect each other but do ***not*** cut the corner angles in half.

Question *ABCD is a parallelogram. Find angle x.*

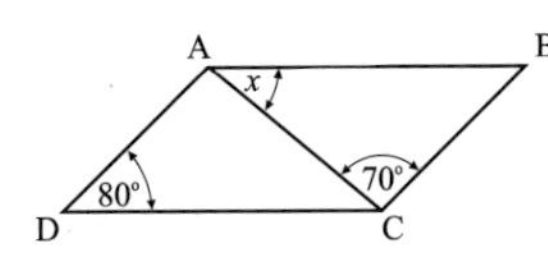

Opposite angles are equal and so angle ABC = 80°.

So, $x+70°+80° = 180°$

$\therefore x = 180°-70°-80 = 30°$

6. Trapezium

A **trapezium** has just two sides parallel. It has no other special properties.

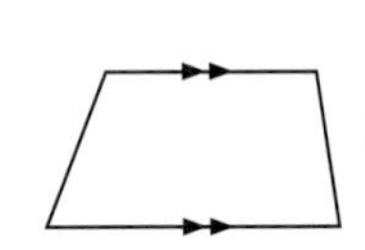

Question *Calculate angle a.*

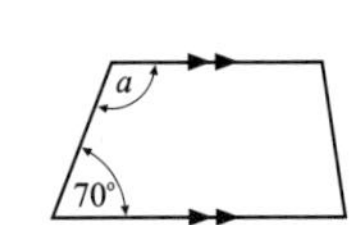

a and 70° are interior angles and so add up to 180° (see Box 6, p79)

$\therefore a = 180°-70° = 110°$

7. Kite

A **kite** has two pairs of equal sides and one pair of equal opposite angles.

The diagonals cross at right angles.

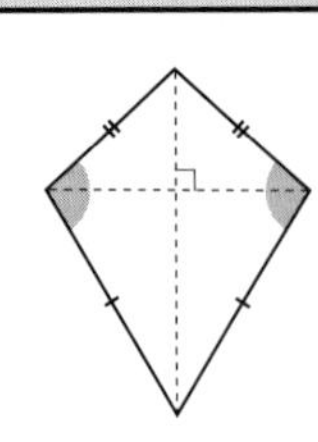

Question *PQRS is a kite. Find angle x.*

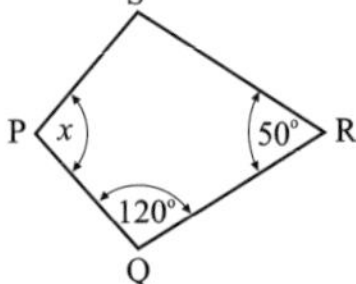

Angle PSR = 120° because opposite angles are equal.

The angles add up to 360° and so:

$x+50°+120°+120° = 360°$

$\therefore x = 360°-50°-120°-120° = 70°$

Polygons

1. Regular Polygons

Regular polygons are geometrical shapes with all sides and angles equal. You need to know the names of the regular polygons below.

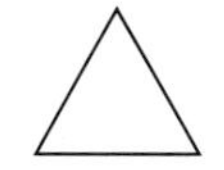
Equilateral triangle (3 sides)

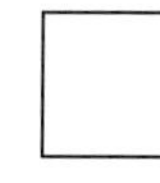
Square (4 sides)

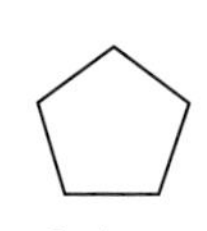
Pentagon (5 sides)

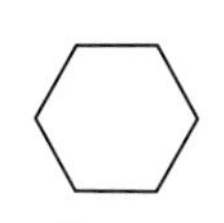
Hexagon (6 sides)

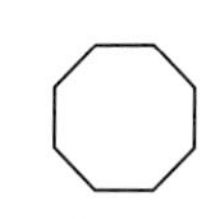
Octagon (8 sides)

2. The Centre of a Regular Polygon

A circle can be drawn around a regular polygon. The centre of the circle is the centre of the polygon.

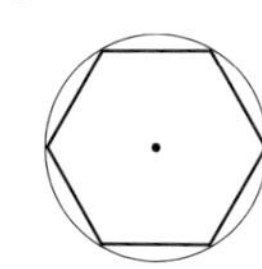

Joining the corners of the polygon to the centre creates identical isosceles triangles. The equal sides of these triangles are radii of the circle.

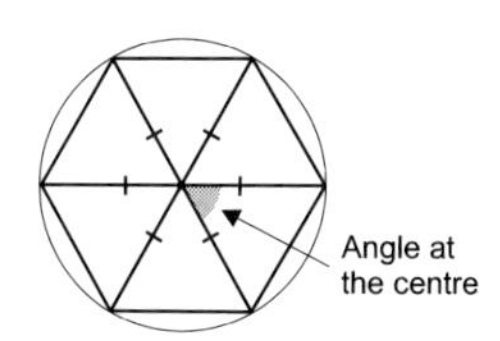

The angles at the centre of a regular polygon are equal and add up to 360°.

Question *Calculate the angle at the centre of a regular pentagon.*

A pentagon has 5 sides and so has 5 equal angles at the centre that add up to 360°.

So, each angle $= 360^\circ \div 5 = 72^\circ$

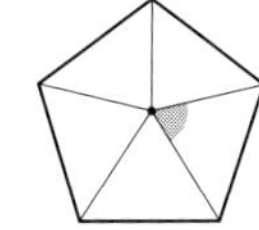

3. Interior and Exterior Angles

The interior angles of a regular polygon are all equal.

The exterior angles of a regular polygon are equal to the angle at its centre (see Box 2) and so:

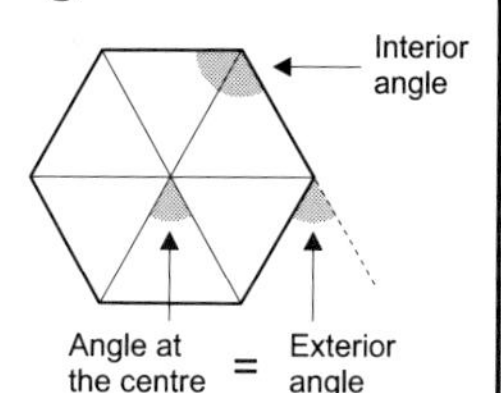

The exterior angles of any polygon add up to 360°.

Question *Find the interior angle of a regular octagon. You must show your working.*

Make a sketch, including the angles at the centre.

It is easiest to find the angle at the centre first.

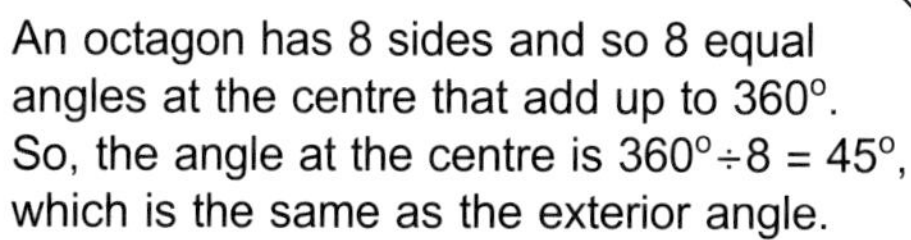

An octagon has 8 sides and so 8 equal angles at the centre that add up to 360°. So, the angle at the centre is $360^\circ \div 8 = 45^\circ$, which is the same as the exterior angle.

Then, interior angle $= 180^\circ - 45^\circ = 135^\circ$
(Angle of a straight line is 180°)

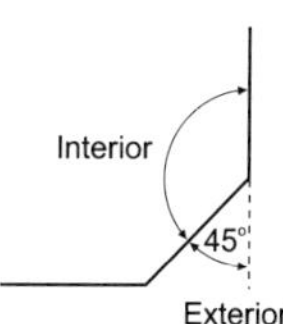

4. Finding the Number of Sides of a Polygon

For each side there is an exterior angle and so there are the same number of sides as exterior angles. It is easy to find the number of exterior angles.

Question *The interior angle of a polygon is 160°. How many sides does it have?*

Find the exterior angle first.

Exterior angle $= 180^\circ - 160^\circ = 20^\circ$

The exterior angles add up to 360°.

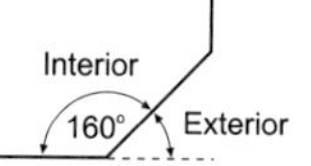

So, number of exterior angles $= 360^\circ \div 20^\circ = 18$

So, the polygon has 18 sides.

5. Problems Involving Hexagons

Regular hexagons are easy polygons to work with and often appear in examination questions.

Question *The diagram shows a new coin made in the shape of a regular hexagon. Calculate the smallest height of slot that the coin could fit into.*

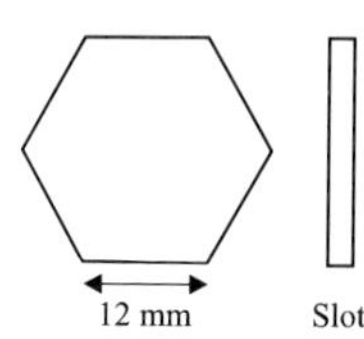

A hexagon can be divided into six equilateral triangles.

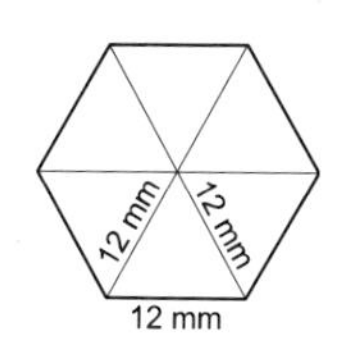

Split an equilateral triangle in half to make two identical right-angled triangles of height h, say. Then by Pythagoras' theorem:

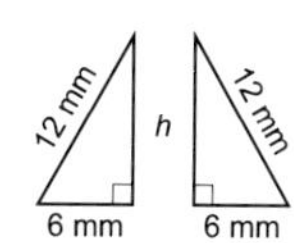

$h^2 + 6^2 = 12^2$

$\therefore\ h^2 = 12^2 - 6^2 = 144 - 36 = 108$

$\therefore\ h = \sqrt{108} = 10.4$ mm

So, the distance between the flat sides of the coin is $2 \times 10.4 = 20.8$ mm, the minimum possible slot height.

6. Sum of Interior Angles of Any Polygon

The following result is true for *all* polygons.

Sum of interior angles = (Number of sides $- 2) \times 180^\circ$

For example, a pentagon has 5 sides, so:

Sum of interior angles $= (5-2) \times 180^\circ$
$= 3 \times 180^\circ = 540^\circ$

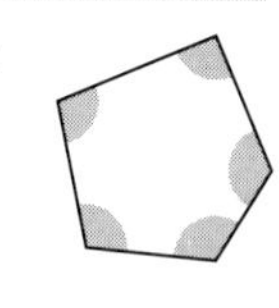

Question *The interior angles of a polygon add up to 900°. How many sides does it have?*

Let n be the number of sides, then:

$(n-2) \times 180 = 900$

$\therefore\ n - 2 = 900 \div 180 = 5$

$\therefore\ n = 5 + 2 = 7$

Circles H

You need to know the following results about circles. These results are called **theorems**.

A **chord** is a straight line that joins any two points on the circumference of a circle.

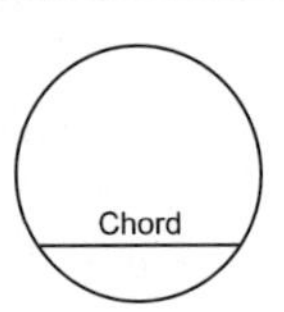

A radius that is perpendicular (at right angles) to a chord cuts the chord in half (bisects the chord). The opposite is also true: if a radius cuts a chord in half, it is perpendicular to the chord.

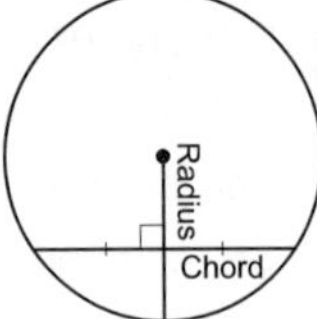

Question *Calculate the drop in water level in this fish bowl.*

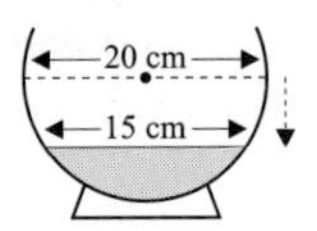

Radius of circle = 10 cm

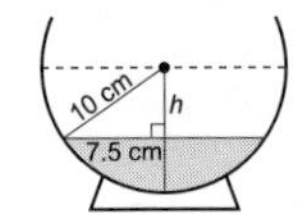

Let h be the distance the water level has dropped. From Pythagoras' theorem:

$h^2+7.5^2 = 10^2$

$\therefore\ h^2 = 10^2-7.5^2 = 100-56.25 = 43.75$

$\therefore\ h = \sqrt{43.75} = 6.6$ cm

If the corners of a triangle lie on the circumference of a circle and one of its sides is a diameter, the angle opposite the diameter is 90°. The opposite is also true: if you draw a circle around a right-angled triangle, the hypotenuse will be a diameter of the circle.

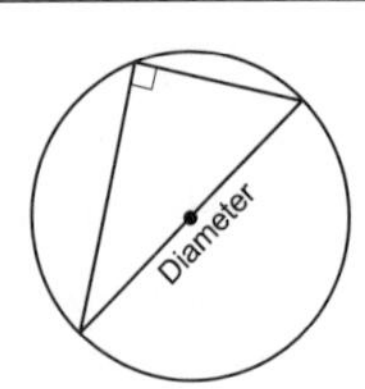

Question *Find angle BAC, given that O is the centre of the circle.*

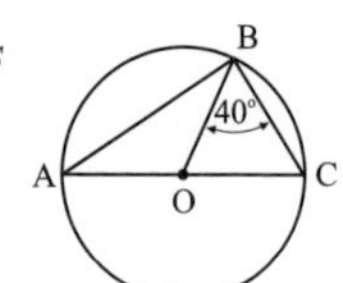

Mark the radii with dashes to show any isosceles triangles.

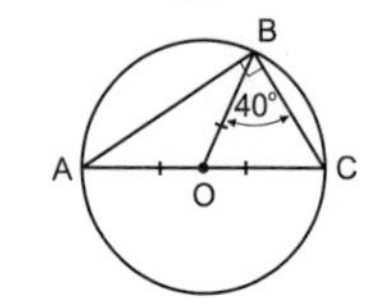

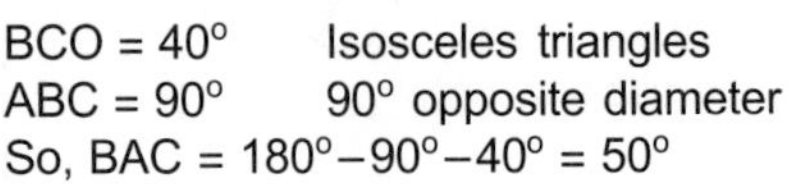

BCO = 40° Isosceles triangles

ABC = 90° 90° opposite diameter

So, BAC = 180°−90°−40° = 50°

When the ends of a chord are joined to a point on the circumference they make an angle, called the **subtended angle**. The subtended angles on the same side of the chord are all equal.

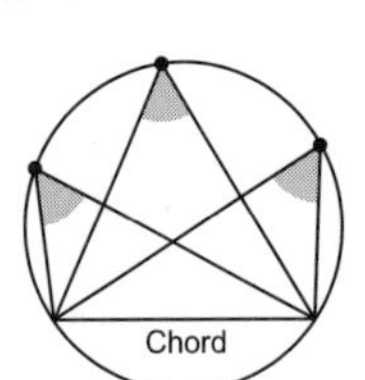

Question *Find angle x.*

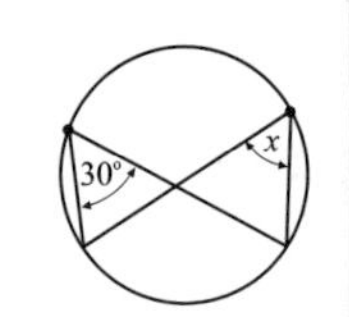

Draw in the missing chord. Then you can see that angles x and 30° are subtended by the same chord. So, x = 30°.

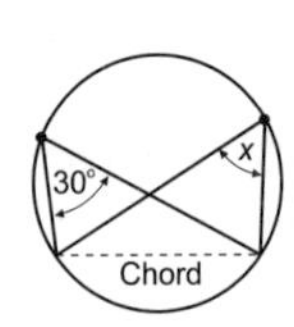

The angle subtended by a chord at the centre of a circle is twice the angle subtended at the circumference by the chord.

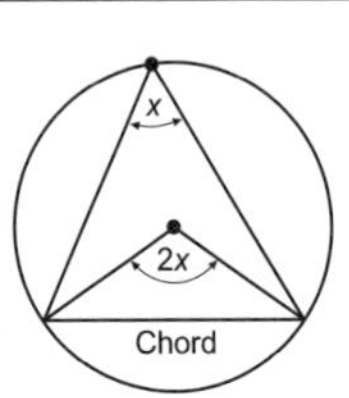

Question *Find angles x and y.*

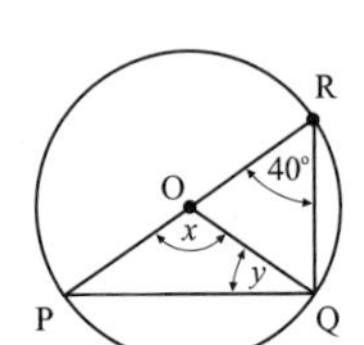

Angle x is subtended by the chord PQ at the centre O. Angle 40° is subtended by the same chord at the circumference. So, $x = 2\times40° = 80°$

Triangle POQ is isosceles.

Base angles of triangle POQ add up to 180°−80° = 100°.

So, $y = 100°\div2 = 50°$

If all four corners of a quadrilateral lie on the circumference of a circle, the quadrilateral is said to be **cyclic**.

Opposite angles of a cyclic quadrilateral add up to 180°.

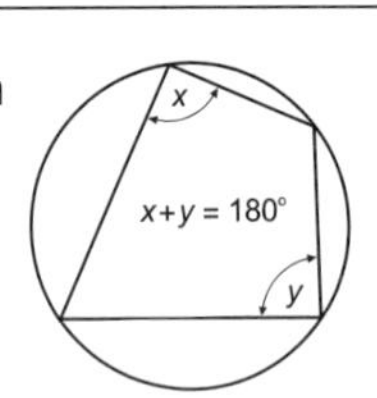

Question *Find angles x and y.*

$x+90° = 180°\quad \therefore\ x = 180°-90° = 90°$

$y+115° = 180°\quad \therefore\ y = 180°-115° = 65°$

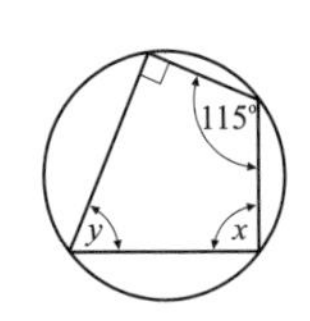

A **tangent** is a line that touches a circle at just one point.The two tangents drawn from point T to the circle are equal and meet radii OA and OB at right angles. Triangles AOT and BOT are congruent (identical).

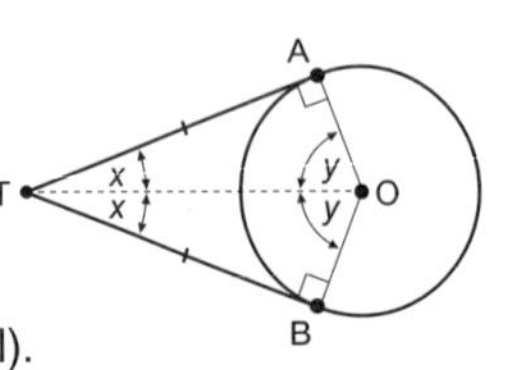

Question *Find angle AOB.*

The angles between the radii and tangents are 90°. The angles of a quadrilateral add up to 360°, so:

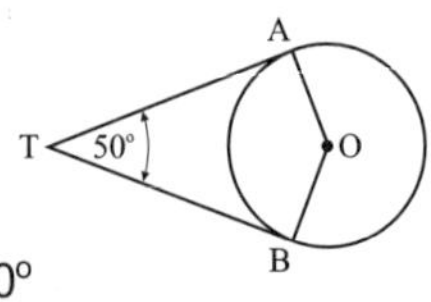

AOB+50°+90°+90° = 360°

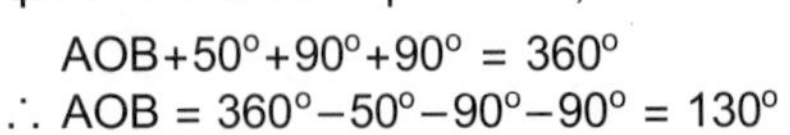

$\therefore$ AOB = 360°−50°−90°−90° = 130°

Measuring. Scale Drawing. Loci

1. Measuring with a Ruler

Measure lengths as accurately as you can. You will lose marks if your answer is more than 1 mm out.

Question *Measure the length of the line AB.*

A B

Align the 0 mark of your ruler with the end of the line.

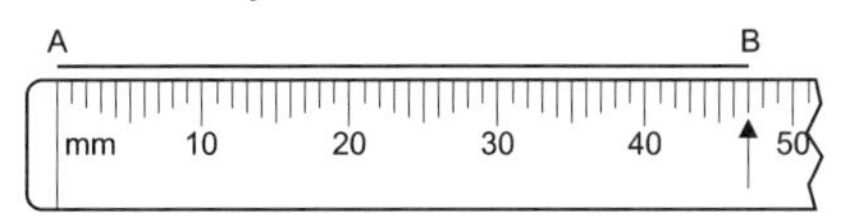

The line AB is approximately 47 mm long (or 4.7 cm).

2. Scale Drawing

Question *The diagram shows the plan of a tennis court, drawn to a scale of 1 cm to 7 yards. Find the length of the serve XY correct to the nearest yard.*

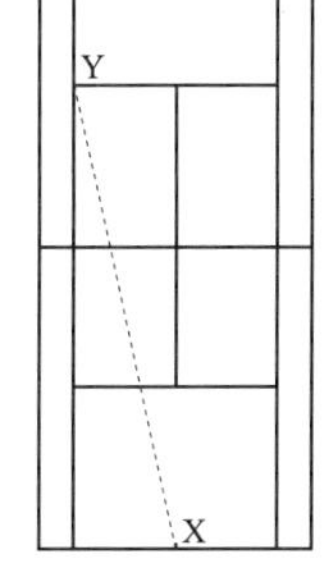

Use your ruler to accurately measure the length XY. You should find that XY ≈ 31 mm = 3.1 cm.

A scale of 1 cm to 7 yards means that 1 cm on the drawing represents a real distance of 7 yards. So,

$$\begin{aligned} XY = 3.1 \text{ cm} &= 3.1 \times 7 \text{ yards} \\ &= 21.7 \text{ yards} \\ &\approx 22 \text{ yards} \end{aligned}$$

3. Measuring Angles with a Protractor

Use a semicircular protractor numbered 1° to 180°, both clockwise and anticlockwise. A clear plastic protractor is best because you can see the diagram underneath it.

Measure angles as accurately as you can. You will lose marks if your answer is more than 1° or 2° out.

Question *Measure the size of angle ABC.*

A

B C

Accurately place the centre point of your protractor on point B with the 0° line over line BC.

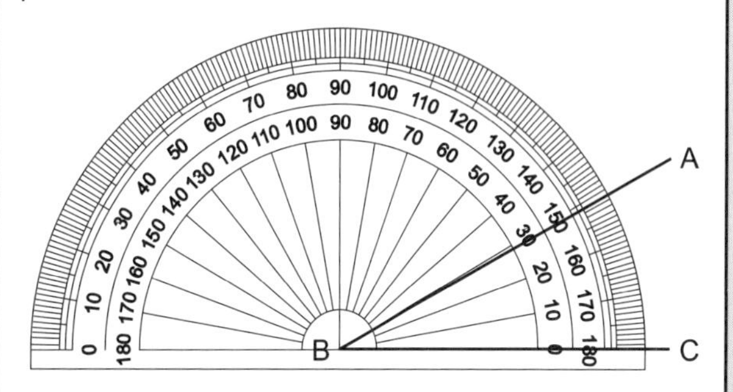

The angles on the protractor increase from 0°, on line BC, through 10°, 20° and up to angle 29° on line AB.

So, the angle ABC is 29°.

4. Drawing Geometrical Shapes

Question *Accurately draw this triangle.*

C

A 30° B

8 cm

Use your ruler to draw side AB, 8 cm long.

Use your protractor to mark a 90° angle at point B.

NOTE Do not estimate right angles (90°) by eye.

Draw a feint line perpendicular to AB. Feint lines like this are called **construction lines**. Don't rub them out, as the examiner will want to see how you made your drawing.

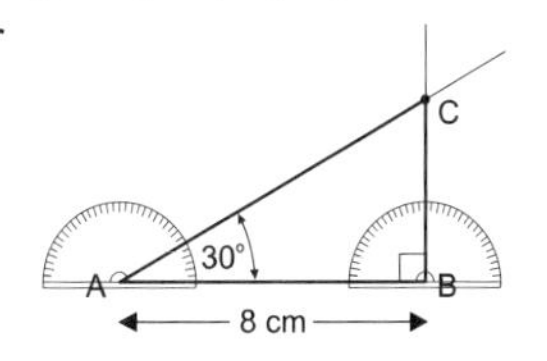

Use your protractor to mark a 30° angle at point A. Draw a feint line at 30° to AB, crossing the perpendicular line at point C.

Draw lines AC and BC to complete the triangle. Label the corners A, B and C.

Question *Make an accurate drawing of this shape. The curved lines are quarter circles.*

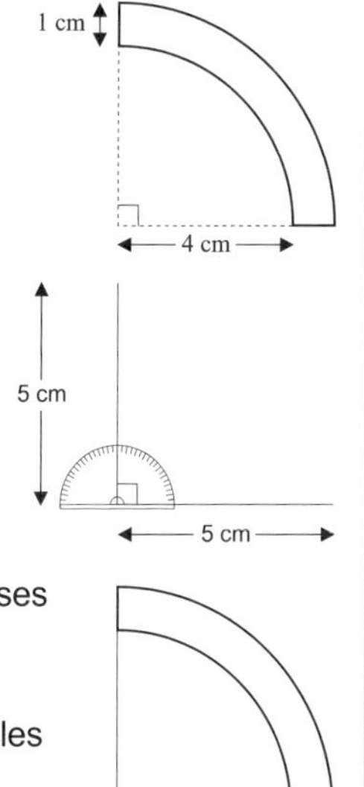

Think about the method you are going to use before you start drawing.

Draw perpendicular construction lines 5 cm long.

Open your compasses to 5 cm, place the point on A and draw a quarter circle. Reduce the compasses to 4 cm and draw another quarter circle.

Join up the ends of the quarter circles to complete the shape.

5. Locus

A **locus** is a line whose points obey a rule. The plural of the word locus is *loci*. Often, this line is the path traced out by a moving object. For example, the dashed line in the diagram shows the locus (path) of a playground swing. You need to know the loci described in the boxes overleaf. The title of each box describes the rule of the locus.

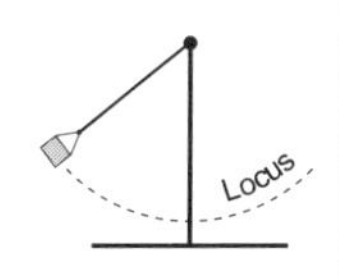

Measuring. Scale Drawing. Loci (Contd)

6. Equal Distance from a Point

Question *A and B represent two radio transmitters. Signals from A can be received 300 km away. Signals from B can be received 350 km away. Shade the region in which signals can be received from both transmitters.*

1 cm represents 100 km

Transmitter A sends signals 300 km in all directions. So the signals can be received within a circle of radius 300 km with centre A. Since 1 cm represents 100 km, draw a circle of radius 3 cm.

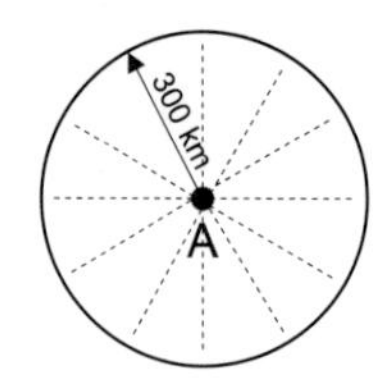

For transmitter B, 350 km is represented by 3.5 cm on the diagram. So draw a circle of radius 3.5 cm, centre B. Shade the intersection, where radio signals can be received from both transmitters.

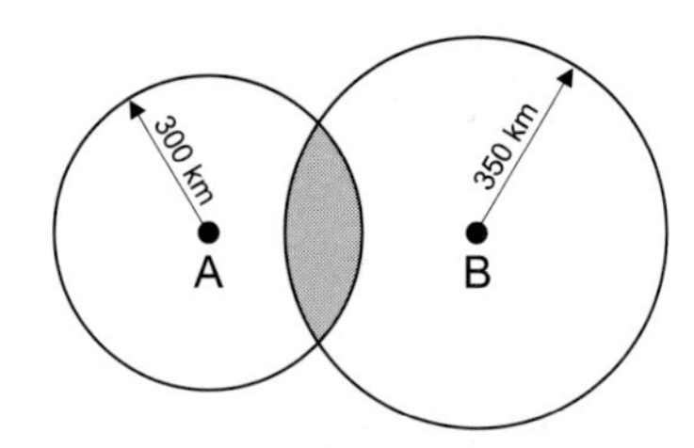

7. Equal Distance from Two Points

Question *A ship sails between the two buoys P and Q, keeping an equal distance from each. Accurately draw the course of the ship.*

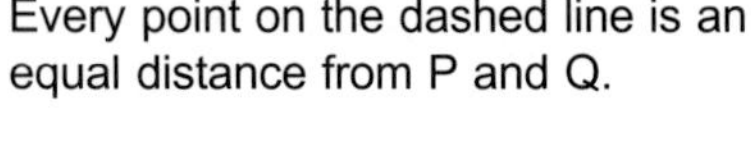

Every point on the dashed line is an equal distance from P and Q.

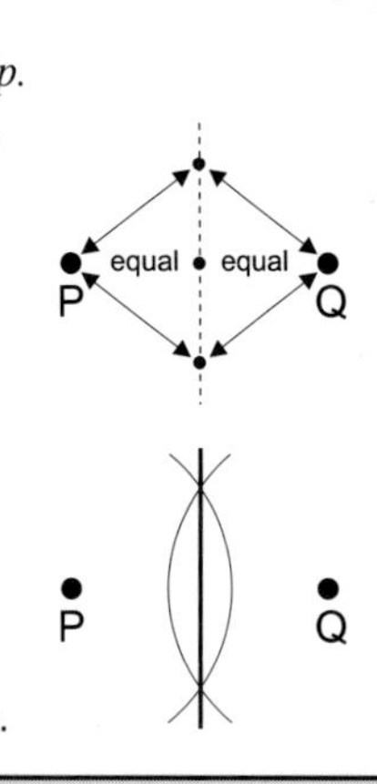

Place the point of your compasses on Q and open them to about $\frac{3}{4}$ of the distance PQ. Draw an arc as shown. Repeat for point P. Using a ruler, join the intersections of these arcs to obtain the course of the ship.

8. Equal Distance from a Line (Contd)

Question *The light, S, above a front door has a sensor which turns on the light when anything moves within a distance of 2 m. A man walks towards the door.*
(a) Draw the locus of point H.
(b) Draw the locus of points 2 m from S.
(c) How far is the point H from the door when the light is switched on?

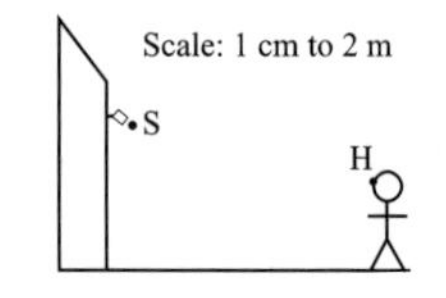

(a) Draw a line parallel to the ground through H.

(b) Draw a circle with centre S and radius 1 cm (representing 2m).

(c) Measure AB to be 0.5 cm, which represents a distance of 1 m.

8. Equal Distance from a Straight Line

Question *In a certain type of cricket match, players must stand within 15 yards of the line AB joining the wickets.*

A B

Use a scale of 1 cm to 5 yards to draw the area in which the players must stand.

All points on the dashed line are 15 yards from the line AB. The straight lines are parallel to AB and 15 yards from AB. The semicircles have radii 15 yards.

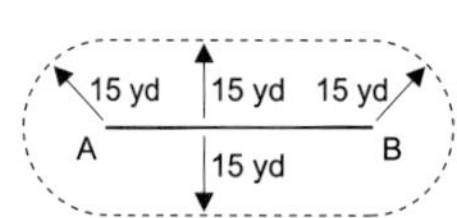

1 cm represents 5 yards and so 3 cm represents 15 yards. Use your protractor to draw construction lines perpendicular to AB through points A and B. Measure 3 cm along these lines away from AB and join up the points. Use your compasses to draw semicircles of radius 3 cm with centres at A and B.

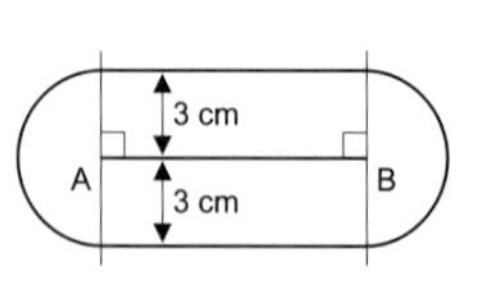

9. Equal Distance from Two Lines

Question *The diagram shows a car park. A guard patrols the park, entering at point B. He walks across the park, keeping the same distance from walls AB and BC until he is 5 m from wall CD. He then walks parallel to wall CD to door E in wall AD. Draw the path the guard takes.*

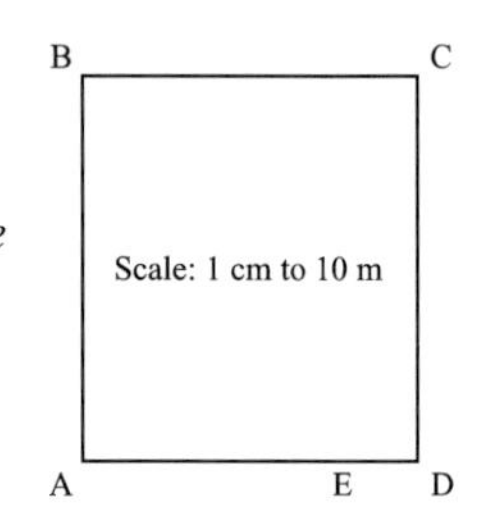

Place the point of your compasses on B and draw an arc cutting AB and BC at P and Q. Place the point of your compasses on P and draw an arc. Repeat for point Q, keeping your compasses the same distance apart. Join corner B to the intersection of these arcs.

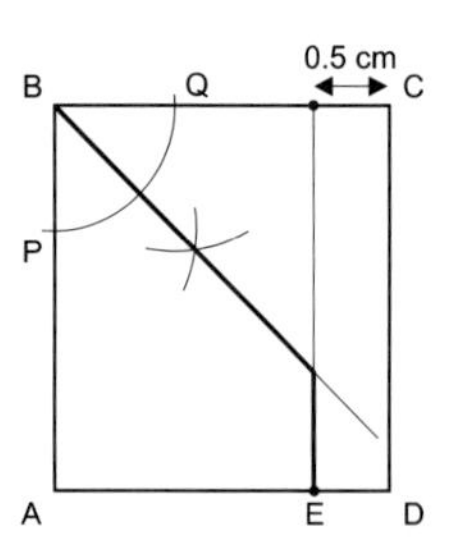

Points on this line are an equal distance from walls AB and BC. Now, 1 cm represents 10 m and so 0.5 cm represents 5 m. Mark points 0.5 cm along CB and DA, join them with a construction line and draw the rest of the guard's path.

more

Bearings

1. Bearings

A **bearing** is an angle measured clockwise from North, and is a way of describing a direction.

Bearings are always given as three digit numbers; so 45° is written 045°.

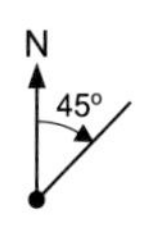

Bearing of 045°

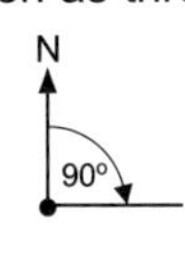

Bearing of 090°

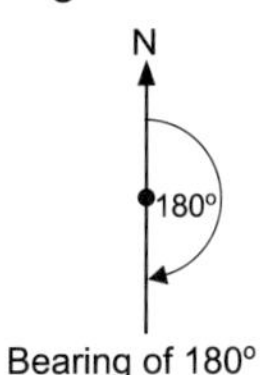

Bearing of 180°

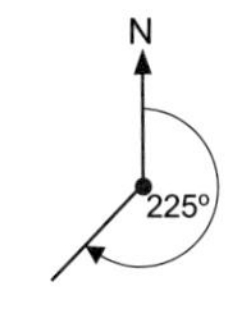

Bearing of 225°

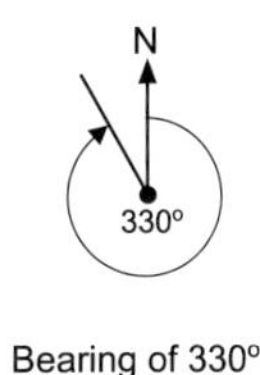

Bearing of 330°

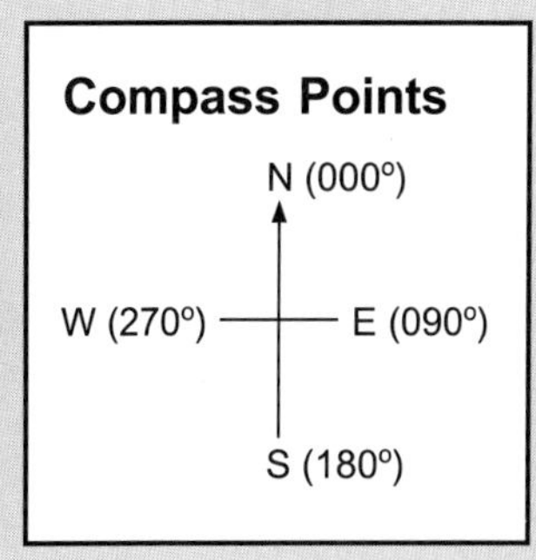

2. Measuring a Bearing

A bearing is always measured **from** a certain point.

Question *Measure the bearing of the buoy B* ***from*** *the ship S.*

Join the two points with the straight line SB.

Draw a North arrow through point S, **from** which you are measuring the bearing. Make sure that your North line is parallel with the given North line.

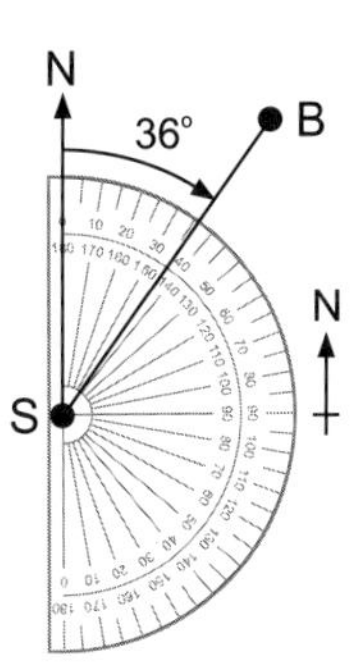

Place the centre of your protractor on point S, aligning 0° with North. Read off the **clockwise** angle the line SB makes with North.

This gives a bearing of 036°.

When the bearing is greater than 180°, turn your protractor around and add 180° to your reading.

Question *The street map opposite is drawn to a scale of 1 cm to 200 m. Calculate:*

(a) the bearing of B from A

(b) the distance between the centres of these two buildings.

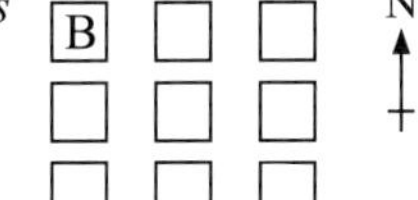

(a) Join the centres of the two buildings with a straight line. Draw a North line through A, from which the bearing is measured. Place the centre of your protractor on A, aligning 0° with North, as shown. Read the angle of 138° in a clockwise direction.

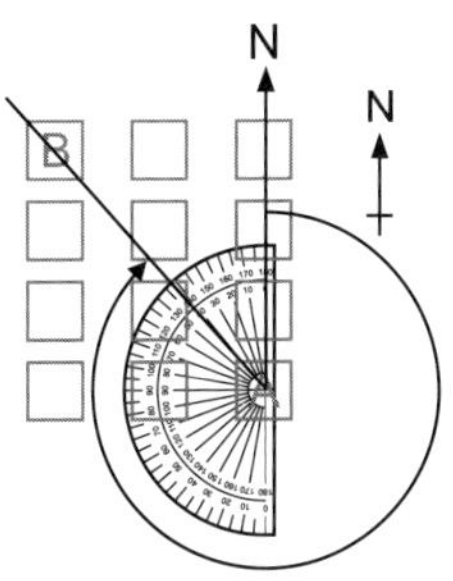

Bearing = 180°+138° = 318°

(b) Measure the distance between the centres of the two buildings:

Distance = 23 mm = 2.3 cm

1 cm represents a real distance of 200 m and so:

Actual distance = 2.3×200 = 460 m

3. Drawing a Bearing (Plotting a Course)

You may be asked to plot the course of, for example, a ship or an aircraft.

Question *A fishing boat sails 50 km from port P to a fishing ground G on a bearing of 240°. Plot the course of the boat and mark the fishing ground G. Use the scale 1 cm to 10 km.*

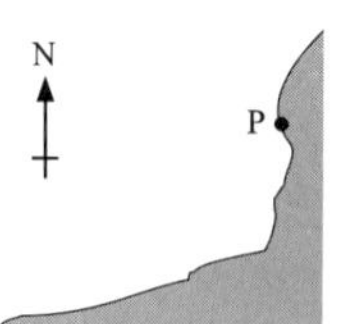

Draw a North line through point P. Place the centre of the protractor on point P, aligning 0° with North. The bearing of 240° can be split into 180°+60°. Mark a point at an angle of 60°, measured clockwise from 0° at the bottom of the protractor. Join point P to this point. This line is the course of the boat.

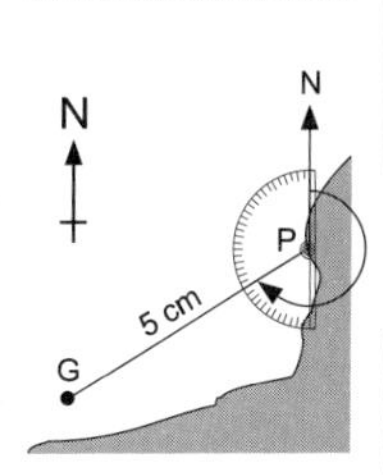

Since 1 cm represents 10 km, then 5 cm represents 50 km. So, mark fishing ground G 5 cm from port P.

4. Locating a Point

Question *A coastguard, C, picks up a distress signal from a yacht Y due East. The same signal is received by a lighthouse L, on a bearing of 050°.*

(a) Plot the position of the yacht Y.

(b) Measure CY and calculate the distance of the yacht from the coastguard.

(c) How long would a helicopter take to reach the yacht from the coastguard, travelling at an average speed of 180 kmlh? Give your answer to the nearest minute.

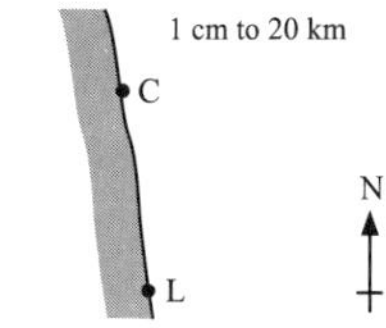

(a) Draw North lines through C and L. Use your protractor to draw bearings of East (090°) from C and 050° from L. Mark the position of yacht Y where these bearings intersect.

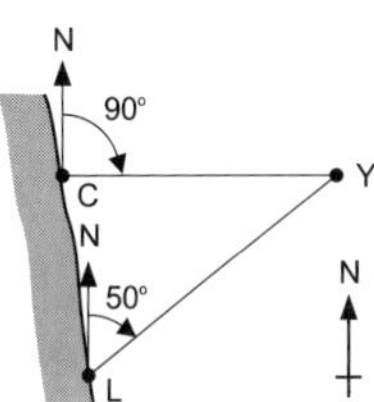

(b) Carefully measure CY to be 1.9 cm. The scale in the diagram tells us that 1 cm represents 20 km and so CY = 1.9×20 = 38 km.

(c) 180 km/h means 180 km travelled in 60 min

So, 1 km travelled in $\frac{60 \text{ min}}{180} = 0.\dot{3}$ min

So, 38km travelled in $38 \times 0.\dot{3}$min $\approx$ 13 min

Vectors H

1. Vectors

A **vector** quantity has both size (magnitude) and direction. For example, a car travelling 50 km/h on a bearing of 045°.

A vector can be represented by a straight line with an arrowhead. The length of the line represents the size of the vector and the arrowhead indicates its direction.

Vectors can be labelled using bold letters.

Or they can be labelled using capital letters.

This vector is written $\overrightarrow{AB}$.

Column vectors

Vectors can be described using a pair of numbers like coordi–nates, only written vertically. The top number represents the horizontal direction, the bottom number the vertical direction.

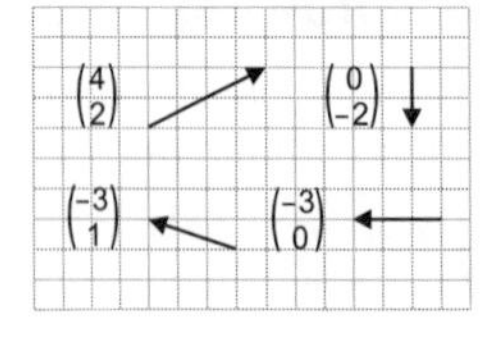

Position vectors

The **position vector** of a point is the vector joining the origin to the point. The position vector of P is described using a column vector $\overrightarrow{OP} = \binom{3}{2}$.

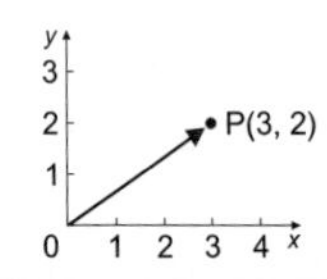

2. Comparing Vectors

Parallel vectors

Parallel vectors have the same (or opposite) direction, but may have different sizes.

Vectors with the same gradient are parallel.

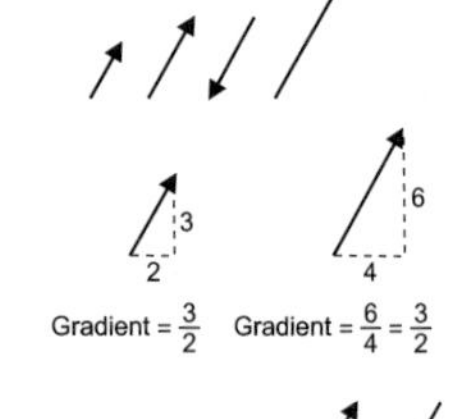

Negative vectors

Vector $-\mathbf{a}$ has the same size as vector $\mathbf{a}$ but opposite direction

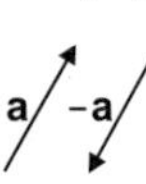

If $\overrightarrow{AB}$ is the vector from A to B, then $-\overrightarrow{AB}$ is the opposite vector from B to A, i.e. $\overrightarrow{BA}$

So, $-\overrightarrow{AB} = \overrightarrow{BA}$

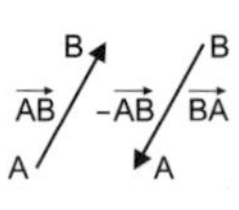

Multiplying vectors by a number

Multiplying a vector by a positive number changes its size but not its direction. Multiplying by a negative number reverses the direction.

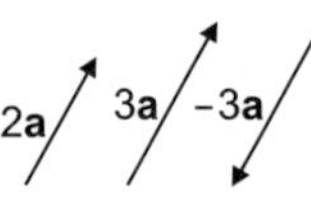

3. Vector Arithmetic

Vectors can be added: $\binom{3}{2} + \binom{5}{4} = \binom{3+5}{2+4} = \binom{8}{6}$

Vectors can be multiplied by a number. Remember to multiply *both* numbers. $2\times\binom{1}{3} = \binom{2\times1}{2\times3} = \binom{2}{6}$

4. Vector Diagrams

In this diagram, $\overrightarrow{OA} = \binom{2}{3}$ and $\overrightarrow{AB} = \binom{4}{2}$

Adding these vectors, we get:

$$\binom{2}{3} + \binom{4}{2} = \binom{2+4}{3+2} = \binom{6}{5}$$

which is the same as vector $\overrightarrow{OB}$. So we have the result: $\overrightarrow{OA} + \overrightarrow{AB} = \overrightarrow{OB}$

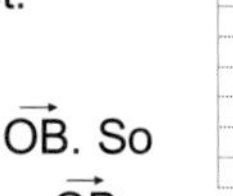

In other words, travelling from O to A and then from A to B is the same as travelling directly from O to B

Question *M is the midpoint of OQ. Given that $\overrightarrow{OM} = \binom{2}{3}$ and $\overrightarrow{OP} = \binom{5}{7}$ find the vectors $\overrightarrow{OQ}$ and $\overrightarrow{PQ}$.*

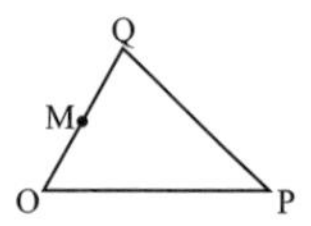

Since M is the mid–point of OQ then $\overrightarrow{OQ} = 2\times\overrightarrow{OM}$

So, $\overrightarrow{OQ} = 2\times\overrightarrow{OM} = 2\times\binom{2}{3} = \binom{4}{6}$

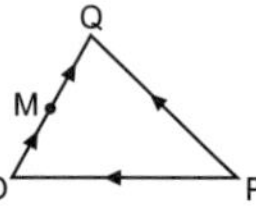

Travelling from P to Q is the same as travelling from P to O and then from O to Q. So, we can write: $\overrightarrow{PQ} = \overrightarrow{PO} + \overrightarrow{OQ} = -\overrightarrow{OP} + \overrightarrow{OQ}$

Thus, $\overrightarrow{PQ} = -\binom{5}{7} + \binom{4}{6} = \binom{-5+4}{-7+6} = \binom{-1}{-1}$

Question *In this diagram, $\overrightarrow{OR} = \mathbf{a}$ and $\overrightarrow{OP} = \mathbf{b}$. Given that $\overrightarrow{PQ} = 2\overrightarrow{OR}$ and $\overrightarrow{OS} = \frac{1}{3}\overrightarrow{OQ}$, express in terms of **a** and **b** the vectors $\overrightarrow{PQ}$, $\overrightarrow{OQ}$ and $\overrightarrow{OS}$. Use your answers to express $\overrightarrow{PS}$ and $\overrightarrow{RS}$ in terms of **a** and **b**. What can you say about points P, S and R?*

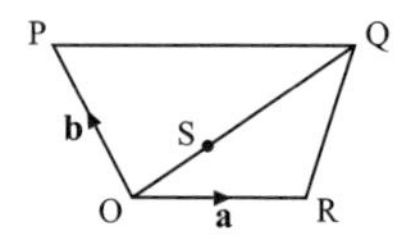

$\overrightarrow{PQ} = 2\times\overrightarrow{OR} = 2\times\mathbf{a} = 2\mathbf{a}$

$\overrightarrow{OQ} = \overrightarrow{OP} + \overrightarrow{PQ} = \mathbf{b} + 2\mathbf{a}$

$\overrightarrow{OS} = \frac{1}{3}\times\overrightarrow{OQ} = \frac{1}{3}(\mathbf{b}+2\mathbf{a}) = \frac{1}{3}\mathbf{b} + \frac{2}{3}\mathbf{a}$

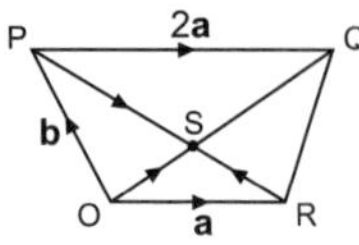

$\overrightarrow{PS} = \overrightarrow{PO} + \overrightarrow{OS} = -\overrightarrow{OP} + \overrightarrow{OS}$

$= -\mathbf{b} + \frac{1}{3}\mathbf{b} + \frac{2}{3}\mathbf{a} = -\frac{2}{3}\mathbf{b} + \frac{2}{3}\mathbf{a}$

$\overrightarrow{RS} = \overrightarrow{RO} + \overrightarrow{OS} = -\overrightarrow{OR} + \overrightarrow{OS} = -\mathbf{a} + \frac{1}{3}\mathbf{b} + \frac{2}{3}\mathbf{a} = \frac{1}{3}\mathbf{b} - \frac{1}{3}\mathbf{a}$

Notice that $\overrightarrow{PS} = -2\times\overrightarrow{RS}$ and so $\overrightarrow{PS}$ must be parallel to $\overrightarrow{RS}$ (see Box 2). But the lines PS and RS are joined at S, and so PSR must be a straight line.

5. Solving Problems Using Vectors

Question *A man wants to swim across a river. He swims through the water at a speed of 4 km/h, represented by the vector in the diagram. A current of 2 km/h drags him along the river.*

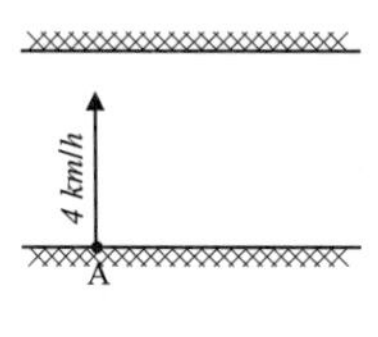

(a) Using a scale of 1 cm to 4 km/h, draw speed vectors for the current and the swimmer crossing the river.

(b) Find the speed of the swimmer by measurement and mark the point B where he reaches the opposite bank.

(a) Draw vector $\overrightarrow{PQ}$ 0.5 cm long to represent the speed of the current, 2 km/h. The actual speed of the swimmer is the combination of his speed through the water, $\overrightarrow{AP}$, and the speed of the current, $\overrightarrow{PQ}$. So, $\overrightarrow{AQ}$ represents the actual speed and course of the swimmer ($\overrightarrow{AQ} = \overrightarrow{AP} + \overrightarrow{PQ}$). Draw this vector.

(b) Carefully measure $\overrightarrow{AQ}$ to be 1.1 cm. The scale is 1 cm = 4 km/h and so the speed of the swimmer is 1.1×4 km/h = 4.4 km/h. Continue the line AQ to B, where the swimmer reaches the opposite bank.

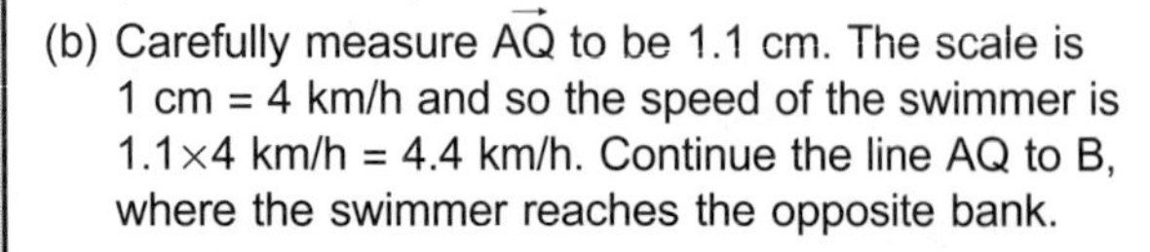

Transformations

1. Transformation

A **transformation** is a way of moving the points of a shape from one position to another.

The corner points A, B and C have been transformed into the points A', B' and C'. We say that triangle A'B'C' is the **image** of triangle ABC under this transformation.

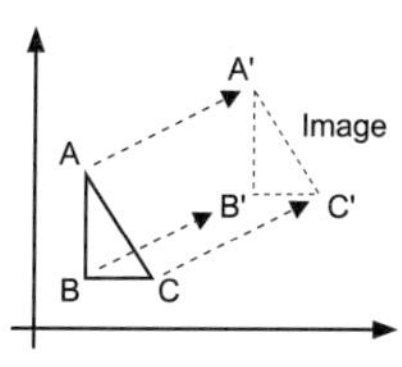

2. Translation

The point A has moved 3 units right and 2 units down. We say that the point A has been **translated** to point A'. This translation can be summarised using a column vector called a **translation vector**:

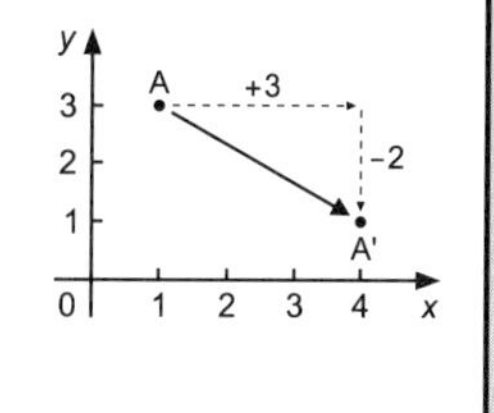

$\begin{pmatrix} 3 \\ -2 \end{pmatrix}$ ← Movement in the x-direction
← Movement in the y-direction

Each corner of triangle ABC has been translated using the vector $\begin{pmatrix} 3 \\ -2 \end{pmatrix}$.

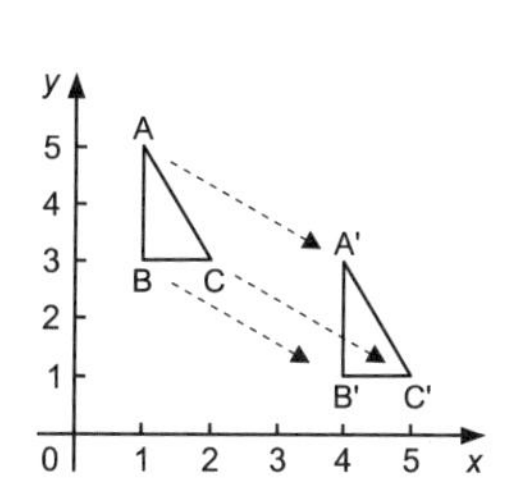

3. Reflection

Flag F' is the **reflection** of flag F in the mirror. Each point of the flag F is the same distance from the mirror as the corresponding point of its reflection F'.

F | Mirror | F'
equal | equal

Question *Draw the reflection of triangle ABC in the y-axis and label the image A'B'C'.*

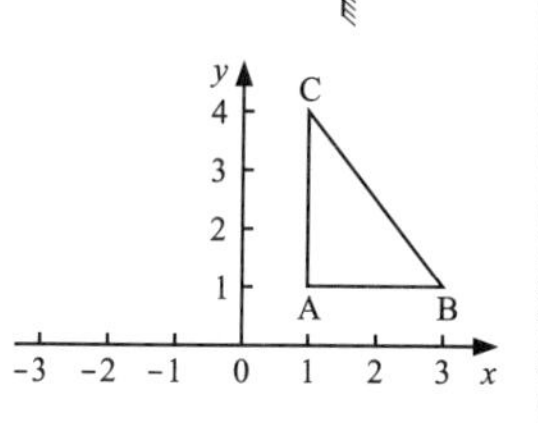

The mirror is the y-axis and is called the **line of reflection**.

Place a piece of tracing paper over the triangle and line of reflection. Trace the triangle and the y-axis. Label the corners A'B'C'. Draw a cross over the origin.

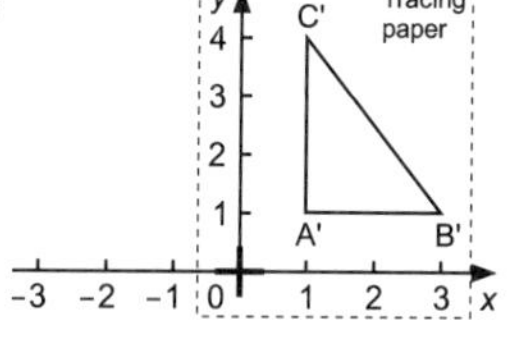

Turn over the tracing paper and align the cross over the origin. Use a pencil or the point of your compasses to mark points A', B' and C' and draw the new triangle A'B'C' (the image).

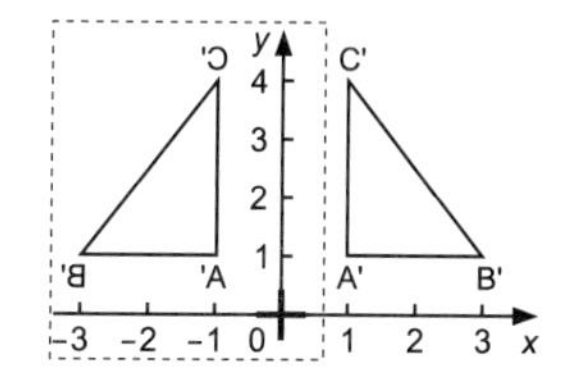

Carefully label the corners of the image A'B'C'. Corner A' should be opposite corner A and the same distance from the line of reflection; and the same for points B and C.

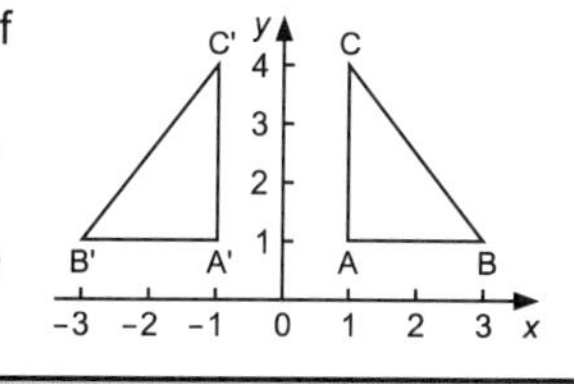

4. Rotation

To **rotate** a shape, you need to know the centre about which it is rotated and the angle of rotation.

Question *Rotate the shape PQRS 90° clockwise about the point (1, 0) and label the image P'Q'R'S'.*

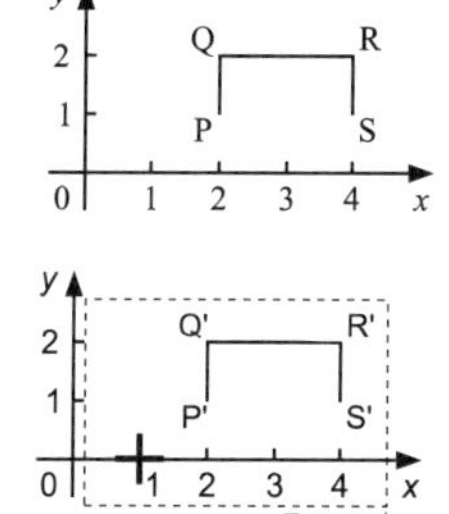

Place a piece of tracing paper over the shape and the point (1, 0). Trace the shape, labelling the corners P'Q'R'S'. Draw a cross over the centre of rotation (1, 0), as shown, and trace part of the x-axis. This will help you to position the image accurately.

Push the point of your compasses through the centre of rotation and rotate the tracing paper 90° clockwise, aligning the cross over the centre of rotation once again.

Mark the points P'Q'R'S' and draw the image.

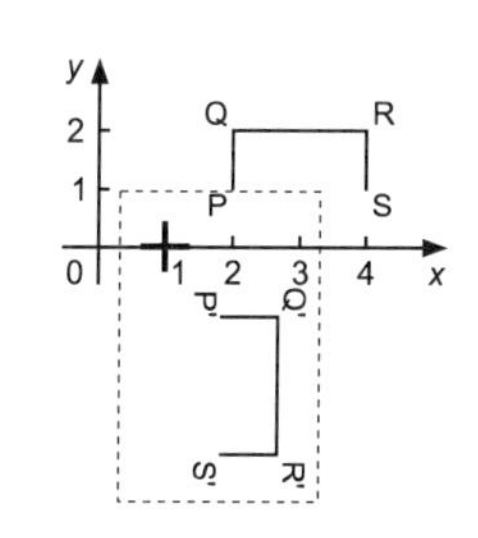

How to find the centre of rotation

Question *The triangle ABC has been rotated to obtain the image A'B'C'. Find the centre and angle of rotation*

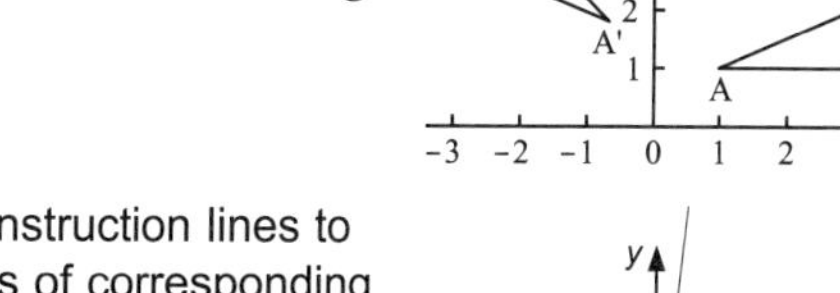

Use feint construction lines to join two pairs of corresponding points, e.g. AA' and CC'.

Use your ruler to find the midpoint of each line and draw a perpendicular line through it.

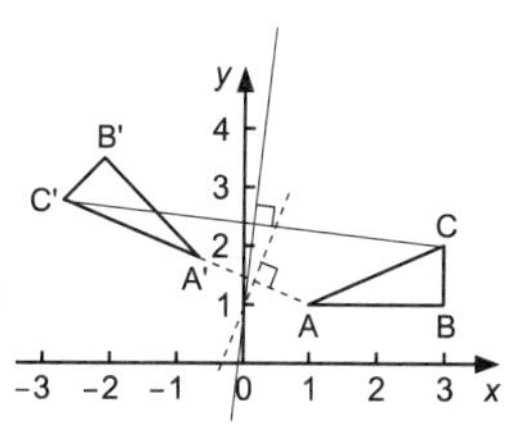

The centre of rotation is where these two lines cross. In this example, the centre of rotation is the point (0, 1).

To find the angle of rotation, join two corresponding points to the centre of rotation, e.g. A and A'. Measure the angle from A to A', 130° anticlockwise.

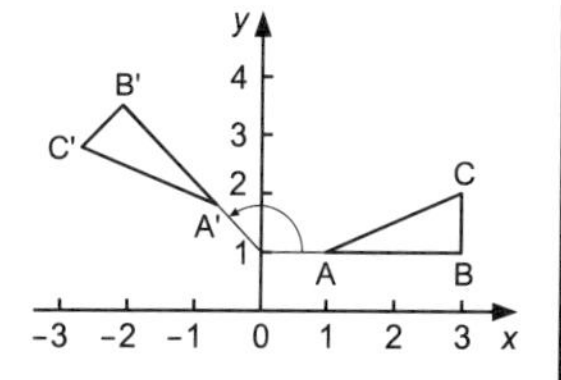

Transformations (Contd)

5. Enlargement

To **enlarge** a shape, you need to know the centre from which to enlarge it and the scale factor.

Question *Enlarge the rectangle PQRS by a scale factor of 3, using the centre (0, 0).*

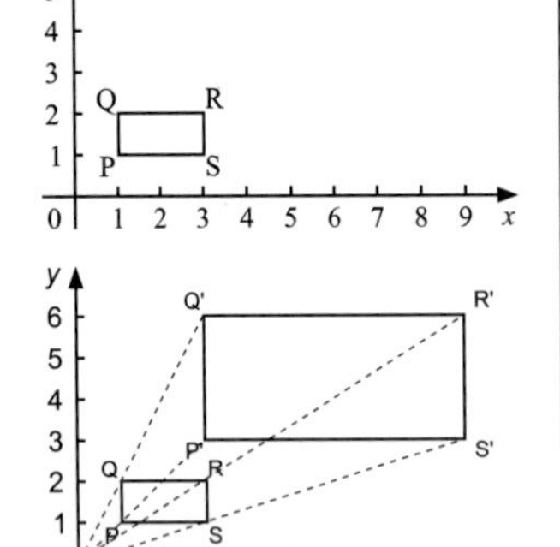

Take each point in turn. Let's start with P.

From the centre to P is 1 unit right, 1 unit up. Multiplying these distances by the scale factor 3 gives the position of the image P', 3 units right and 3 units up from the centre.

Similarly, from the centre to Q is 1 unit right, 2 units up. After multiplying by 3, these distances become 3 units right and 6 units up, giving the position of the image Q'. And so on. Join up the points P'Q'R'S' to give the enlarged image. Notice that the length and breadth of the rectangle P'Q'R'S' are 3 times those of PQRS.

Here, square ABCD has been enlarged by a scale factor of $\frac{1}{2}$, using point B as centre.

Because the scale factor is a fraction (less than 1), this enlargement has *reduced* the size of square ABCD.

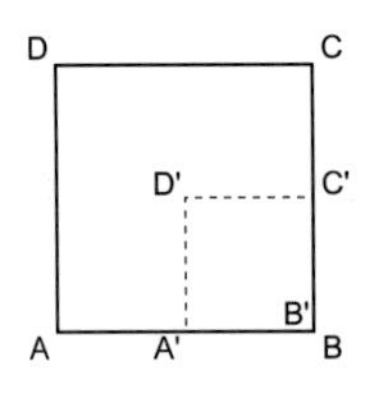

How to find the centre and scale factor of an enlargement

Question *Triangle A'B'C' is an enlargement of triangle ABC. Find the centre and scale factor of the enlargement.*

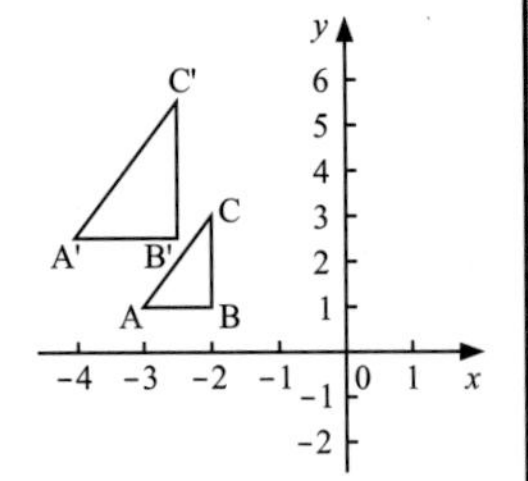

Draw straight lines through pairs of corresponding points, e.g. A to A'. The centre of enlargement is where these lines meet, i.e. (−1, −2).

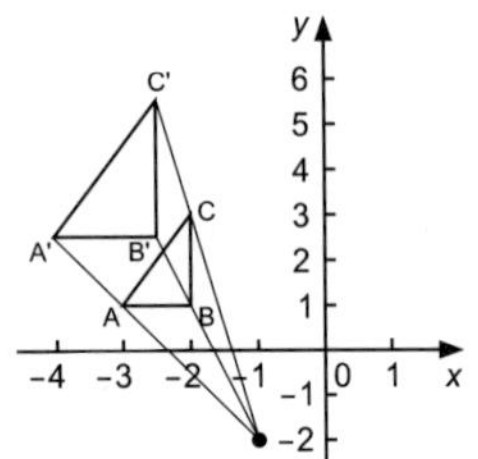

To find the scale factor of enlargement, divide a length of the image A'B'C' by the corresponding length of triangle ABC. For example, A'B' = 1.5 and AB = 1. So, the scale factor = 1.5÷1 = 1.5.

Negative scale factor

A negative scale factor, e.g. −2, means that the enlarged image of a shape will be on the opposite side of the centre.

The shape FGH has been enlarged by a scale factor of −2 using M as the centre.

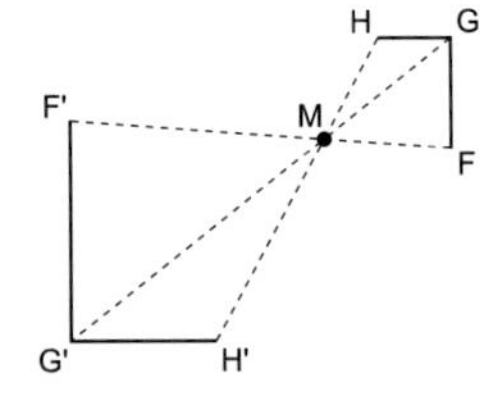

The distance from M to F' is 2 times the distance from M to F, but in the opposite direction.

6. Identifying Transformations

Question *P, Q, R and S are the images of different transformations of the shape T. Fully describe these transformations.*

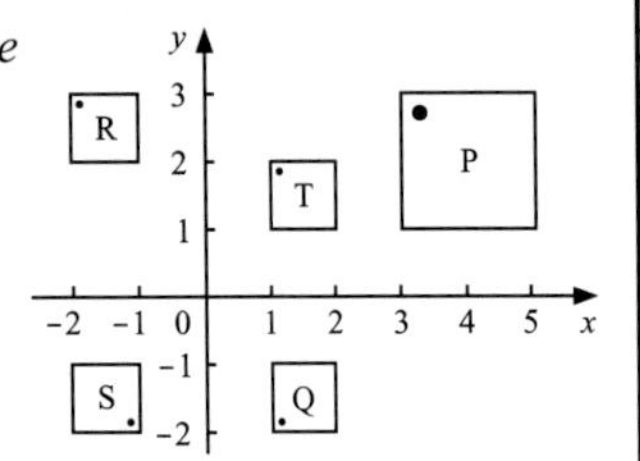

P is an enlargement of T, with scale factor 2. Joining up the corresponding points shows the centre to be (−1, 1).

Q is a reflection of T in the x-axis.

R is a translation with vector $\binom{-3}{1}$.

You can see from the position of the dot that S is a 180° rotation. The centre is the origin (0, 0).

7. Combining Transformations

Question *Triangle ABC has been reflected in the x-axis to give image A'B'C'. This image has then been reflected in the y-axis to give image A"B"C". Fully describe the single transformation that changes ABC into A"B"C".*

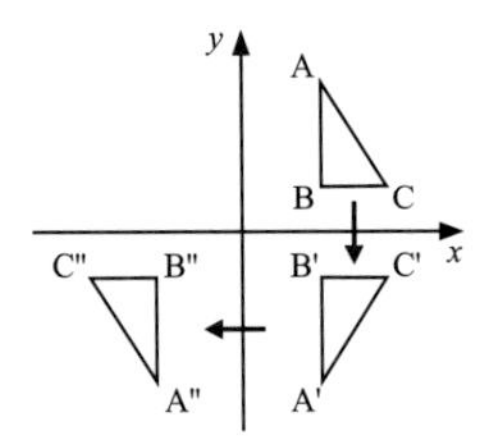

It cannot be a reflection in the dashed line because the reflection of A is not A". So it must be a rotation of 180° with centre (0, 0). Check this deduction using tracing paper (see Box 4, p89).

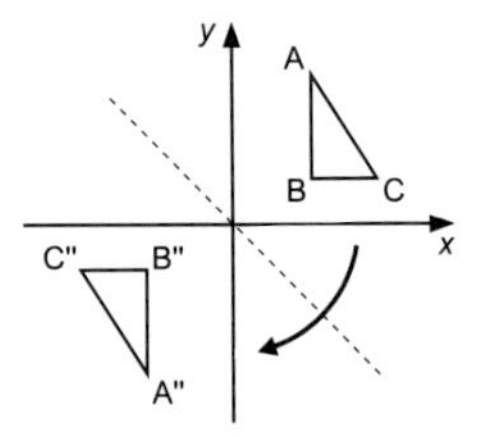

8. Transformation Matrix

A **transformation matrix** is used to transform the points of a shape by multiplying their coordinates in a particular way. Transformation matrices are labelled using capital letters. For example, T = $\begin{pmatrix} -1 & 0 \\ 0 & 1 \end{pmatrix}$.

Question *Draw the image of the trapezium PQRS under the transformation*

$$T = \begin{pmatrix} -1 & 0 \\ 0 & 1 \end{pmatrix}$$

Fully describe the transformation.

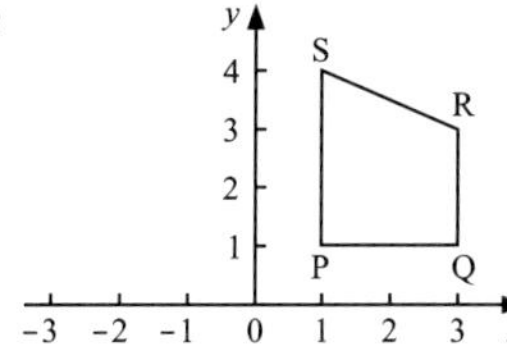

① Write the coordinates of each corner of the trapezium as a vector.

P(1, 1) becomes $\begin{pmatrix} 1 \\ 1 \end{pmatrix}$ Q(3, 1) becomes $\begin{pmatrix} 3 \\ 1 \end{pmatrix}$

R(3, 3) becomes $\begin{pmatrix} 3 \\ 3 \end{pmatrix}$ S(1, 4) becomes $\begin{pmatrix} 1 \\ 4 \end{pmatrix}$

② Multiply each vector by the matrix T to give the coordinates of the corners of the image.

For corner P: $\begin{pmatrix} -1 & 0 \\ 0 & 1 \end{pmatrix} \times \begin{pmatrix} 1 \\ 1 \end{pmatrix} = \begin{pmatrix} -1\times1 + 0\times1 \\ 0\times1 + 1\times1 \end{pmatrix} = \begin{pmatrix} -1+0 \\ 0+1 \end{pmatrix} = \begin{pmatrix} -1 \\ 1 \end{pmatrix}$

So, the image P' of P has coordinates (−1, 1).

For corner Q: $\begin{pmatrix} -1 & 0 \\ 0 & 1 \end{pmatrix} \times \begin{pmatrix} 3 \\ 1 \end{pmatrix} = \begin{pmatrix} -1\times3 + 0\times1 \\ 0\times3 + 1\times1 \end{pmatrix} = \begin{pmatrix} -3+0 \\ 0+1 \end{pmatrix} = \begin{pmatrix} -3 \\ 1 \end{pmatrix}$

So, the image Q' of Q has coordinates (−3, 1).

Similarly, R' has coordinates (−3, 3) and S' has coordinates (−1, 4).

③ Plot the coordinates of points P'Q'R'S'. Join the points to give the image P'Q'R'S'.

The diagram shows that the transformation T is a reflection in the *y*-axis.

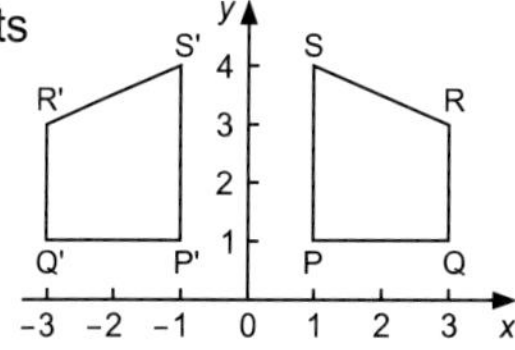

H

9. Identifying a Transformation Matrix

You may be given a transformation matrix and asked to describe the transformation it represents.

Question *Fully describe the transformation represented by the matrix:*

$$T = \begin{pmatrix} 0 & -1 \\ 1 & 0 \end{pmatrix}$$

Make a sketch of the **unit square** OABC.

Use matrix T to transform points A, B and C.

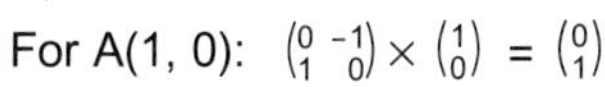

For A(1, 0): $\begin{pmatrix} 0 & -1 \\ 1 & 0 \end{pmatrix} \times \begin{pmatrix} 1 \\ 0 \end{pmatrix} = \begin{pmatrix} 0 \\ 1 \end{pmatrix}$

For B(1, 1): $\begin{pmatrix} 0 & -1 \\ 1 & 0 \end{pmatrix} \times \begin{pmatrix} 1 \\ 1 \end{pmatrix} = \begin{pmatrix} -1 \\ 1 \end{pmatrix}$

For C(0, 1): $\begin{pmatrix} 0 & -1 \\ 1 & 0 \end{pmatrix} \times \begin{pmatrix} 0 \\ 1 \end{pmatrix} = \begin{pmatrix} -1 \\ 0 \end{pmatrix}$

Sketch the image OA'B'C'. This shows that T represents a 90° anticlockwise rotation, centre (0, 0).

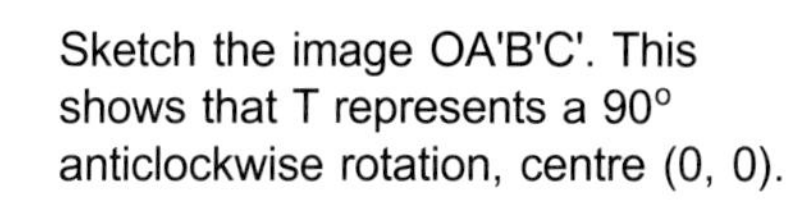

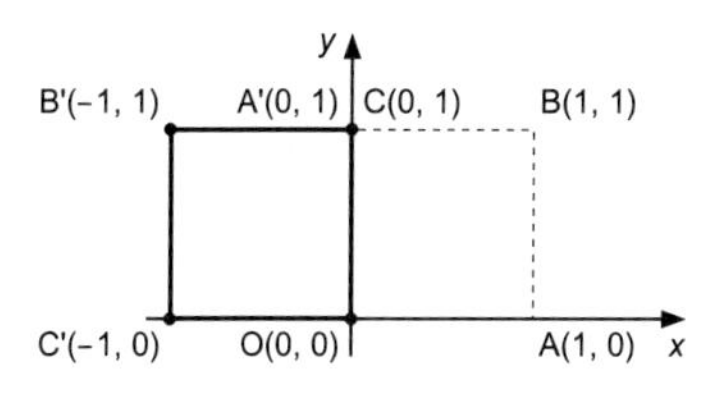

H

10. Combinations of Transformation Matrices

Question *(a) Fully describe the transformations represented by the matrices* $A = \begin{pmatrix} -1 & 0 \\ 0 & 1 \end{pmatrix}$ *and* $B = \begin{pmatrix} 0 & -1 \\ 1 & 0 \end{pmatrix}$

(b) The shape T is transformed using the combination BA. Draw the image of T.

(c) Fully describe the single transformation that BA represents.

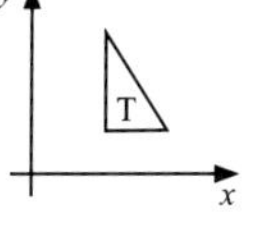

(a) From Boxes 8 and 9, A represents a reflection in the *y*-axis and B an anticlockwise rotation of 90° with centre (0, 0).

(b) 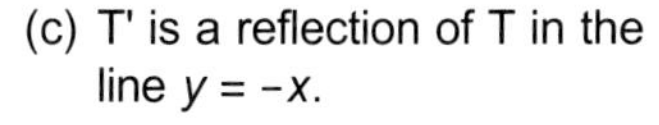
The combination BA means 'apply A first, then B'.

Reflecting T in the *y*-axis and then rotating the image 90° anticlockwise about (0, 0) gives the image T'.

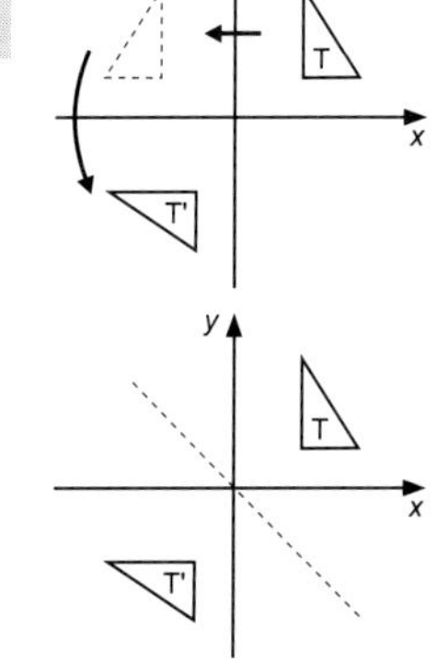

(c) T' is a reflection of T in the line *y* = −*x*.

H

11. Inverse of a Transformation

The **inverse** of a transformation has the opposite effect. Here, T is a 90° anticlockwise rotation and so the inverse of T is a 90° clockwise rotation. The inverse of T is written T^{-1}. Applying T followed by its inverse T^{-1} leaves the shape unchanged. The inverse of T can be found using the formula:

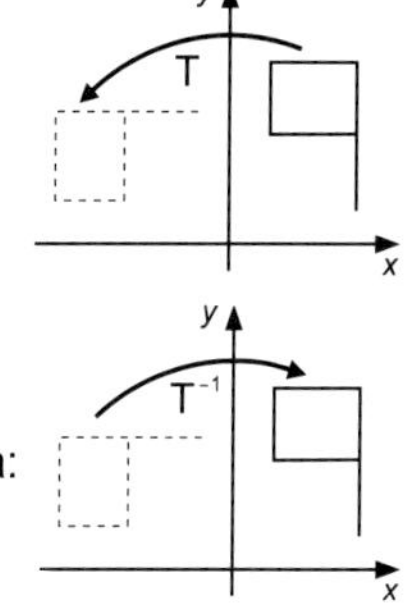

$T = \begin{pmatrix} a & b \\ c & d \end{pmatrix}$ $T^{-1} = \frac{1}{ad-bc}\begin{pmatrix} d & -b \\ -c & a \end{pmatrix}$

Question *T is the transformation represented by the matrix* $T = \begin{pmatrix} 0 & -1 \\ 1 & 0 \end{pmatrix}$.

(a) Describe the transformation T.

(b) Calculate the inverse T^{-1}.

(c) Describe the transformation represented by T^{-1}.

(a) From Box 9, we can see that T represents an anticlockwise rotation of 90° with centre (0, 0).

(b) For $T = \begin{pmatrix} 0 & -1 \\ 1 & 0 \end{pmatrix}$, *a* = 0, *b* = −1, *c* = 1, *d* = 0 and so

$$T^{-1} = \frac{1}{0\times0 - -1\times1}\begin{pmatrix} 0 & --1 \\ -1 & 0 \end{pmatrix} = \frac{1}{1}\begin{pmatrix} 0 & 1 \\ -1 & 0 \end{pmatrix} = \begin{pmatrix} 0 & 1 \\ -1 & 0 \end{pmatrix}$$

(c) T^{-1} represents a clockwise rotation of 90° with centre (0, 0).

Symmetry. Nets. Tessellations

1. Line Symmetry

A **line of symmetry** divides a shape in half. It is like a mirror: each half is a reflection of the other.

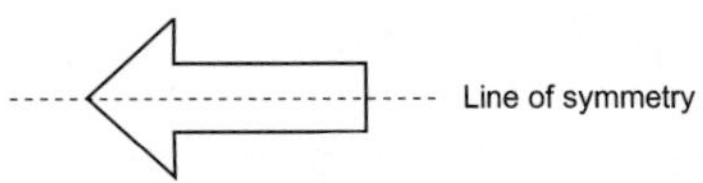

A shape can have several lines of symmetry:

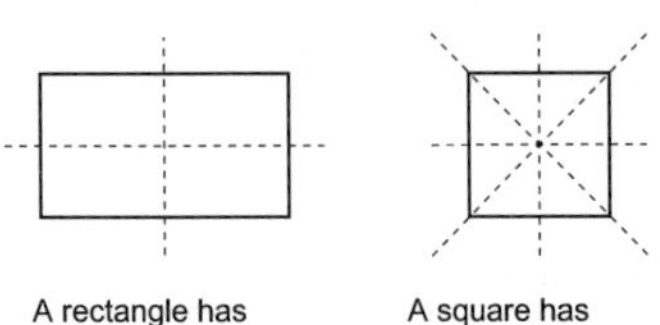

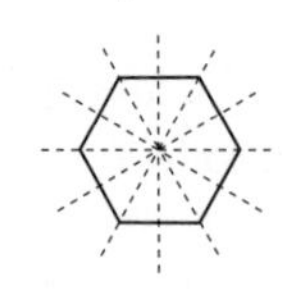

A rectangle has 2 lines of symmetry

A square has 4 lines of symmetry

A regular polygon has the same number of lines of symmetry as sides

Some shapes do not have line symmetry.

2. Rotational Symmetry

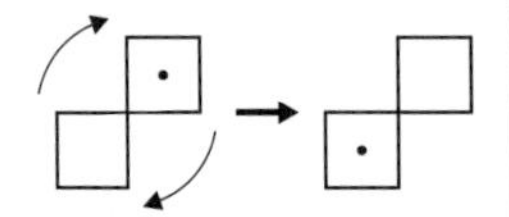

If the left-hand shape is rotated half a turn (180°), it becomes the right-hand shape. Ignoring the dot, these shapes appear the same. We say the shape has **rotational symmetry**. There are two positions in which the shape appears the same, so we say that the **order** of rotational symmetry is 2.

A square has rotational symmetry of order 4

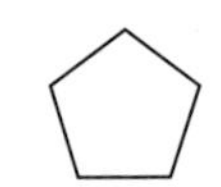

A regular pentagon has rotational symmetry of order 5

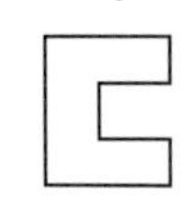

This shape does not have rotational symmetry

Question *Which of the shapes below has*
(a) line symmetry but not rotational symmetry
(b) rotational symmetry but not line symmetry
(c) both line and rotational symmetry?

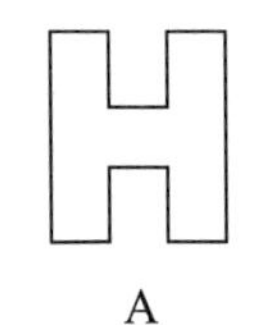

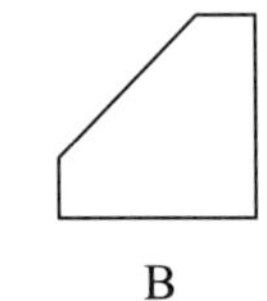

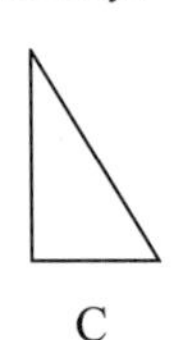

A B C D

(a) B has line symmetry but not rotational symmetry.

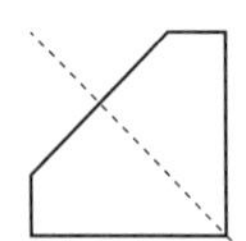

(b) D has rotational symmetry of order 4 but no lines of symmetry.

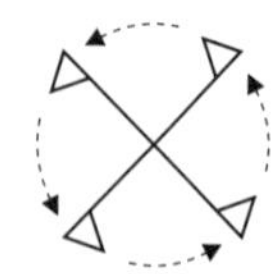

(c) A has both line symmetry and rotational symmetry of order 2.

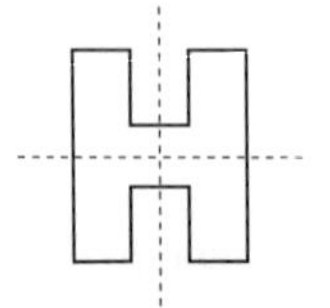

3. Nets

A **net** is a flat pattern that can be cut out and folded into a 3-D shape. The net opposite can be folded up to make a cube.

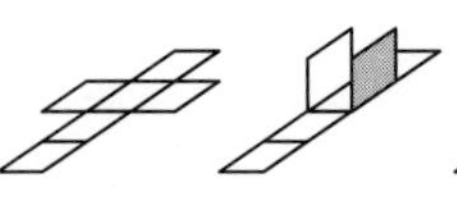

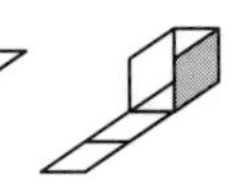

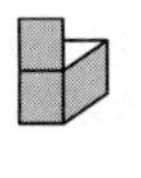

There are several different nets for each 3-D shape. Some of the nets for a cube are shown below, together with a pattern that is not a net.

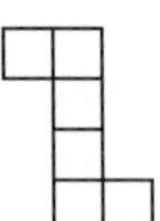

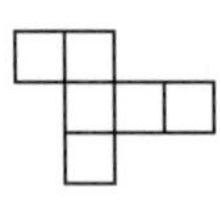

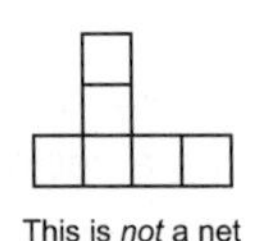

This is *not* a net

Question *Accurately draw a net of this prism.*

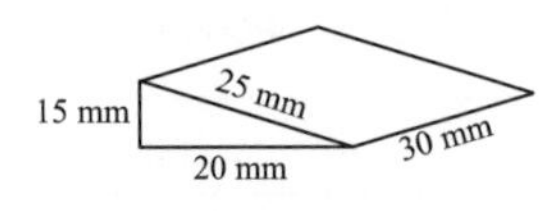

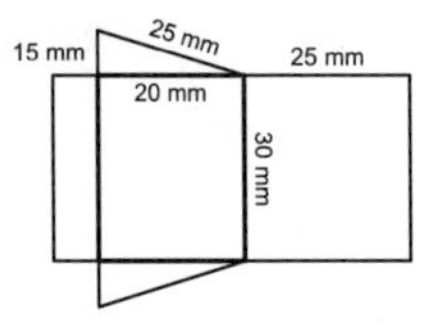

Start by drawing one of the central faces in the middle of the paper (see the bold lines in the diagram).

Add adjacent faces, mentally checking that they fold up correctly.

4. Tessellation

A tessellation is a repeating pattern made from one or more shapes. There are no gaps between the shapes.

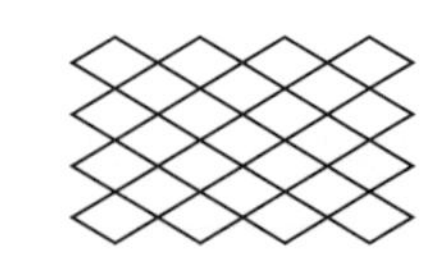

This tessellation is made from two shapes: a regular octagon and a square.

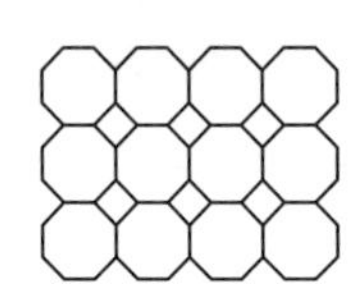

Any regular polygon whose interior angle divides exactly into 360° can be used to make a tessellation. This tessellation uses a hexagon, with an interior angle of 120° (see Box 3, p83).

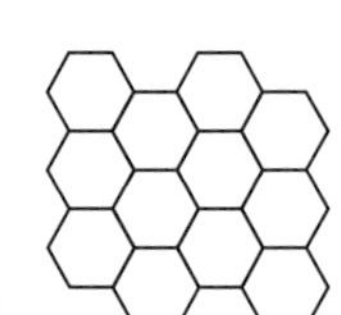

Any triangle can be used to make a tessellation. This is because the corner angles add up to 180° (half a circle) when placed next to each other.

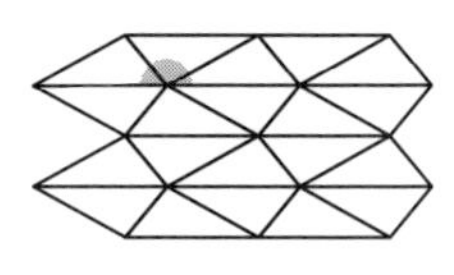

Any quadrilateral can be used to make a tessellation. This is because the corner angles add up to 360° (a circle) when placed next to each other.

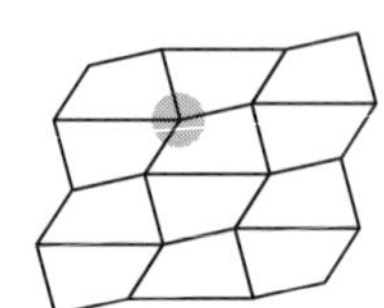

Trigonometry and Right-angled Triangles

1. Sides of a Right-angled Triangle

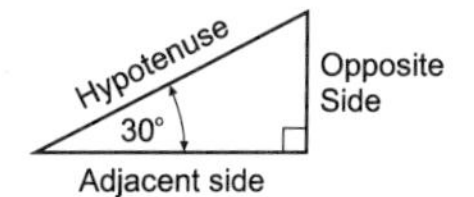

The side opposite the right angle is called the **hypotenuse**. It is the longest side.

The side opposite the 30° angle is called the **opposite** side.

The side next to the 30° angle is called the **adjacent** side (because adjacent means 'next to').

2. Sin, Cos and Tan

Sine, cosine and tangent are the names of three fractions (called **trigonometric ratios**) made using the sides of a right-angled triangle. They are written briefly as sin, cos and tan.

$$\sin\theta = \frac{\text{Opposite}}{\text{Hypotenuse}}$$

$$\cos\theta = \frac{\text{Adjacent}}{\text{Hypotenuse}}$$

$$\tan\theta = \frac{\text{Opposite}}{\text{Adjacent}}$$

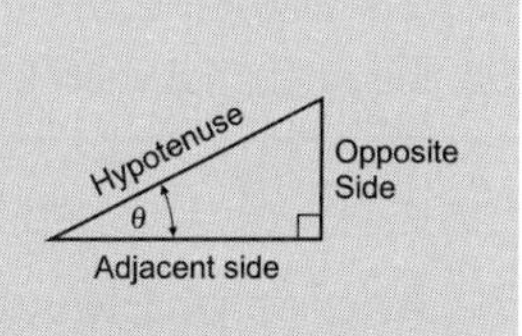

NOTE sin θ is written instead of just sin because the ratio depends on the size of the angle θ.

Question *Write down sin 30° as a fraction, using the sides of this triangle.*

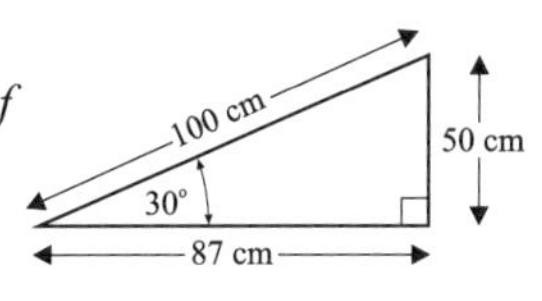

Label the sides as in Box 1

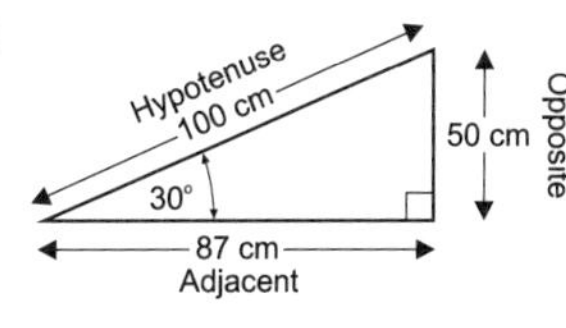

$$\sin 30° = \frac{\text{Opposite}}{\text{Hypotenuse}} = \frac{50}{100}$$

3. Using a Calculator to find Sin, Cos and Tan

Instead of drawing a triangle to find sin 30°, we can use a calculator. Make sure that your calculator is in **degrees mode**.

So, sin 30° = 0.5

NOTE More sophisticated calculators let you press the [sin] button first: [sin] [3] [0] [=]

Question *Calculate the value of tan 20° correct to 3 decimal places.*

0.3639702

So, tan 20° = 0.364 (3 dp)

4. Finding an Unknown Side

Question *Find the length of side AB, correct to 2 decimal places.*

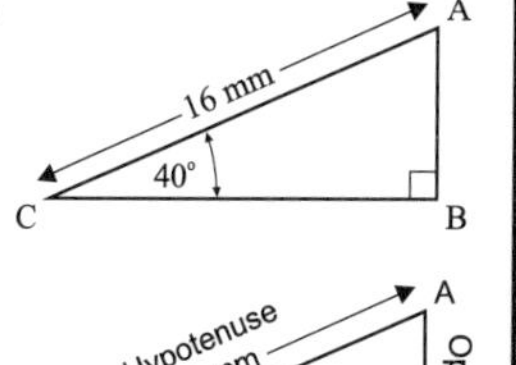

① Label the side you know (AC = 16 cm) and the side you want to find (AB).

② Write down the equation in Box 2 that contains these two sides:

$$\sin\theta = \frac{\text{Opposite}}{\text{Hypotenuse}}$$

③ Fill in the angle and sides for this triangle:

$$\sin 40° = \frac{AB}{16}$$

④ Use your calculator to find the value of sin 40°

Keep this value displayed in your calculator, or store it in the memory. Write down an approximate value, e.g. sin 40° = 0.643.

⑤ Rewrite the equation and solve it:

$$0.643 = \frac{AB}{16}$$

$\therefore$ 0.643×16 = AB

$\therefore$ AB = 0.643×16 = 10.28 mm (2 dp)

All the calculator steps are shown below.

10.2846018

Question *A ladder leans against a wall and makes an angle of 72° with the ground. The foot of the ladder is 1.2 m from the wall. Calculate the length of the ladder.*

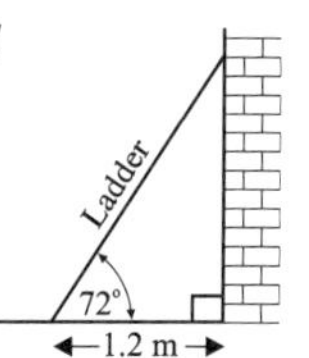

Let y be the length of the ladder

The ladder is the hypotenuse and the length 1.2 m is adjacent to the angle. From Box 2, use the equation:

$$\cos\theta = \frac{\text{Adjacent}}{\text{Hypotenuse}}$$

$$\therefore \cos 72° = \frac{1.2}{y}$$

0.30901699

$\therefore 0.309 = \frac{1.2}{y}$ Move $\div y$ to LHS, and change to $\times y$

$\therefore 0.309y = 1.2$ Divide both sides by 0.309

$\therefore y = \frac{1.2}{0.309} = 3.88$ m

All the calculator steps are shown below:

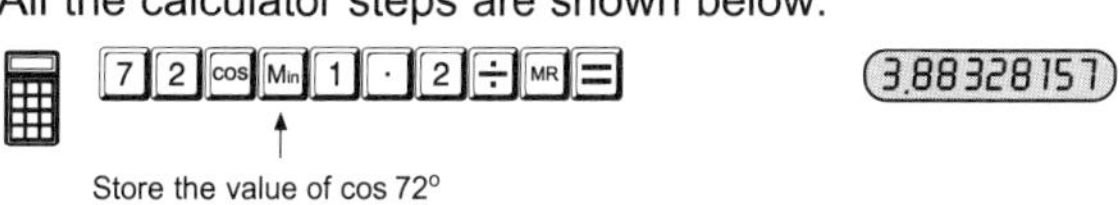

Trigonometry and Right–angled Triangles (Contd)

5. Sin^{-1}, Cos^{-1} and Tan^{-1}

If you enter an angle into your calculator and press the [sin] button you get a number. For example, pressing [3][0][sin] changes the angle 30° into the number 0.5.

The opposite (inverse) of sin is written $\sin^{-1}$. So, if you enter a number into your calculator and press [INV][sin] you get an angle. For example, pressing [0][·][5][INV][sin] changes the number 0.5 into the angle 30°.

Question *If $\tan x = 1.3$ find the angle x.*

When tan moves to the RHS it becomes the opposite (inverse) of tan, written $\tan^{-1}$.

$\tan x = 1.3$

$\therefore\ x = \tan^{-1} 1.3$

$= 52.43°$

[1][·][3][INV][tan] (52.4314080)

6. Finding an Unknown Angle

Question *Calculate the size of angle x, correct to the nearest 0.1°.*

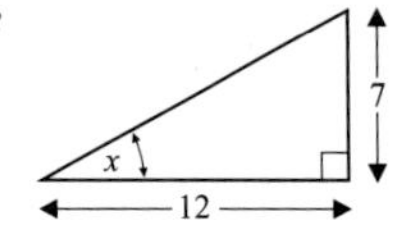

① Label the sides you know (12 and 7).

② Write down the equation in Box 2 that contains these two sides:

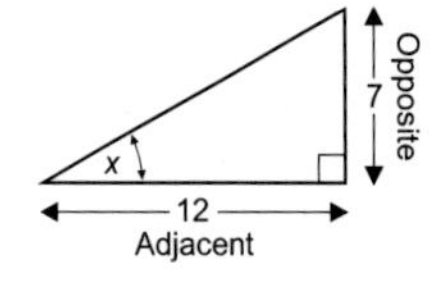

$$\tan x = \frac{\text{Opposite}}{\text{Adjacent}}$$

③ Fill in the sides for this triangle:

$$\tan x = \frac{7}{12}$$

④ Calculate the RHS using a calculator:

(0.58333333)

So, $\tan x = 0.58\dot{3}$

Keep this value displayed in your calculator.

⑤ Move tan to the RHS and change it to $\tan^{-1}$:

$\tan x = 0.58\dot{3}$

$\therefore\ x = \tan^{-1} 0.58\dot{3}$

⑥ Use your calculator to find the value of x.

You should still have 0.58333333 displayed on your calculator, from step 4. If not, calculate $7 \div 12$ again. Here are all the calculator steps:

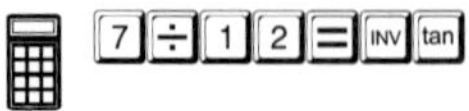

(30.2564372)

So, $x = 30.3°$

more

6. Finding an Unknown Angle (Contd)

Question *Find the angle between the blades of these scissors.*

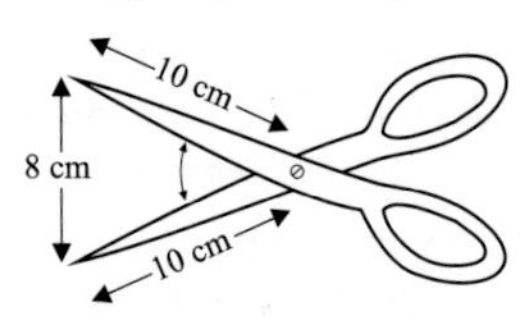

Draw the isosceles triangle made by the blades of the scissors:

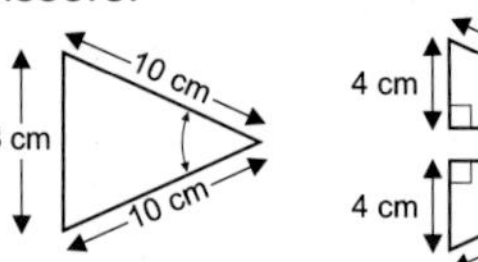

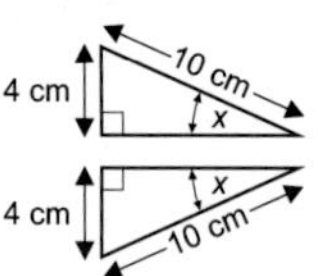

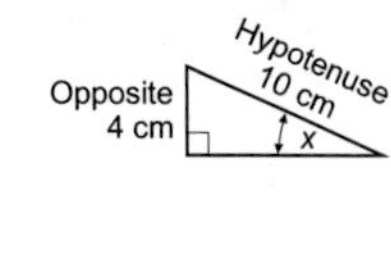

Split this into two identical right–angled triangles, each with angle x, say. Use one of the triangles to find x:

$\sin x = \frac{4}{10} = 0.4$

$\therefore\ x = \sin^{-1} 0.4 = 23.6°$

So, the angle between the blades $= 2 \times 23.6 = 47.2°$.

7. Angles of Elevation and Depression

A person, P, looking straight ahead would have to look up (elevate) through an angle of 40° to see the bird and look down (depress) through an angle of 30° to see the ship.

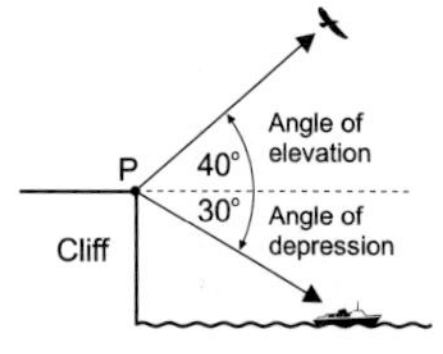

Question *A person looks out of a window 6 m above ground at a vertical flagpole. The angle of elevation of the top of the flagpole is 20°. The angle of depression of the foot of the flagpole is 40°.*

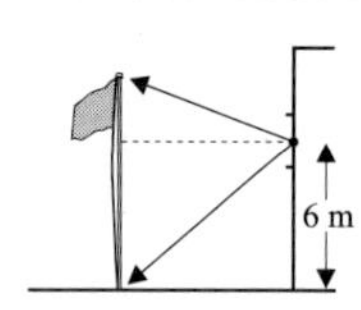

(a) Mark these angles on the diagram.

(b) Calculate the horizontal distance between the person and the flagpole.

(c) Calculate the height of the flagpole.

(a) See diagram.

(b) The diagram contains two right–angled triangles.

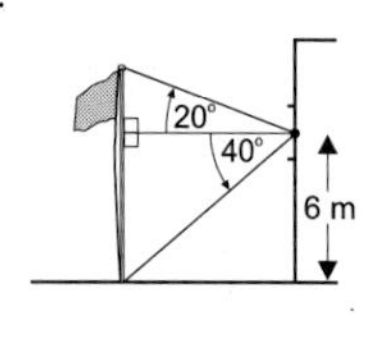

For this triangle:

$\tan 40° = \dfrac{6}{x}$

$\therefore\ 0.839 = \dfrac{6}{x}$

$\therefore\ 0.839x = 6$

$\therefore\ x = \dfrac{6}{0.839} = 7.15 \text{ m}$

Mark this length on the diagram to help you below.

For this triangle:

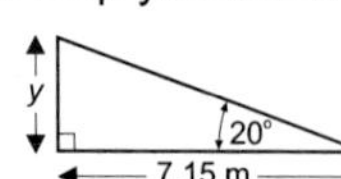

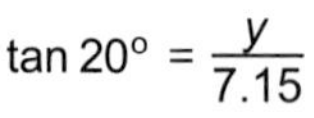

$\tan 20° = \dfrac{y}{7.15}$

$\therefore\ 0.364 = \dfrac{y}{7.15}$

$\therefore\ 0.364 \times 7.15 = y$

$\therefore\ y = 2.60 \text{ m}$

So, height of flagpole $= 6 + 2.60 = 8.60$ m.

8. Trigonometry and Bearings

Question *Reading is 85 km due East of Bristol and 52 km due North of Portsmouth. Calculate*
(a) the bearing of Portsmouth from Bristol
(b) the distance between Portsmouth and Bristol.

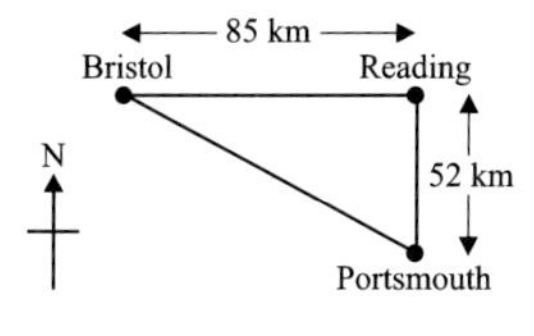

(a) The diagram shows that the bearing of Portsmouth from Bristol is 90° plus angle x. So, we must find x

$$\tan x = \frac{52}{85} = 0.612$$

$\therefore\ x = \tan^{-1} 0.612 = 31.5°$

So, the bearing is $90° + 31.5° = 121.5°$

(b) From Pythagoras' theorem, we have:

$$(\text{Distance})^2 = 85^2 + 52^2 = 9929$$

$\therefore$ Distance $= \sqrt{9929} = 99.6 \approx 100$ km

Sine and Cosine Rules H

1. Sine and Cosine Rules

The sine and cosine rules can be used to find the unknown sides and angles of any kind of triangle. They are normally used with triangles that do not have a right angle.

It is easy to decide which rule to use:

Use the sine rule if you know a side and the angle opposite.
Use the cosine rule if you cannot use the sine rule.

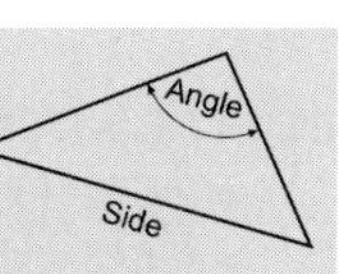

2. Labelling a Triangle

The capital letters A, B and C represent the corner angles.

The lower case letters a, b and c represent the sides opposite the angles A, B and C.

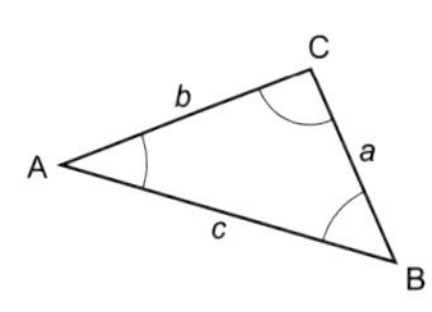

3. Sine Rule

The sine rule says that the fraction

$$\frac{\text{Side}}{\text{Sine of opposite angle}}$$

is the same for all three sides of the triangle.

The sine rule can be expressed algebraically:

$$\frac{a}{\sin A} = \frac{b}{\sin B} = \frac{c}{\sin C}$$

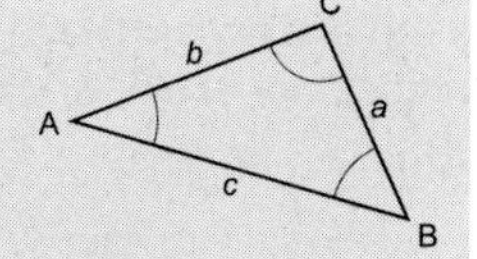

more

3. Sine Rule (Contd)

Question *Area ABC is a fenced area of woodland. Find the length of BC.*

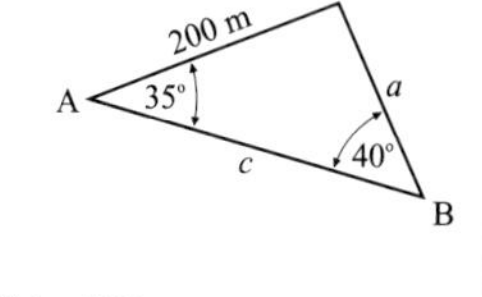

Here, $b = 200$, $A = 35°$ and $B = 40°$.

We want to find a, the length of side BC.

Substitute these values in the sine rule:

$$\frac{a}{\sin 35°} = \frac{200}{\sin 40°} \left(= \frac{c}{\sin C}\right)$$

Discard this unwanted part

$$\therefore\ \frac{a}{0.574} = \frac{200}{0.643}$$

$$\therefore\ \frac{a}{0.574} = 311.14$$

$\therefore\ a = 311.14 \times 0.574 = 178.5$ m

Question *Q is 25 km from P on a bearing of 075° and 40 km from R. P is due North of R. Calculate the bearing of Q from R, correct to the nearest degree.*

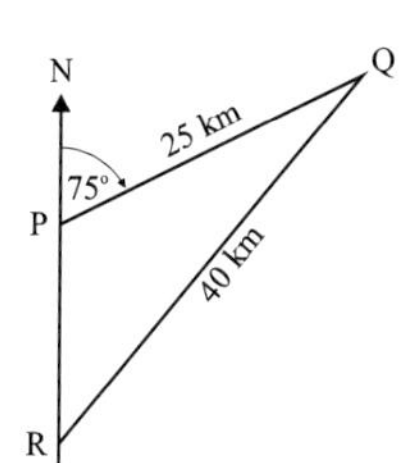

Angle $P = 180° - 75° = 105°$

We want to find angle R.

Applying the sine rule, we have:

$$\frac{25}{\sin R} = \frac{40}{\sin 105°}$$

Turn both sides of the equation upside down, to get R on top:

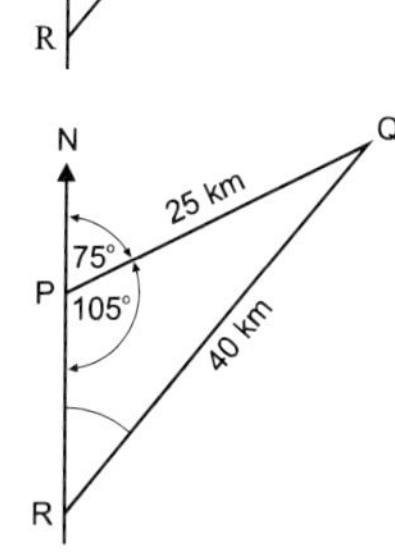

$$\therefore\ \frac{\sin R}{25} = \frac{\sin 105°}{40}$$

$$\therefore\ \frac{\sin R}{25} = 0.024$$

$\therefore\ \sin R = 25 \times 0.024 = 0.604$

$\therefore\ R = \sin^{-1} 0.604 = 37.1° \approx 37°$

The bearing of Q from R is 037°.

Sine and Cosine Rules (Contd)

4. Cosine Rule

There are two formulae for the cosine rule: one to find lengths, the other to find angles.

To find the length a, use:

$$a^2 = b^2 + c^2 - 2bc \cos A$$

To find the angle A, use:

$$\cos A = \frac{b^2 + c^2 - a^2}{2bc}$$

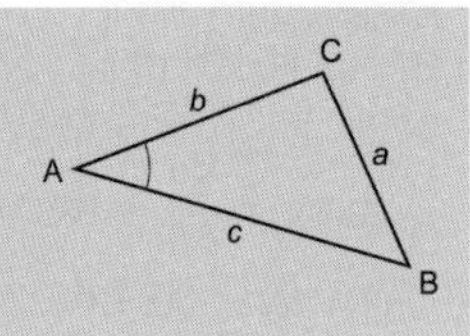

Question *Find the length BC.*

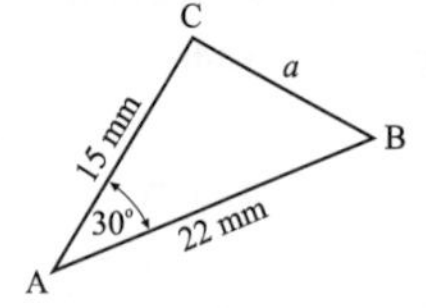

We do not know a side and its opposite angle and so cannot use the sine rule. So, we must use the cosine rule.

Here, $b = 15$, $c = 22$ and $A = 30°$
We want to find a:

$$a^2 = b^2 + c^2 - 2bc \cos A$$
$$= 15^2 + 22^2 - 2 \times 15 \times 22 \times \cos 30°$$
$$= 225 + 484 - 571.6$$
$$= 137.4$$

So, $a = \sqrt{137.4} = 11.7$ mm

Question *The diagram shows the cross-section of a roof. Calculate angles x, y and z.*

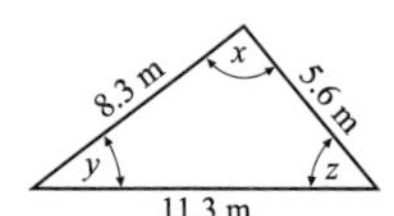

If we consider angle x to be angle A in the cosine rule, then $a = 11.3$, $b = 5.6$ and $c = 8.3$

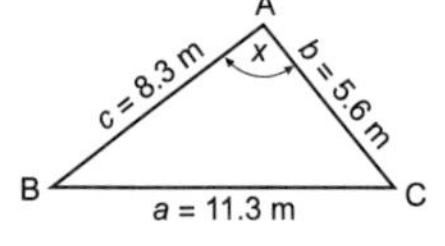

$$\cos x = \frac{b^2 + c^2 - a^2}{2bc}$$
$$= \frac{5.6^2 + 8.3^2 - 11.3^2}{2 \times 5.6 \times 8.3}$$
$$= \frac{-27.44}{92.96}$$
$$= -0.295$$

So, $x = \cos^{-1} -0.295 = 107.2°$

Mark this angle on the diagram; it may help you to find other sides and angles.

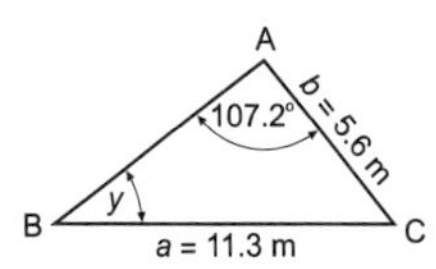

We now know a side (11.3 m) and the opposite angle (107.2°) and so can use the easier sine rule to find angle y:

$$\frac{5.6}{\sin y} = \frac{11.3}{\sin 107.2°}$$

$$\therefore \frac{\sin y}{5.6} = \frac{\sin 107.2°}{11.3}$$ Turn both sides of the equation upside down

$$\therefore \frac{\sin y}{5.6} = 0.085$$

$\therefore \sin y = 5.6 \times 0.085 = 0.473$

$\therefore y = \sin^{-1} 0.473 = 28.3°$

Since the angles of a triangle add up to 180° we have:

$z = 180° - 107.2° - 28.3° = 44.5°$

more

4. Cosine Rule (Contd)

Question *Calculate the length of the ramp, BC.*

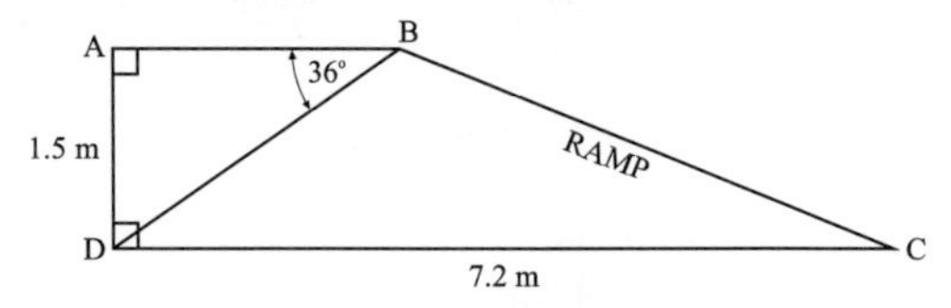

Triangle BCD contains the side BC we want.

To use the cosine rule with triangle BCD, we need to know sides BD and DC and angle BDC (opposite BC).

We know side DC = 7.2 m.

We can also find angle BDC. Sides AB and DC are parallel because they are both perpendicular to side AD. So, angle BDC = 36° (alternate angles).

We can find side BD from the right-triangled ADB using trigonometry:

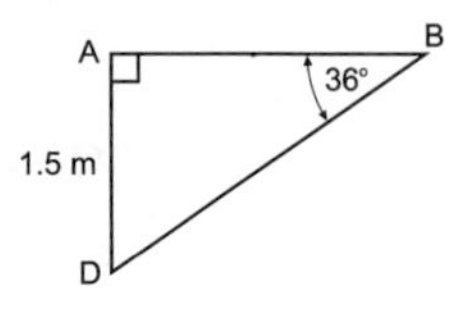

$$\sin 36° = \frac{1.5}{BD}$$

$\therefore BD \sin 36° = 1.5$

$$\therefore BD = \frac{1.5}{\sin 36°} = 2.552 \text{ m}$$

Now we can apply the cosine rule to triangle BCD:

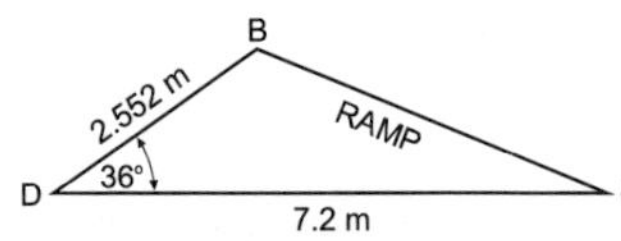

$$BC^2 = BD^2 + DC^2 - 2 \times BD \times DC \times \cos D$$
$$= 2.552^2 + 7.2^2 - 2 \times 2.552 \times 7.2 \times \cos 36°$$
$$= 6.513 + 51.84 - 29.73$$
$$= 28.62$$

So, $BC = \sqrt{28.62} \approx 5.4$ m (1 dp)

5. Area of a Triangle = $\frac{1}{2}ab \sin C$

When you do not know the height of a triangle, use the following formula to calculate its area:

$$\text{Area} = \tfrac{1}{2}ab \sin C$$

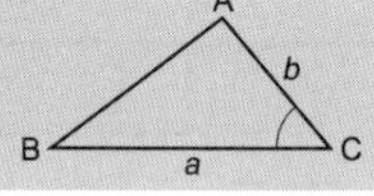

Question *The diagram shows a postage stamp in the shape of an equilateral triangle. Calculate its area.*

You could split this triangle into two right-angled triangles and calculate its height (see Box 6, p94).

But it is quicker to use the $\frac{1}{2}ab \sin C$ formula.

All the sides of this triangle are 3 cm and so $a = 3$ and $b = 3$. The angles are all 60° and so $C = 60°$.

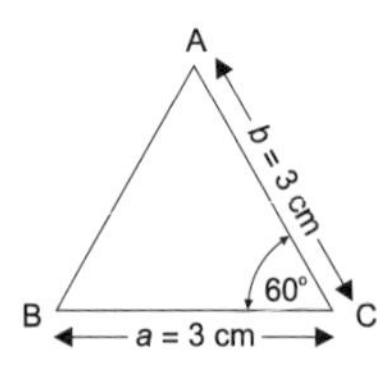

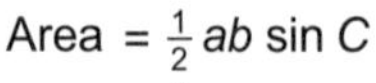

Area $= \frac{1}{2}ab \sin C$

$= \frac{1}{2} \times 3 \times 3 \times \sin 60°$

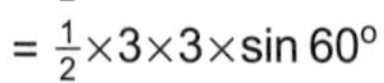

$= 0.5 \times 3 \times 3 \times 0.866$

$= 3.9 \text{ cm}^2$

Three–dimensional Trigonometry

Triangles can be used to find unknown sides and angles of three–dimensional shapes.

The method is to find a triangle that contains the side or angle you want. Then draw the triangle, marking on it the lengths and angles you know. Look out for isosceles triangles and right–angled triangles.

Question *A road sign is made from an equilateral triangle of side 45 cm and is supported by two struts, each 30 cm long.*

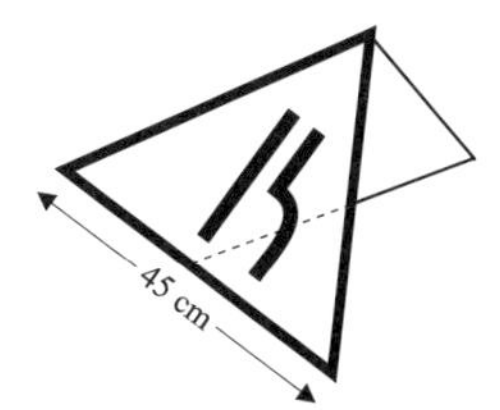

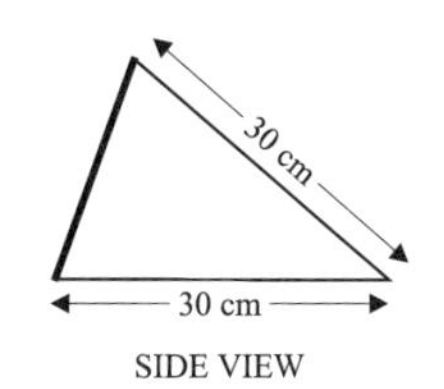

(a) Calculate the height of the equilateral triangle.
(b) Calculate the angle the sign makes with the ground.

(a) The angles of an equilateral triangle are all 60°. Let h be the height of the triangle, then:

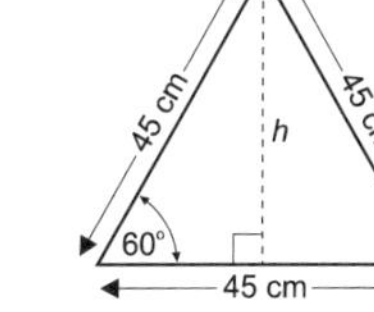

$$\sin 60^\circ = \frac{h}{45}$$

$$\therefore\ 0.866 = \frac{h}{45}$$

$\therefore\ 0.866 \times 45 = h$

$\therefore\ h = 39.0$ cm

(b) Split the isosceles triangle into two identical right–angled triangles and let x be the angle between the sign and the ground. Then

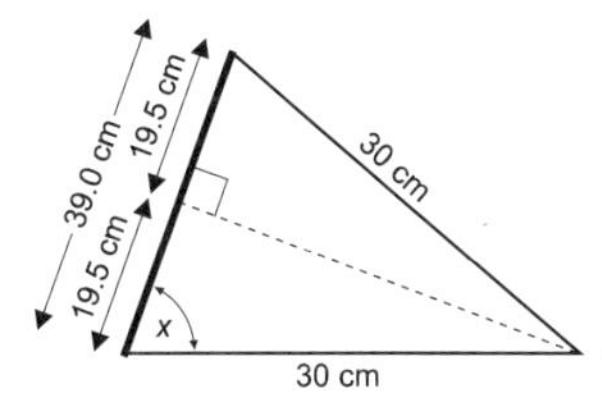

$$\cos x = \frac{19.5}{30} = 0.65$$

$\therefore\ x = \cos^{-1} 0.65 = 49.5^\circ$

NOTE You could also use the cosine rule since you know all three sides of the triangle.

Question **H** *The angle of elevation of the top of the Eiffel tower from Notre–Dame, 4.1 km away, is 4.5°. The Arc de Triomphe is 1.6 km from the Eiffel tower.*

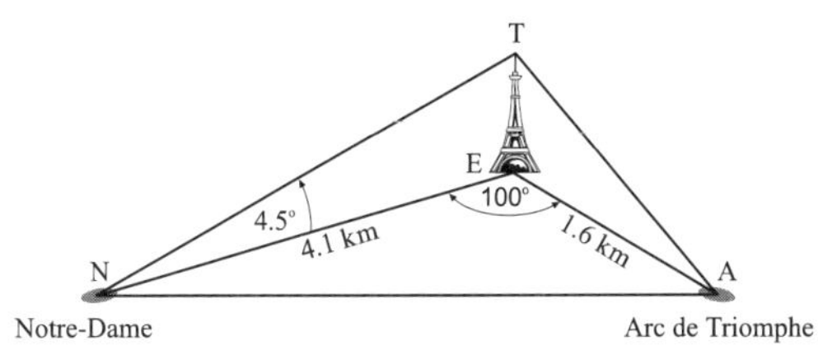

Calculate:
(a) the height of the Eiffel tower, correct to the nearest 10 m
(b) the angle of elevation of the top of the Eiffel tower from the Arc de Triomphe
(c) the distance between Notre–Dame and the Arc de Triomphe.

(a) Use the right–angled triangle NET to find the height of the Eiffel tower ET:

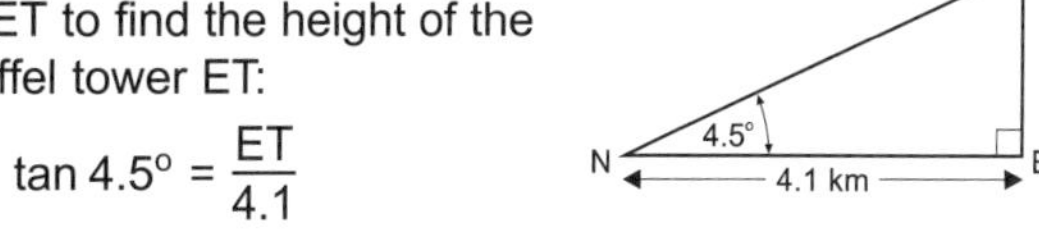

$$\tan 4.5^\circ = \frac{ET}{4.1}$$

$\therefore\ 4.1 \times \tan 4.5^\circ = ET$

$\therefore\ ET = 0.3227\text{ km} = 322.7\text{ m} \approx 320\text{ m}$

(b) Use the right–angled triangle EAT to find the angle of elevation EAT of the top of the Eiffel tower from the Arc de Triomphe:

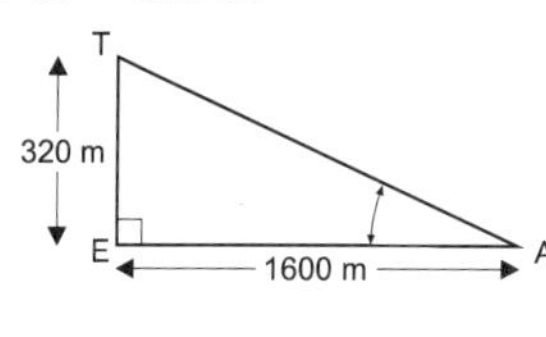

$$\tan A = \frac{322.7}{1600} = 0.2017$$

$\therefore\ A = \tan^{-1} 0.2017 \approx 11.4^\circ$ (1 dp)

(c) Apply the cosine rule to triangle NAE to find the distance NA between Notre–Dame and the Arc de Triomphe:

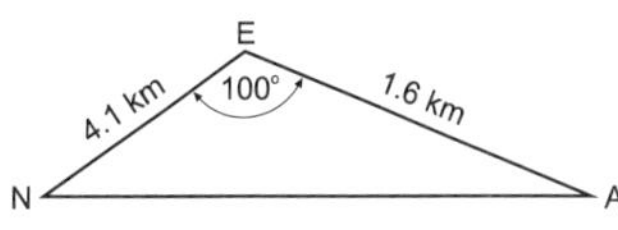

$$\begin{aligned} NA^2 &= NE^2 + EA^2 - 2 \times NE \times EA \times \cos E \\ &= 4.1^2 + 1.6^2 - 2 \times 4.1 \times 1.6 \times \cos 100^\circ \\ &= 16.81 + 2.56 - -2.278 \\ &= 21.648 \end{aligned}$$

So, BC = $\sqrt{21.648} \approx 4.7$ km (1 dp)

Question **H** *The diagram shows a rectangular block of butter.*

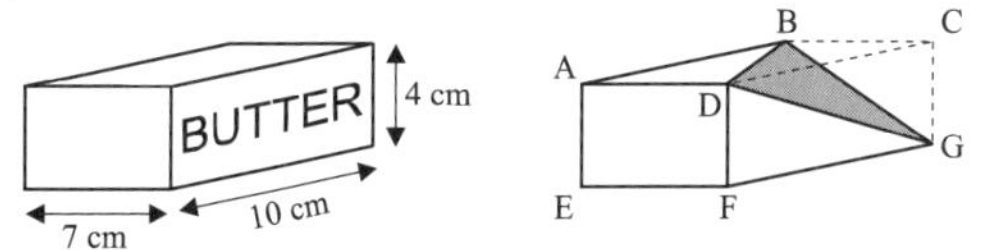

A corner of the butter is removed with a single knife cut. Calculate the area of the cut face of the remaining block.

We must first find the sides of triangular cut face BDG.

Using Pythagoras' theorem, we have:

$DG^2 = 4^2 + 10^2 = 116 \quad \therefore\ DG = \sqrt{116} = 10.77$ cm

$BD^2 = 10^2 + 7^2 = 149 \quad \therefore\ BD = \sqrt{149} = 12.21$ cm

$BG^2 = 4^2 + 7^2 = 65 \quad \therefore\ BG = \sqrt{65} = 8.06$ cm

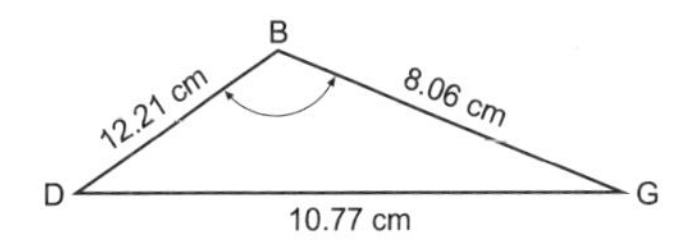

We can use $\frac{1}{2}ab \sin C$ to find the area of triangle BDG if we can find an angle. Using the cosine rule, we can find angle DBG:

$$\cos B = \frac{12.21^2 + 8.06^2 - 10.77^2}{2 \times 12.21 \times 8.06} = 0.4982$$

$\therefore\ B = \cos^{-1} 0.4982 = 60.12^\circ$

Area of triangle BDG $= \frac{1}{2} \times 12.21 \times 8.06 \times \sin 60.12^\circ$
$= 42.7\text{ cm}^2$ (1 dp)

Graphs of Trigonometric Functions H

1. Graphs of Trigonometric Functions

Sine is a function that changes angles into numbers. If we calculate the value of $\sin x$ for different angles x, we will obtain a table of values like the one below

x	0°	30°	60°	90°	120°	150°	180°	210°	240°	270°	300°	330°	360°
$y = \sin x$	0	0.5	0.87	1	0.87	0.5	0	−0.5	−0.87	−1	−0.87	−0.5	0

Using these values, we can plot the graph of $y = \sin x$:

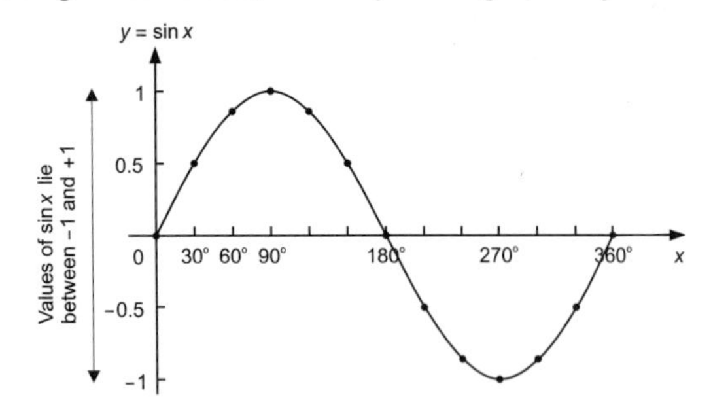

From the graph you can see that the values of $\sin x$ lie between −1 and +1. Also, the graph repeats itself every 360°. Each repetition is called a **cycle**.

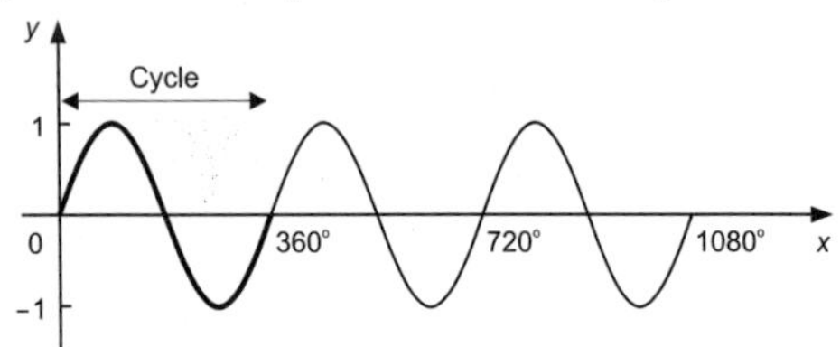

The graph of $y = \cos x$ is the same as the graph of $y = \sin x$ only shifted 90° left.

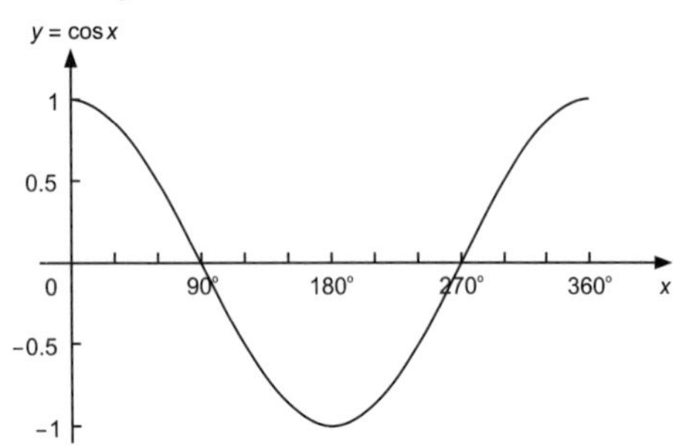

The graph of $y = \tan x$ is completely different:

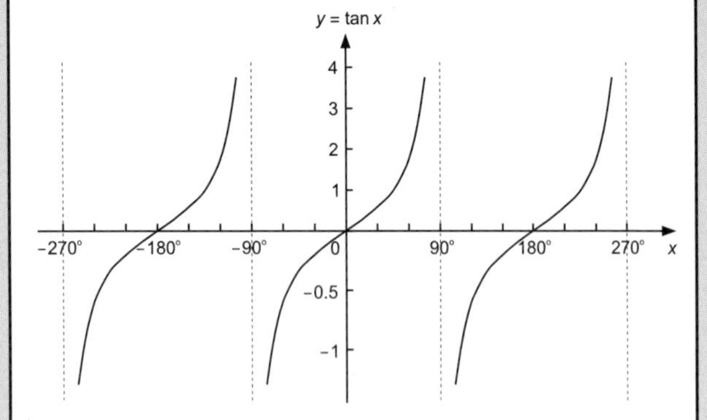

The graph is broken into separate sections (called **branches**). As x gets closer to 90° from the left, the y-values become very large. When x reaches 90°, y is infinitely large and cannot be calculated. Try calculating tan 90°: you will get a calculator error.

2. Graphs of Related Trigonometric Functions

Here is a cycle of the graph of $y = \sin x$.

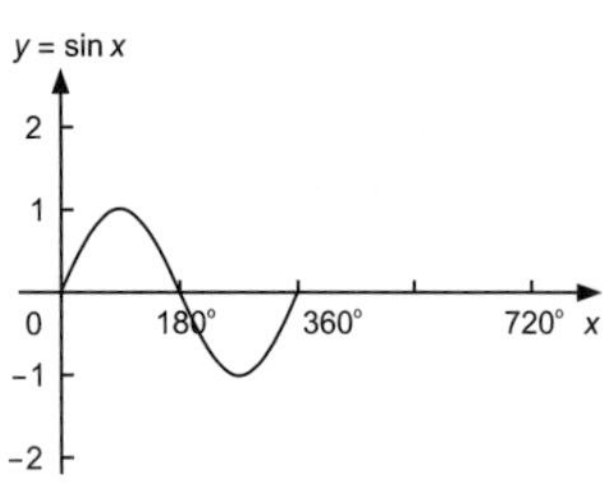

Here is a cycle of the graph of $y = 2 \sin x$. The y-values of $\sin x$ have been multiplied by 2 and so now lie between −2 and 2.

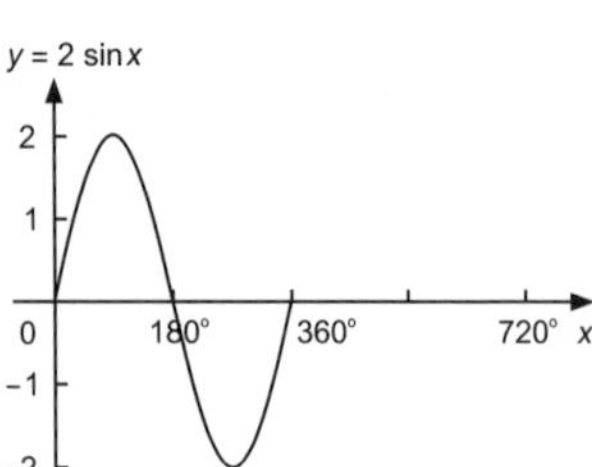

Here is a cycle of the graph of $y = \sin \frac{1}{2}x$. It is $\sin x$ stretched by a factor of 2 in the x-direction and so the cycle now repeats itself every 720° (360°×2).

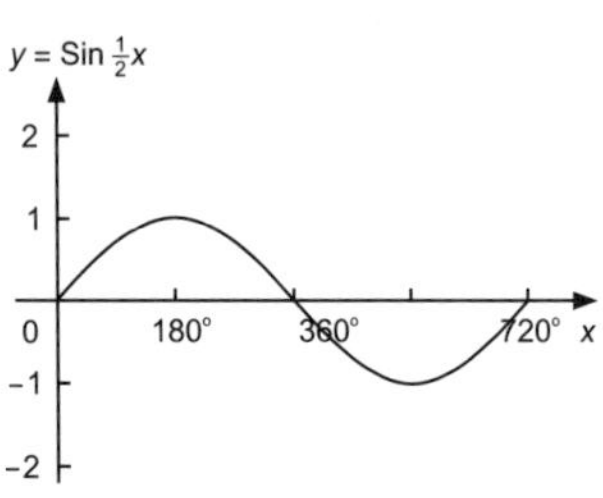

Here is a cycle of the graph of $y = \sin 2x$. It is $\sin x$ stretched by a factor of $\frac{1}{2}$ in the x-direction and so the cycle now repeats itself every 180° (360°÷2).

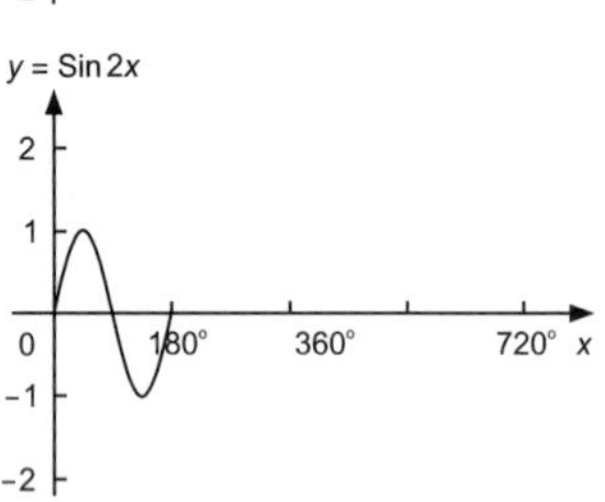

3. Solving Practical Problems

Question *The graph shows the tidal flow in a harbour over a 24-hour period.*

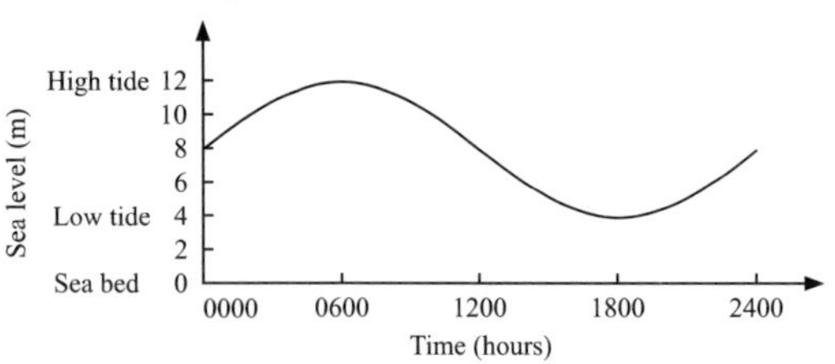

A ship needs 6 m of water to enter the harbour. Between which times is the ship unable to enter the harbour?

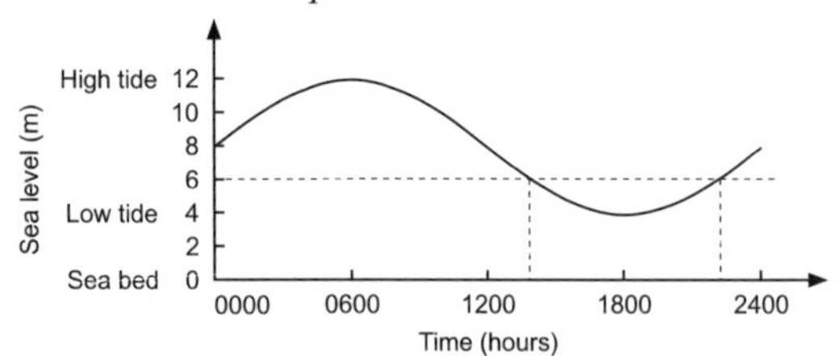

The dashed line shows that the ship cannot enter the harbour between approximately 1330 and 2230 hours.

4. Using Graphs to Solve Trigonometric Equations

Question *Complete the table below and plot the graph of* $y = \cos \frac{1}{2}x$.

x	0°	60°	120°	180°	240°	300°	360°
$y = \cos \frac{1}{2}x$		0.87		0		−0.87	

(a) Use your graph to solve the equation $\cos \frac{1}{2}x = -0.75$.

(b) By drawing a suitable straight line, solve the equation $\cos \frac{1}{2}x = \dfrac{x}{180}$

(a) When $x = 0$, $y = \cos \frac{1}{2}x = \cos \frac{1}{2} \times 0 = \cos 0 = 1$, etc., giving the table below:

x	0°	60°	120°	180°	240°	300°	360°
$y = \cos \frac{1}{2}x$	1	0.87	0.5	0	−0.5	−0.87	−1

Plot these points and join them with a smooth line.

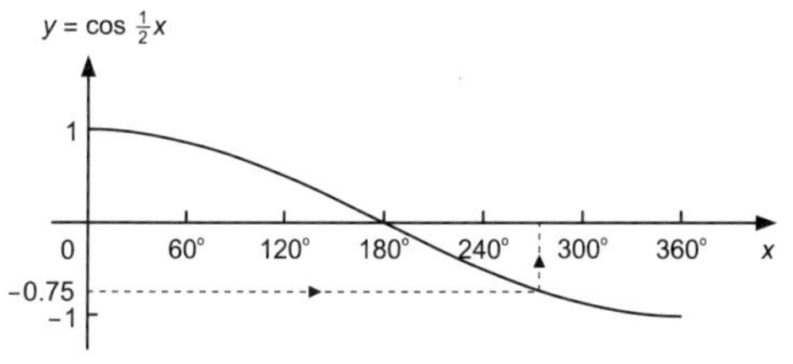

(b) We must solve the equation $\cos \frac{1}{2}x = -0.75$. We have drawn the graph of $y = \cos \frac{1}{2}x$ and so need to find the value of x when $y = -0.75$. Read off this value (see dashed line), giving $x \approx 277°$.

(c) Draw the straight line with equation $y = \dfrac{x}{180}$.

First, make a table of values:

When $x = 0$ $y = \frac{0}{180} = 0$

When $x = 180$ $y = \frac{180}{180} = 1$

When $x = 360$ $y = \frac{360}{180} = 2$

x	0°	180°	360°
$y = \frac{x}{180}$	0	1	2

Draw the straight line and read off the values where it intersects the curve.

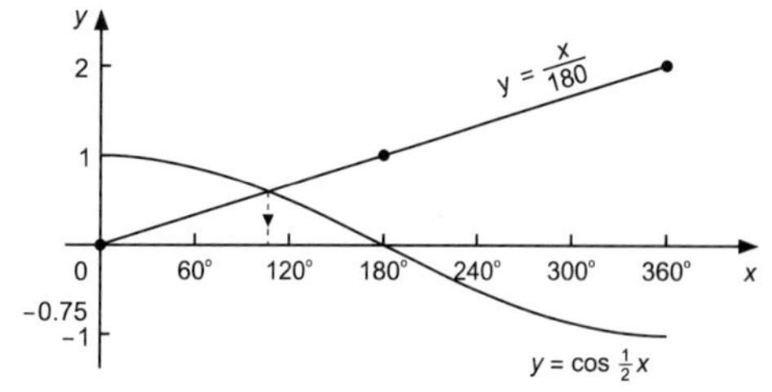

The solution of $\cos \frac{1}{2}x = \dfrac{x}{180}$ is $x \approx 107°$.

Collecting Data

1. Data

Data is information collected from the real world. There are several ways of collecting data:

Counting. For example, counting the number of tomatoes on a tomato plant.

Measuring. For example, measuring the height of children in a classroom.

Asking questions. For example, a questionnaire designed to find out what people think about mobile telephones.

Some data is **numerical**. For example, the numbers of tomatoes on 7 tomato plants: 15 28 7 14 32 21 20

The possible values of **discrete** data increase in steps, e.g. numbers of tomatoes increase by steps of 1. Each dot represents a possible number of tomatoes.

0 1 2 3 4 5

The possible values of **continuous** data increase smoothly, e.g. lengths of leaves. Each dot on the line represents a possible length of a leaf.

25 mm 75 mm

Non-numerical data can often be organised numerically. For example, 50 people were asked 'Do mobile telephones annoy you? YES/NO'. Although 'YES' and 'NO' are not numbers, it was recorded that 20 said 'YES' and 30 said 'NO'.

2. Populations and Samples

The collection of all objects being studied in an investigation is called the **population**.

For example, Katrina investigated the use of contact lenses and spectacles amongst the students of a college. The population under investigation was 'all students studying at the college'.

As the college population was very large, it would have been difficult for Katrina to get information about *every* student. Instead, she chose a **sample** of 60 students from the college population.

Provided her sample was *representative* of the college population and was *large enough*, she could then generalise her findings to the whole college.

Choosing a representative sample from a population

There were twice as many women as men studying at the college. Katrina felt that this aspect of the population should be reflected in the sample of 60 students (perhaps women prefer to wear contact lenses). So she made sure that the sample contained the same proportion of men and women, i.e. 40 women and 20 men. This is called **proportional sampling**.

Katrina enlisted the help of four research assistants to interview the 60 students. She gave each assistant a **quota** of 10 women and 5 men to interview.

It is important that the interviewees are chosen in an *unbiased* way. So each assistant was instructed to stand at a busy part of the college on a Monday morning and approach the first student that walked past. Each assistant was to continue in this way until they had filled their quota of 10 women and 5 men.

Random sample

Someone pointed out to Katrina that many students in the college did not have a chance of being included in her sample. A **random sample** is where *every* member of the population has an *equal chance* of being included.

Katrina thought up a way of choosing a random sample of 40 women and 20 men. Each student in the college had a three digit enrolment number, e.g. 378. She borrowed a **table of random numbers** from the library. Here are the first few numbers:

77803 61872 86245 68220 66267 01379 11304 01658
82404 46728 35228 49673 53552 51215 45611 83927

She read the numbers from left to right in groups of three digits: 778 036 187 286 245 682 etc.

She then wrote down the names of the students with these enrolment numbers, making a list of 40 female students and a list of 20 male students for interviewing. If one of the three digit numbers was not an enrolment number, she ignored it and moved on to the next one. The listed students were then interviewed.

3. Questionnaires

Use these guidelines when designing a questionnaire:

- **Not too many questions (could get boring)**
- **Make it clear how each question should be answered, e.g. tick one of the boxes, circle your preference**
- **Force the person to choose from a limited number of answers. Make sure that you include all possible answers**

  'Do you enjoy studying mathematics?'
  Invites too many possible answers.

  'Do you enjoy studying mathematics?' YES/NO
  Better. Forces a YES or NO answer.

  'Do you enjoy studying mathematics?'
  Not at all A little Quite a lot Very much
  Better still. Covers all degrees of enjoyment.
- **Make sure the question has only one meaning**

  'Do you and your family go to the beach?' YES/NO
  Should you answer YES if you go to the beach on your own, or with your family, or some of your family?
- **The question should be unbiased**

  'Do you agree that TV violence should be banned because it causes violence in teenagers?' YES/NO
  This question is strongly suggesting that violence on TV does in fact cause violence in teenagers.

Frequency Distributions

1. Tally Charts and Frequency Distributions

Tally charts are a convenient way of recording data.

Peter investigated the hair colour of fellow students in a college. He prepared a record sheet like the one below.

Hair colour	
Brown	
Black	
Fair	
Other	

As students entered the college, he made a **tally mark** next to their hair colour. He recorded the hair colour of 60 students, as shown in the table below.

Hair colour	Tally
Brown	卌 卌 卌 卌 II
Black	卌 卌 IIII
Fair	卌 卌 卌 I
Other	卌 III

NOTE 卌 represents a group of 5 students

Peter observed that brown was the most common hair colour.

He replaced the tally marks by numbers, called **frequencies**, which are represented by the letter f. The table of frequencies below is called a **frequency distribution**.

Hair colour	Number of students (Frequency, f)
Brown	22
Black	14
Fair	16
Other	8
Total	60

The table shows that 22 students had brown hair, 14 had black hair, 16 had fair hair and 8 students had some other hair colour. A total of 60 students.

This total can be found by adding together the frequencies in the table. The total frequency is represented by the letter n. In this example, $n = 60$.

Question *Eugenia investigated the number of occupants of cars passing her school. She prepared the record sheet below and recorded a tally mark for each car passing the school.*

Number of occupants	Tally
1	卌 卌 卌 III
2	卌 卌 卌
3	卌 卌 I
4	卌 I

(a) Make a frequency distribution table for the data.
(b) How many cars did she record altogether?
(c) Suggest a way in which the record sheet could be improved.
(d) Eugenia noticed that the most common number of occupants was 1. She concluded that most cars are travelling around almost empty. Give a reason why this might not be true.

(a) Replace the tally marks by numbers (frequencies).

Number of occupants	Number of cars (Frequency, f)
1	18
2	15
3	11
4	6
Total	50

(b) The total number of cars Eugenia recorded is 50, found by adding up the frequencies.

(c) A large car could have 5 or more occupants and so Eugenia should have included this category in her record sheet.

(d) Some of the drivers may be parents who have just taken their children to school. Another way of describing the data is to say that most of the cars had 2 or more occupants. This gives a different impression.

2. Grouped Frequency Distributions

Ms French recorded the number of minutes it took her to drive to work over a period of 30 days. The results are shown below.

31 37 49 25 35 33 39 29 25 43
41 45 32 33 33 27 43 20 35 39
37 38 44 35 32 38 37 30 31 44

The values range from 20 to 49 minutes. This range could be divided into smaller **classes** (or **intervals**) of values. The class 20–24 contains the values 20, 21, 22, 23 and 24. We say that the values have been **grouped** into classes.

Classes
20–24
25–29
30–34
35–39
40–44
45–49

Each recorded time can be placed into one of these classes using a tally mark.

Time (min)	Tally
20-24	I
25-29	IIII
30-34	卌 III
35-39	卌 卌
40-44	卌
45-49	II

Replacing the tally marks by frequency numbers gives the **grouped frequency distribution**, as shown in this table.

Time (min)	No. of journeys
20-24	1
25-29	4
30-34	8
35-39	10
40-44	5
45-49	2
Total	30

more

Frequency Distributions (Contd)

2. Grouped Frequency Distributions (Cont)

Question *A fisherman's catch is recorded in the table below.*

Weight, w (kg)	Number of fish
$0.5 \leqslant w < 1.0$	75
$1.0 \leqslant w < 2.0$	150
$2.0 \leqslant w < 3.0$	90
$3.0 \leqslant w < 4.0$	45
$4.0 \leqslant w < 5.0$	25

(a) How many fish did he catch altogether?
(b) How many fish weighed between 1.0 kg and 3.0 kg?
(c) One fish weighed exactly 3.0 kg. Which class contains this weight?

(a) Add up the frequencies (numbers of fish) in the right column:
Total no. of fish = 75+150+90+45+25 = 385

(b) 150 fish weighed between 1.0 kg and 2.0 kg.
90 fish weighed between 2.0 kg and 3.0 kg.
So, 150+90 = 240 fish weighed between 1.0 kg and 3.0 kg.

(c) A weight of 3.0 kg is contained in the class $3.0 \leqslant w < 4.0$, because the sign $\leqslant$ means 'less than or *equal* to'. It is ***not*** contained in the class $2.0 \leqslant w < 3.0$, because the sign < means 'less than'.

Illustrating Data

1. Illustrating Data

Data can be illustrated using a variety of diagrams: pictograms, bar charts, line charts, pie charts, graphs, histograms, cumulative frequency diagrams. You will usually be asked to draw one of these, but sometimes you may have to choose an appropriate diagram for the given data.

2. Pictograms

A **pictogram** uses a symbol to represent a unit of data, e.g. 10 men. The symbol is usually related to the data, e.g. the symbol 웃 might represent 10 men

Question *The table shows the methods of transport used by the employees of a company. Illustrate this data using a pictogram.*

Mode of transport	Number of employees
Car	40
Train	15
Bus	7
Bicycle	2

Using the symbol 웃 to represent 5 employees, the pictogram for the data is:

Car 웃웃웃웃웃웃웃웃
Train 웃웃웃
Bus 웃 (part)
Bicycle (part)

Some of the symbols are incomplete, representing less than 5 employees.

3. Bar Charts and Line Charts

A vertical (or horizontal) bar can be used to represent the amount of data in a category: the taller the bar, the more data it represents. The bars are of equal width and are separated from each other by narrow gaps. Lines can be used instead of bars.

Question *The table below shows the distribution of accommodation in Greater London during 1995.*

Owner occupied	Council housing	Housing association	Privately rented
56%	22%	7%	15%

Illustrate this data using a suitable chart.

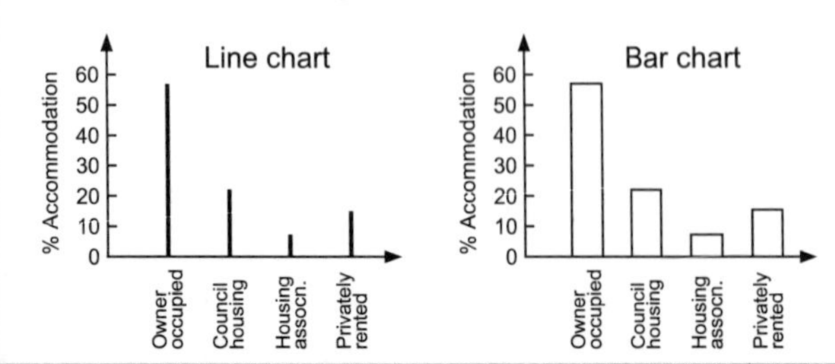

Question *100 students each took two exam papers in science. The bar chart shows the distribution of marks in both papers.*

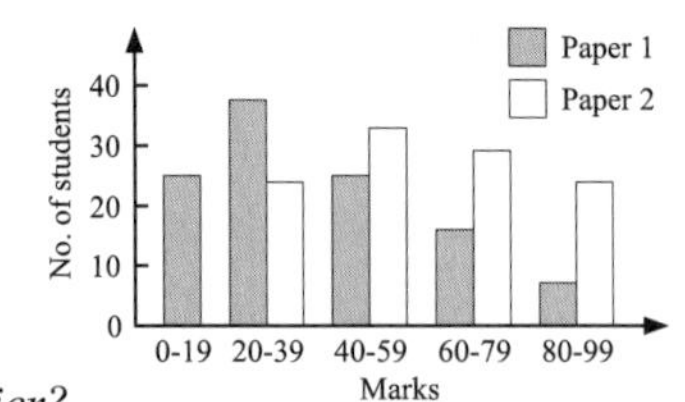

(a) Which paper was easier?
(b) In which exam was there a greater spread of marks?
(c) How many students scored 40 to 59 marks in Paper 2?

(a) Paper 2 appears to have been easier because more students got high marks (40 or more) than in Paper 1 (the white bars are higher than the shaded bars).

(b) The shaded bars show that students scored between 0 and 99 in Paper 1. But the white bars show they scored between 20 and 99 in Paper 2. So, the spread of marks is higher for Paper 1.

(c) The white bar for class 40–59 has a height of 33, so 33 students scored between 40 and 59 in Paper 2.

Illustrating Data

4. Pie Charts

A **pie chart** uses a circle to represent the total data. Each category of data is represented by a sector of the circle.

Question *Chantal's weekly expenditure is illustrated in the pie chart below. She spends £12 per week altogether.*
(a) How much does she spend on fares?
(b) How much does she spend on clothes?
(c) Measure the angle of the Entertainment sector.
(d) How much does she spend on entertainment?

(a) The whole circle represents £12.
There are 360° in a whole circle.
The angle of the Fares sector is 90°, which is $\frac{1}{4}$ of the whole circle ($\frac{90}{360} = \frac{1}{4}$).
So, money spent on fares = $\frac{1}{4}$ of £12 = £3

(b) The angle for the Clothes sector is 60°.
So, money spent on clothes = $\frac{60}{360}$ of £12
= 60÷360×£12 = £2

(c) Carefully measure the angle for the Entertainment sector to be 135°.

(d) Money spent on entertainment
= $\frac{135}{360}$ of £12 = 135÷360×£12 = £4.50

Question *Complete the pie chart for the distribution of British people living abroad.*

Location	Percentage
Asia & Australia	30
Africa	15
Middle East	15
Contintental Europe	20
Americas	20

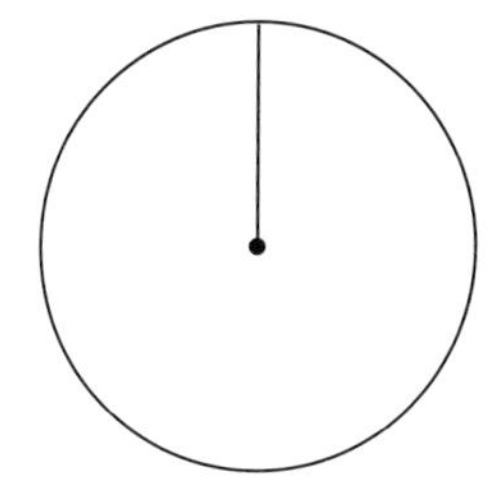

There are 360° in a circle. So:
Asia & Australia = 30% of a circle
= 30% of 360° = 30÷100×360° = 108°
Repeating this calculation for the other locations, we get:

Location	%	Angle
Asia & Australia	30	108°
Africa	15	54°
Middle East	15	54°
Contintental Europe	20	72°
Americas	20	72°

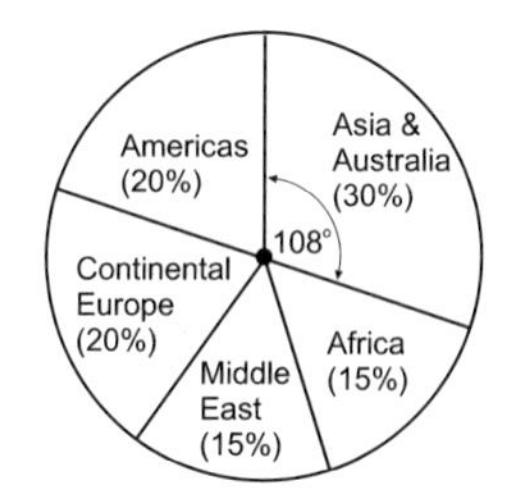

Place the centre of your protractor on the centre of the circle, aligning 0° with the given radius. Mark an angle of 108° and draw a new radius, labelling the sector 'Asia & Australia (30%)'. Repeat for the other locations.

Histograms

1. Histograms

A **histogram** is like a bar chart. The main differences are:

- There are no gaps between the bars.
- The horizontal axis has a continuous scale, just like a graph, e.g. 1 cm = 20 kg.
- The **areas** of the bars represent the frequencies (see Box 2).

Question *A student investigated the lengths of worms in the topsoil of an allotment. She measured the lengths of 115 worms and recorded them in the frequency distribution table. Draw a histogram to illustrate this data.*

Length (cm)	No. of worms
0–5	20
5–10	45
10–15	20
15–20	15
20–25	10
25–30	5
Total	115

The horizontal axis represents the recorded values (length of worms in cm). Mark the axis from 0 to 30 cm.

The vertical axis represents the frequencies (numbers of worms). Mark the axis from 0 to 45, the greatest number of worms in the table.

All the classes have the *same width*, 5 cm. For example, the width of the class 10–15 cm is 5 cm, as shown in the diagram below:

15–10 = 5 cm
5 10 15 20

When all of the classes have the same width, make the height of each bar equal to the frequency of the class it represents.

Draw a bar above each class, with height equal to the frequency of the class. For example, the bar for the class 10–15 cm should have a height of 20.

NOTE The side of the first bar is part of the y-axis and there should be no gaps between the bars.

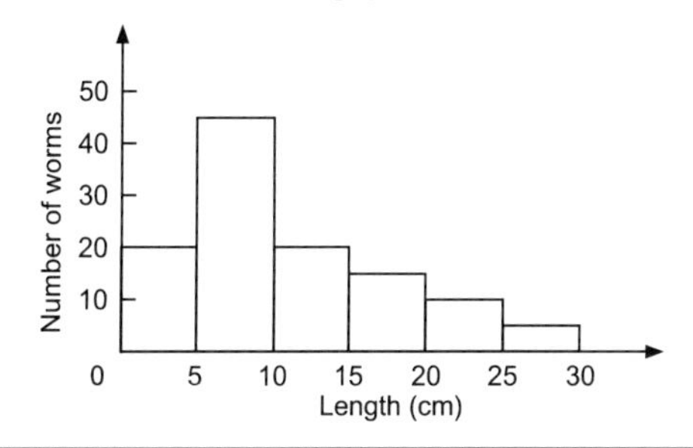

Histograms (Contd)

2. Histograms and Unequal Classes

When the class widths are unequal, the *areas* of the bars must be used to represent the frequencies.

Question *The weights of 60 rice portions from a Chinese take-away were measured and recorded in the table. Draw a histogram to illustrate this distribution.*

Weight, w (g)	No. of portions
$0 \leqslant w < 30$	6
$30 \leqslant w < 50$	14
$50 \leqslant w < 60$	20
$60 \leqslant w < 70$	12
$70 \leqslant w < 90$	8
Total	60

The class $0 \leqslant w < 30$ has a width of 30 g, whereas the class $30 \leqslant w < 50$ has a width of 20 g. So, the classes have different widths and we cannot simply make the heights of the bars equal to the frequencies.

Instead, we must make sure that the *area* of a bar represents the frequency of its class:

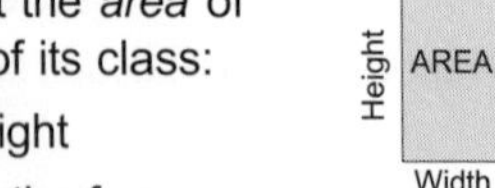

Area of a bar = Width × Height

But the area of a bar represents the frequency of the class and so the formula becomes:

Frequency = Class width × Bar height

Rearranging this formula, we get:

$$\text{Bar Height} = \frac{\text{Frequency}}{\text{Class width}}$$

The heights of the bars calculated in this way are called **frequency densities**.

Use this formula to calculate the bar height for each of the classes in the table of values.

Weight w (g)	Class width	No. of portions (Frequency)	Bar height (Frequency density)
$0 \leqslant w < 30$	30	6	0.2
$30 \leqslant w < 50$	20	14	0.7
$50 \leqslant w < 60$	10	20	2.0
$60 \leqslant w < 70$	10	12	1.2
$70 \leqslant w < 90$	20	8	0.4

Draw the histogram using these bar heights, choosing an easy scale for the y-axis.

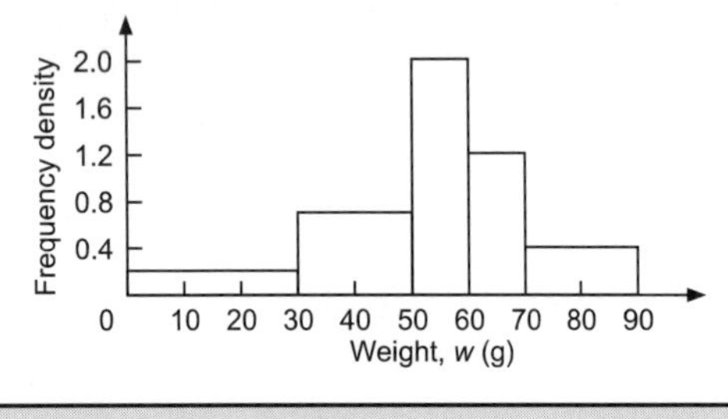

Question *The histogram below shows the distribution of spectators at professional football matches in England on a Saturday in 1993.*

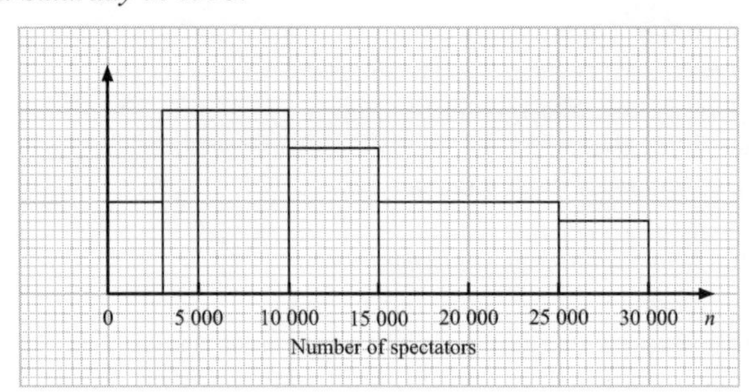

Use the information in the histogram to complete the frequency table.

No. of spectators	No. of matches
$0 \leqslant n < 3000$	
$3000 \leqslant n < 5000$	
$5000 \leqslant n < 10\,000$	10
$10\,000 \leqslant n < 15\,000$	
$15\,000 \leqslant n < 25\,000$	
$25\,000 \leqslant n < 30\,000$	

Remember that the area of a bar represents the frequency of its class. The area of the bar for the class $5000 \leqslant n < 10\,000$ is 1 cm × 2 cm = 2 cm^2 and the frequency for this class is 10. So:

2 cm^2 represents a frequency of 10

$\therefore$ 1 cm^2 represents a frequency of $10 \div 2 = 5$

Now we can calculate the areas of the other bars and convert them to frequencies.

For the class $0 \leqslant n < 3000$:

Area of bar = $0.6 \times 1 = 0.6$ cm^2 which represents a frequency of $0.6 \times 5 = 3$

Repeating this calculation for the other classes gives the remaining frequencies.

No. of Spectators	No. of Matches
$0 \leqslant n < 3000$	3
$3000 \leqslant n < 5000$	4
$5000 \leqslant n < 10\,000$	10
$10\,000 \leqslant n < 15\,000$	8
$15\,000 \leqslant n < 25\,000$	10
$25\,000 \leqslant n < 30\,000$	4

3. Frequency Polygons

Joining the mid-points of the tops of the bars of a histogram with straight lines makes a **frequency polygon**. It gives a good impression of the shape of the histogram.

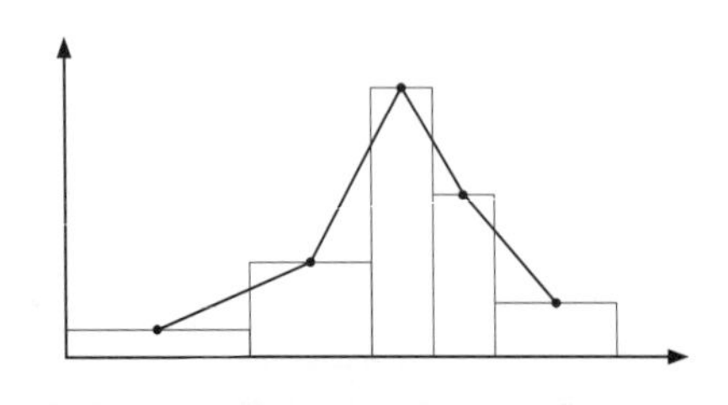

4. Shape of a Frequency Distribution

The shape of a frequency distribution is the shape of its frequency polygon. The diagram below shows three shapes you should know.

NORMAL	POSITIVELY SKEWED	NEGATIVELY SKEWED
A normal distribution has a symmetrical shape with most values clustered around the centre	Not symmetrical. The longer right tail represents a few extremely large values, compared to the centre	Not symmetrical. The longer left tail represents a few extremely small values, compared to the centre

Averages

1. Averages

There are three ways of finding the average of a set of numbers: mean, median and mode. You need to be able to calculate all three.

2. Mode and Modal Class

The **mode** is the most frequently occurring value.

The mode of this set of numbers is 5 because it occurs more frequently than the others.

2 3 3 5 5 5 7 9 (5 5 5: Mode)

A student recorded the numbers of occupants travelling in 50 cars. The most frequent number of occupants is 1. We say that the mode is 1 occupant per car (or the modal number of occupants is 1).

No. of occupants	No. of cars
Mode 1	20
2	15
3	9
4	6

The **modal class** (or **modal interval**) is the class with the highest frequency. The numbers of words on the pages of a book are recorded in this table. The modal class is 360–379 words because this class has the highest frequency, 65.

No. of words	No. of pages
300–319	25
320–339	39
340–359	48
360–379	65
380–399	58

The mode does ***not*** tell you anything about the other values. Both these sets of numbers have a mode of 5 and yet their other values are very different.

2 3 3 5 5 5 7 9

5 5 5 10 50 100 200

3. Median

The **median** of a set of values is the middle value after all the values have been put in ascending order of size.

Janet recorded the number of dental fillings in 5 of her classmates, as shown below:

Number of fillings 7 4 8 3 6

She rearranged the values from smallest to largest:

3 4 6 7 8

(6: Median)

She could then see that the middle number is 6. We say that the median is 6 fillings per child.

A sixth classmate had 16 fillings! The values are now:

3 4 6 7 8 16

(Median between 6 and 7)

The median is now halfway between the middle two values 6 and 7, and so is 6.5.

Notice that half (50%) of the values lie below the median and half (50%) lie above it.

Notice also that adding a large value, like 16, to the data has only slightly affected the median: it was 6 and is now 6.5. Very large and very small values are called **extreme values**.

4. Median of a Frequency Distribution

Question *In an experiment, 50 people were asked to estimate the length of a rod, to the nearest centimetre. The results are recorded in the table below:*

Length (cm)	8	9	10	11	12	13	14	15	16
No. of people	3	4	6	6	9	13	7	2	0

Calculate the median for the data.

Imagine the 50 estimated lengths in the table spread out from smallest to largest

8	8	8	9	9	9	....	?	?	....	14	14	14	14	15	15
1st	2nd	3rd	4th	5th	6th		25th	26th		45th	46th	47th	48th	49th	50th

(Median between 25th and 26th)

The median lies halfway between the 25th and 26th values.

Add up the frequencies from left to right until you reach the 25th and 26th values:

3rd value is 8

3+4 = 7th value is 9

3+4+6 = 13th value is 10

3+4+6+6 = 19th value is 11

3+4+6+6+9 = 28th value is 12

So, the 25th and 26th values must both be 12. The median is therefore halfway between 12 and 12, which is 12.

5. Mean

The **mean** of a set of values is found by adding them up and dividing the total by the number of values.

$$\text{Mean} = \frac{\text{Total of values}}{\text{Number of values}}$$

Question *Rachna took a typing speed test. She typed 5 pages as fast as possible. The numbers of errors on the 5 pages are shown below:*

3 2 0 1 5

Calculate the mean number of errors per page.

$$\text{Mean} = \frac{\text{Total of values}}{\text{Number of values}}$$

$$= \frac{3+2+0+1+5}{5} = \frac{11}{5} = 2.2 \text{ errors per page}$$

NOTE The mean may not be a possible value. In this example, it is impossible to make 2.2 typing errors.

Rachna was then asked to type a sixth page and made 25 mistakes (due to nerves). Her results are now:

3 2 0 1 5 25

We can now recalculate the mean:

$$\text{Mean} = \frac{3+2+0+1+5+25}{6} = \frac{36}{6} = 6 \text{ errors per page}$$

Adding this single, extremely large value has had a considerable effect on the mean, dragging it up from 2.2 to 6 errors per page.

more

Averages (Contd)

5. Mean (Contd)

Question *A greengrocer counted the numbers of potatoes in 5 bags and calculated their mean to be 46 potatoes per bag.*

(a) Calculate the total number of potatoes contained in the 5 bags.

(b) He counted the potatoes in another 2 bags and found them both to contain 52 potatoes. Calculate the mean number of potatoes for all 7 bags.

(a) Mean = $\dfrac{\text{Total number of potatoes}}{\text{Number of bags}}$

$\therefore$ 46 = $\dfrac{\text{Total number of potatoes}}{5}$

$\therefore$ 46×5 = Total number of potatoes

$\therefore$ Total number of potatoes = 230

(b) Total potatoes in all 7 bags = 230+52+52 = 334
So, mean = $334 \div 7$ = 47.7 potatoes per bag

6. Mean of a Frequency Distribution

Question *The frequency distribution table below shows the numbers of occupants of houses living in a certain area. Calculate the mean number of occupants per house.*

No. of occupants	0	1	2	3	4	5	6	7
No. of houses	2	8	15	34	48	41	22	16

① First, make sure you know what the numbers in the table mean.

The numbers in the top row are the **possible values** (the possible numbers of occupants living in a house).

The numbers in the bottom row are the **frequencies** (how often each value occurs).

② Calculate the total number of values (the total frequency).

There is a value (number of occupants) for each house. So:

Total no. of values = Total no.of houses
= Total frequency
= 2+8+15+34+48+41+22+16
= 186

③ Calculate the total of the values.

There are 2 values of 0; these total $2 \times 0 = 0$
There are 8 values of 1; these total $8 \times 1 = 8$
There are 15 values of 2; these total $15 \times 2 = 30$
etc.

Total of values
= $2\times0+8\times1+15\times2+34\times3+48\times4+41\times5+22\times6+16\times7$
= 781

④ Calculate the mean.

Mean = $\dfrac{\text{Total of values}}{\text{Number of values}}$

= $\dfrac{781}{186}$ = 4.2 occupants per house

7. Mean of a Grouped Frequency Distribution

Question *833 people took a new kind of IQ test. Their results are recorded in the table. Calculate the mean IQ per person.*

IQ score	No. of people
60–79	52
80–99	145
100–119	392
120–139	165
140–159	58
160–179	21

The problem with calculating the mean here is that we do not know any values precisely. For example, we know that 52 people scored between 60 and 79 but we do not know their exact IQ scores. To get around this problem, we replace the class of scores 60–79 by its middle value, called the **mid–class value**. This can be found by adding the upper and lower class limits together and dividing by 2. For the class 60–79:

Mid–class value = $\dfrac{60+79}{2} = \dfrac{139}{2} = 69.5$

The table shows all of the mid–class values.

We can now calculate the mean using the method described in Box 6.

Mid–class value	No. of people (Frequency)
69.5	52
89.5	145
109.5	392
129.5	165
149.5	58
169.5	21

Number of values = Total frequency
= 52+145+392+165+58+21
= 833 Also given in question

Total of values = $52\times69.5+145\times89.5+....+21\times169.5$
= 93 113.5

$\therefore$ Mean IQ = $\dfrac{\text{Total of values}}{\text{Number of values}}$

= $\dfrac{93\,113.5}{833} \approx 111.8$ per person

8. Using a Calculator

You can use the statistics mode of your calculator to find the mean of a frequency distribution and are less likely to make mistakes. However, you must still show the examiner how the mean is calculated.

Let's recalculate the mean of the distribution in Box 6, using a calculator.

First, put your calculator into **statistics mode**. See your instruction manual.

Now enter the first value, 0, and the frequency with which it occurs, 2. See your instruction manual.

Repeat this for all the values.

Press [n] to find the number of values entered (the total frequency). In this example, this is the total number of houses. You should get 186.

Press [Σx] to find the total of the values. You should get 781.

Press [$\bar{x}$] to find the mean. You should get 4.199.

Write down the working shown in Box 6, using these values obtained from your calculator.

NOTE If you do not show your working and calculate the wrong answer, you will get no marks.

9. Comparing Mean, Median and Mode

Mean and median

The mean and median have been calculated for the values below:

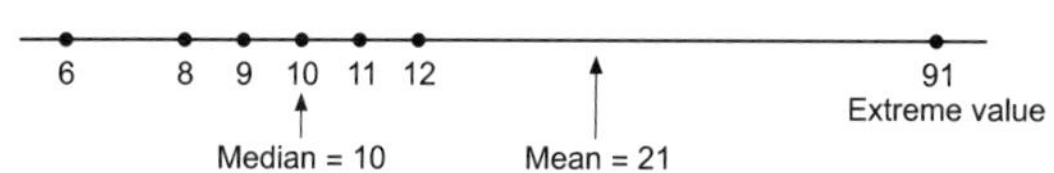

The median is the middle value, 10. The mean is greater than the median because of the extremely large value of 91 being included in its calculation.

The mean is greater than the median when the distribution is positively skewed (see Box 4, p104). The mode lies beneath the highest point of the curve.

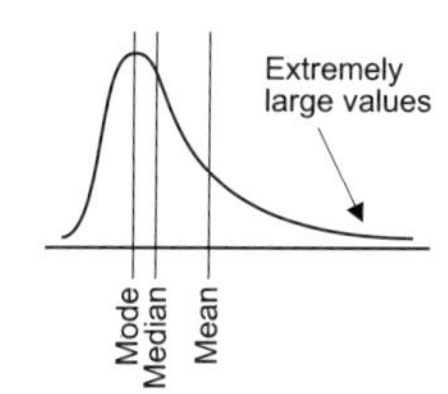

Similarly, if there are extremely small values (negatively skewed distribution), the mean will be less than the median

Mode

The mode only tells you which value occurs the most often. It tells you nothing about the other values (except that they occur less often).

You ***cannot*** calculate the mode by knowing the mean and median. You have to look at the values themselves. The two sets of values below have the same mean and median but completely different modes.

1 1 5 6 8 10 11 Mode = 1

Mean & Median

1 2 5 6 8 10 10 Mode = 10

Question *The table shows the mean and median heights of Jane's and Bill's friends. Jane says that Bill's friends are taller than her friends. Explain why this may not be true.*

	Mean height (cm)	Median height (cm)
Jane's friends	175	175
Bill's friends	180	175

The median height of Bill's friends is 175 cm and so half of his friends are shorter than 175 cm.

The median height of Jane's friends is also 175 cm and so half of her friends are taller than 175 cm.

So, half of Jane's friends are taller than half of Bill's friends. So, not all of Bill's friends are taller than Jane's.

Measures of Spread

1. Spread of Values

In an experiment at a health clinic, two methods of weight reduction were tried by different groups of people.

Group A were simply given a diet sheet.

Group B were given the same diet sheet and met once a week to give each other support.

The weight losses, in lb, for both groups are shown below:

Group A	0	1	2	4	6	8	10	11	12
Group B	4	5	5	6	6	6	7	7	8

Staff at the clinic calculated the mean weight loss for both groups and found them both to be 6 lb. So it appeared that the two methods had the same effect.

However, they noticed that the weight losses in Group A were more widely spread than those in Group B.

The clinic staff reasoned that the people in Group B ate in a more similar way than those in Group A because of their influence on each other at the weekly meetings.

There are three ways of measuring how spread out the values are: **range**, **standard deviation** (and **variance**) and **interquartile range**.

2. Range

The **range** of a set of values is simply the difference between the smallest and largest values. Here are the values from Groups A and B in Box 1:

Group A	0	1	2	4	6	8	10	11	12
Group B	4	5	5	6	6	6	7	7	8

Range for Group A = 12−0 = 12 lb

Range for Group B = 8−4 = 4 lb

The greater range for Group A reflects the greater spread of values.

3. Standard Deviation and Variance

H

The standard deviation is based on the differences (**deviations**) between the values and their mean.

Here are the values for Groups A and B in Box 1. Each dot represents a value:

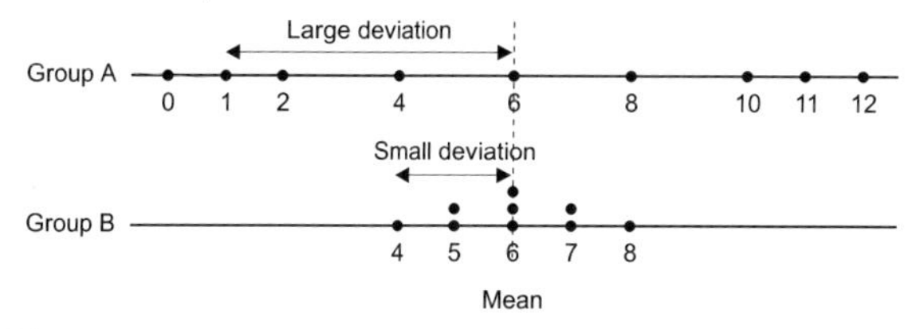

You can see that the deviations from the mean in Group A are greater, overall, than those in Group B.

more

Measures of Spread (Contd)

3. Standard Deviation & Variance (Contd)

The following steps show how to calculate the standard deviation for Group A.

Group A 0 1 2 4 6 8 10 11 12

Let x represent any value.

① Calculate the mean of the values and call it $\bar{x}$.

$$\text{Mean} = \bar{x} = \frac{0+1+2+4+6+8+10+11+12}{9} = \frac{54}{9} = 6$$

② Square the mean, giving $\bar{x}^2$.

$\bar{x} = 6$ and so $\bar{x}^2 = 6^2 = 36$

③ Square each value of x.

x	0	1	2	4	6	8	10	11	12
x^2	0	1	4	16	36	64	100	121	144

④ Add up the squares and call the sum $\sum x^2$.

Sum of squares = $\sum x^2 = 0+1+4+....+144 = 486$

⑤ Divide the sum of the squares, $\sum x^2$, by the number of values, n.

Number of values = $n = 9$

So, $\frac{\sum x^2}{n} = \frac{486}{9} = 54$

⑥ Subtract the square of the mean, $\bar{x}^2$, from $\frac{\sum x^2}{n}$. The result is called the **variance,** represented by s^2.

$$\text{Variance} = s^2 = \frac{\sum x^2}{n} - \bar{x}^2 = 54 - 36 = 18$$

⑦ Square root the variance to give the **standard deviation**, represented by s.

$$\text{Standard deviation} = s = \sqrt{\text{Variance}} = \sqrt{18} = 4.2 \text{ lb}$$

The standard deviation for group B was calculated in the same way and found to be 1.2 lb, which shows that the values of Group A are more spread out than those of Group B.

4. Standard Deviation of a Frequency Distribution

H

Question *The table below shows the numbers and costs of surgical operations at a hospital during a one month period. The mean cost of an operation was calculated to be £4810. Calculate the standard deviation, correct to the nearest £100.*

Type of operation	Number of operations	Cost of operation (£)
Plastic surgery	3	2000
Varicose veins	3	4500
Knee replacement	1	5200
Hip replacement	3	7800

① Mean = $\bar{x}$ = £4810 Given in the question

② Square of mean = $\bar{x}^2 = 4810^2 = 23\,136\,100$

③ Square each value, x, giving x^2.

Type of operation	Number of operations, f	Cost of operation, x	x^2
Plastic surgery	3	2000	4 000 000
Varicose veins	3	4500	20 250 000
Knee replacement	1	5200	27 040 000
Hip replacement	3	7800	60 840 000

more

4. Standard Deviation of a Frequency Distribution (Contd)

④ Multiply each square, x^2, by its frequency, f, giving fx^2.

Type of operation	Number of operations, f	Cost of operation, x	x^2	fx^2
Plastic surgery	3	2000	4 000 000	12 000 000
Varicose veins	3	4500	20 250 000	60 750 000
Knee replacement	1	5200	27 040 000	27 040 000
Hip replacement	3	7800	60 840 000	182 520 000

Sum of squares = $\sum fx^2$ = 282 310 000

⑤ Calculate the sum of squares, $\sum fx^2$.

Sum of squares = $\sum fx^2 = 282\,310\,000$
(See table above)

⑥ Divide the sum of the squares, $\sum fx^2$, by the number of values, n (total frequency).

Number of values = $n = 3+3+1+3 = 10$

So, $\frac{\sum fx^2}{n} = \frac{282\,310\,000}{10} = 28\,231\,000$

⑦ Subtract the square of the mean, $\bar{x}^2$, from $\frac{\sum fx^2}{n}$ to give the variance, s^2.

$$\text{Variance} = s^2 = \frac{\sum fx^2}{n} - \bar{x}^2$$
$$= 28\,231\,000 - 23\,136\,100$$
$$= 5\,094\,900$$

⑧ Square root the variance to give the standard deviation, s.

$$\text{Standard deviation} = s = \sqrt{\text{Variance}}$$
$$= \sqrt{5\,094\,900}$$
$$= 2257$$
$$\approx £2300$$

5. Standard Deviation of a Grouped Frequency Distribution

H

Question *Calculate the standard deviation of the IQ scores recorded in this table.*

IQ score	No. of people
60–79	52
80–99	145
100–119	392
120–139	165
140–159	58
160–179	21
Total	833

① Calculate the mid-class values (see Box 7, p106).

② Calculate the mean, $\bar{x}$, of these mid-class values.

The mean IQ was found to be $\bar{x} = 111.8$ in Box 7 on page 105

Mid-class value	No. of people (Frequency, f)
69.5	52
89.5	145
109.5	392
129.5	165
149.5	58
169.5	21
Total	833

③ Square the mean.

$\bar{x}^2 = 111.8^2 = 12\,499.2$

④ Square each mid-class value, x, giving x^2.

Mid-class value, x	x^2	No. of people (Frequency, f)
69.5	4830.25	52
89.5	8010.25	145
109.5	11 990.25	392
129.5	16 770.25	165
149.5	22 350.25	58
169.5	28 730.25	21

more

5. Standard Deviation of a Grouped Frequency Distribution (Contd)

⑤ Multiply each square, x^2, by its frequency, f, giving fx^2.

Mid-class value, x	x^2	No. of people (Frequency, f)	fx^2
69.5	4830.25	52	251 173
89.5	8010.25	145	1 161 486.3
109.5	11 990.25	392	4 700 178
129.5	16 770.25	165	2 767 091.3
149.5	22 350.25	58	1 296 314.5
169.5	28 730.25	21	603 335.25
		$\sum fx^2 =$	10 779 578

⑥ Calculate the sum of squares, $\sum fx^2$.

$\sum fx^2 = 10\,779\,578$ (See table above)

⑦ Divide the sum of the squares, $\sum fx^2$, by the number of values, n (total frequency).

Number of values = n = 833 (See table in question)

So, $\dfrac{\sum fx^2}{n} = \dfrac{10\,779\,578}{833} = 12\,940.7$

⑧ Subtract the square of the mean, $\bar{x}^2$, from $\frac{\sum fx^2}{n}$ to give the variance, s^2.

$$\text{Variance} = s^2 = \frac{\sum fx^2}{n} - \bar{x}^2$$
$$= 12\,940.7 - 12\,499.2$$
$$= 441.5$$

⑨ Square root the variance to give the standard deviation, s.

$$\text{Standard deviation} = s = \sqrt{\text{Variance}}$$
$$= \sqrt{441.5}$$
$$= 21.0 \text{ (1 dp)}$$

6. Special Problem

H

You may be asked how changing the values affects their mean and standard deviation.

Question *Five people invested £1000 in different bank accounts. At the end of 1 year, the bank accounts contained the following amounts:*

£1080 £1100 £1120 £1125 £1130

The mean amount was calculated to be £1111 and the standard deviation was £18.55. The sum of £1000 was subtracted from each amount to calculate the interest earned during the year. Calculate

(a) the mean interest earned

(b) the standard deviation of the interest earned.

(a) Increasing/decreasing every value by the same amount has the same effect on their mean.

Each amount has been reduced by £1000 and so the mean £1111 will also be reduced by £1000

So, mean interest earned = £1111−£1000 = £111

(b) Increasing/decreasing every value by the same amount has no effect on the standard deviation

The standard deviation of the amounts is £18.55

Reducing the amounts by £1000 has no effect on the standard deviation.

So, the standard deviation of the interest earned is also £18.55.

7. Comparing Distributions

Question *Two machines, A and B, were set to cut broom handles to a length of 180 cm. As part of a quality control check, 40 broom handles were taken from each machine and measured. The results are shown below together with their histograms. Comment on the performance of the machines.*

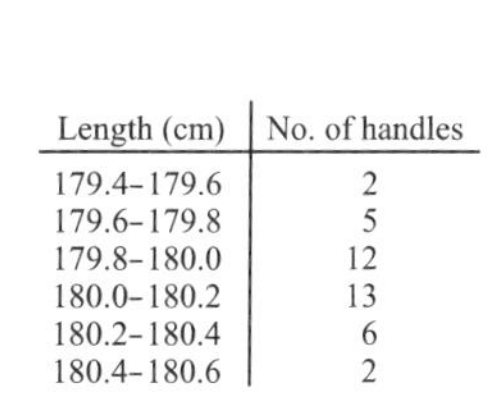

Length (cm)	No. of handles
179.4-179.6	2
179.6-179.8	5
179.8-180.0	12
180.0-180.2	13
180.2-180.4	6
180.4-180.6	2

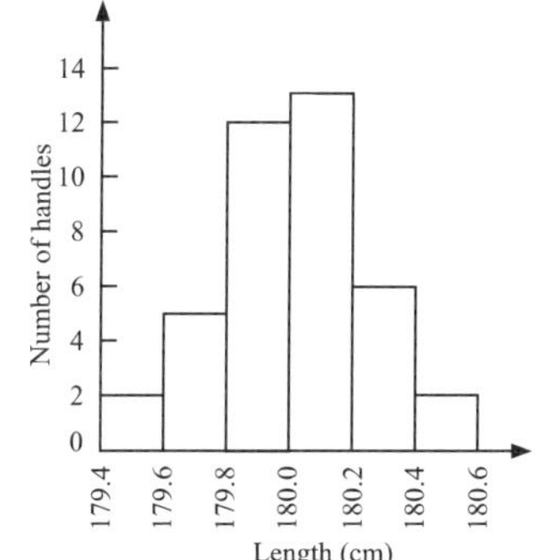

Machine B

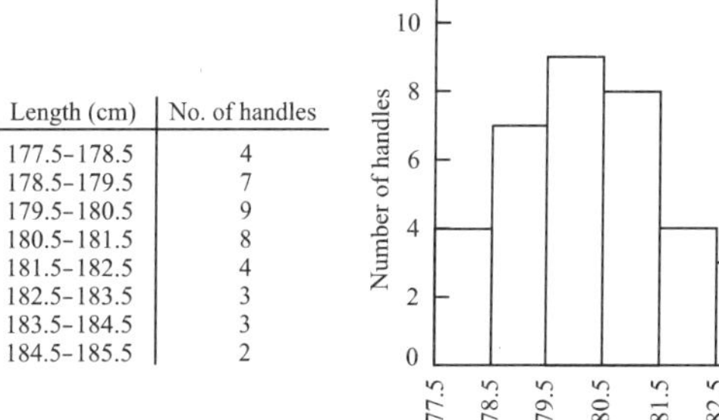

Length (cm)	No. of handles
177.5-178.5	4
178.5-179.5	7
179.5-180.5	9
180.5-181.5	8
181.5-182.5	4
182.5-183.5	3
183.5-184.5	3
184.5-185.5	2

Machine A is working well, producing handles with lengths close to 180 cm. The lengths are not spread very much; the difference between the lowest and highest class limits is 180.6−179.4 cm = 1.2 cm (this is the maximum possible range of the values). The shape of the distribution is symmetrical and so the machine is producing a similar number of handles above and below 180 cm.

Machine B needs overhauling. The machine is producing a wide range of handle lengths; the difference between the lowest and highest class limits is 185.5−177.5 = 8 cm. The modal class (see tallest bar) is 179.5-180.5 cm and contains the machine setting of 180 cm. However, the shape of the distribution is positively skewed and so the mean and median handle lengths are above 180 cm (see Box 9. p107). This shows that the machine is producing more handles above 180 cm than below 180 cm.

Cumulative Frequency

1. Cumulative Frequency

The speeds of cars (mph) travelling along a main road are recorded in this table.

Speed (mph)	No. of cars (Frequency)
0–20	4
20–30	13
30–40	52
40–50	75
50–60	40
60–70	16
Total	200

This table shows that:

4 cars travelled at speeds between 0 and 20 mph
13 cars travelled at speeds between 20 and 30 mph
52 cars travelled at speeds between 30 and 40 mph
and so on

From this table we can deduce that:

4 cars travelled at speeds less than 20 mph
4+13 = 17 cars travelled at less than 30 mph
4+13+52= 69 cars travelled at less than 40 mph
and so on

Adding up the frequencies like this gives the so-called **cumulative frequencies** 4, 17, 69, ... These are summarised in the table below:

Speed (mph)	No. of cars (Cumulative frequency)
Less than 20	4
Less than 30	17
Less than 40	69
Less than 50	144
Less than 60	184
Less than 70	200

This table tells us, for example, that 144 cars travelled at speeds less than 50 mph.

2. Cumulative Frequency Curve

We can plot a graph of the cumulative frequencies in Box 1. Make sure that:

- The graph starts where the axes cross
- The points are joined with a smooth curve

This graph is called a **cumulative frequency curve** (or **ogive**) and has an S shape.

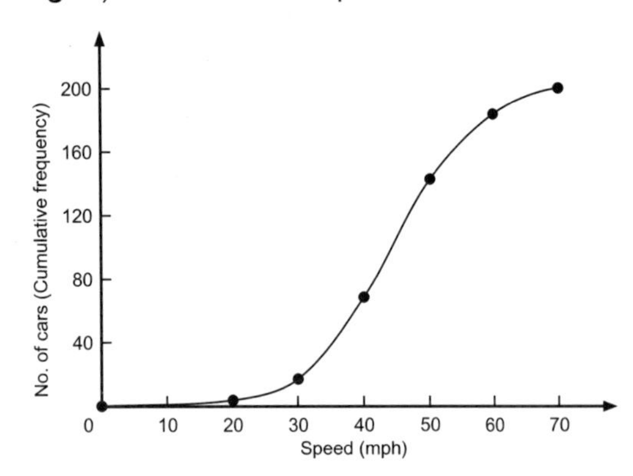

Question *Use the above cumulative frequency curve to answer the following questions.*

(a) How many cars had a speed less than 45 mph?
(b) How many cars had a speed above 45 mph?
(c) How many cars had a speed between 30 mph and 45 mph?
(d) 23 cars were travelling above the speed limit for this road. Use the graph to estimate the speed limit.

more

2. Cumulative Frequency Curve (Contd)

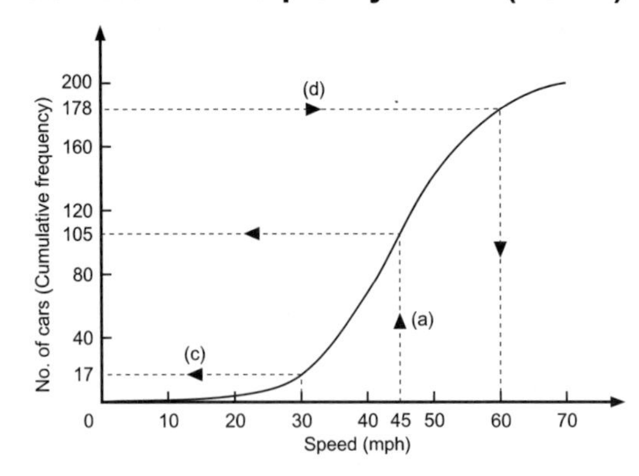

(a) From the graph, the cumulative frequency corresponding to 45 mph is 105. This tells us that 105 cars had a speed below 45 mph.

(b) There are 200 cars altogether (this is the highest cumulative frequency on the graph). So, if 105 cars had a speed below 45 mph, then, 200 − 105 = 95 cars had a speed above 45 mph.

(c) The graph shows that 105 cars had a speed below 45 mph and, of these, 17 cars had a speed below 30 mph. So, 105 − 17 = 88 cars had a speed between 30 mph and 45 mph.

(d) The 23 fastest cars correspond to the last 23 cumulative frequencies 178 to 200. The speed corresponding to the cumulative frequency 178 is 60 mph. So, the fastest 23 cars exceeded this speed limit.

3. Finding the Median

The median is the middle value. This means that half (50%) of the values are less than the median (see Box 3, p105). We can estimate the median from a cumulative frequency diagram.

Question *30 students took a memory test. The numbers of words they recalled are given in the table below.*

No. of words recalled	No. of students
16–20	2
21–25	5
26–30	12
31–35	8
36–40	3
Total	30

No. of words recalled	Cumulative frequency
20 or less	2
25 or less	
30 or less	
35 or less	
40 or less	

(a) Complete the cumulative frequency table.
(b) Draw the cumulative frequency curve.
(c) Use your graph to estimate the median number of words recalled per student.

(a) Add up the frequencies to give the cumulative frequencies.

No. of words recalled	Cumulative frequency
20 or less	2
25 or less	7
30 or less	19
35 or less	27
40 or less	30

more

3. Finding the Median (Contd)

(b) Carefully plot a cumulative frequency curve.

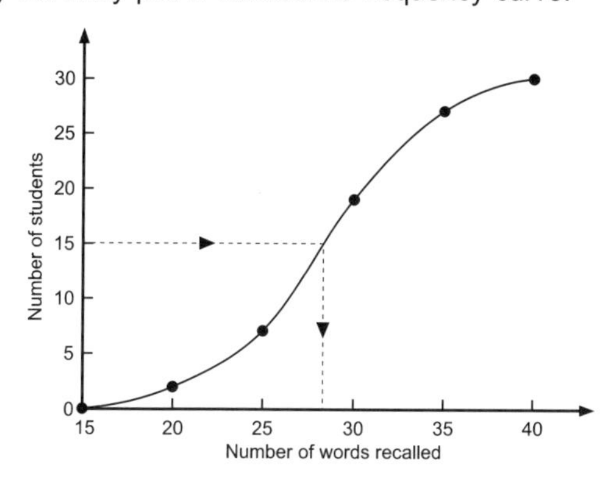

(c) There are 30 values altogether (see question). Half of these values are less than the median; so, 15 values are less than the median. From the graph, 15 students recalled less than 28 words. So, the median number of words recalled is 28 per student.

4. Interquartile Range

The yields (kg) from 12 dwarf apple trees are recorded below, arranged from smallest to largest:

6 8 8 12 15 16 18 19 22 24 25 26

The median yield is 17 kg. Half of the 12 values lie below this median. Now, half of 12 is 6 and so the first 6 trees each yielded less than 17 kg of apples:

Half (50%) of the values

6 8 8 12 15 16 ↑ 18 19 22 24 25 26

Median = 17

Similarly, a quarter of the 12 values lie below the **lower quartile**, 10 kg. Now, a quarter of 12 is 3 and so the first 3 trees each yielded less than 10 kg of apples:

Quarter (25%) of the values

6 8 8 ↑ 12 15 16 18 19 22 24 25 26

Lower quartile = 10

And three quarters of the 12 values lie below the **upper quartile**, 23 kg. Now, three quarters of 12 is 9 and so the first 9 trees each yielded less than 23 kg of apples:

Three quarters (75%) of the values

6 8 8 12 15 16 18 19 22 ↑ 24 25 26

Upper quartile = 23

The **interquartile range** is the difference between the two quartiles. In this example:

Interquartile range = Upper quartile − Lower quartile

= 23 − 10 = 13 kg

The middle half (50%) of the values lie within the interquartile range:

Middle half of the values

6 8 8 ↑ 12 15 16 18 19 22 ↑ 24 25 26

Lower quartile ← Interquartile range → Upper quartile

more

4. The Interquartile Range (Contd)

The quartiles can be estimated using a cumulative frequency curve, as shown in the following example.

Question *The cumulative frequency table shows the prices of houses for sale in an estate agent's window.*

(a) Draw a cumulative frequency curve.

(b) Use your graph to estimate

(i) the median, (ii) the interquartile range.

House price (£1000s)	No. of houses
$0 \leqslant p < 25$	5
$0 \leqslant p < 50$	23
$0 \leqslant p < 75$	39
$0 \leqslant p < 100$	51
$0 \leqslant p < 125$	58
$0 \leqslant p < 150$	60

(a) Carefully draw the cumulative frequency curve:

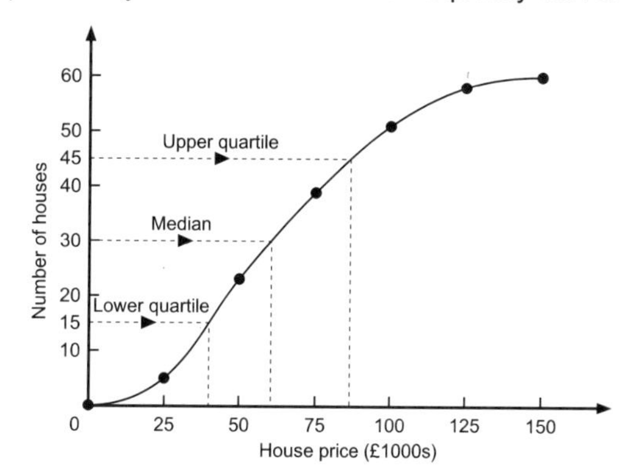

(b) (i) There are 60 values altogether (the highest cumulative frequency). The median corresponds to half of these, i.e. 30 values. From the graph, the median is £60 000.

(ii) First, find the lower and upper quartiles. The lower quartile corresponds to a quarter of the 60 values, i.e. 15 values. From the graph, the lower quartile is £40 000.

The upper quartile corresponds to three quarters of the 60 values, i.e. 45 values. From the graph, the upper quartile is £87 000.

So, interquartile range = £87 000 − £40 000
= £47 000

Question *25% of the employees of a company earn more than £23 000 per annum. The interquartile range of employees' incomes is £9000. 25% of the employees earn below a certain income. Calculate this income.*

The diagram shows that the lowest paid 25% of employees earn below £23 000 − £9000 = £14 000

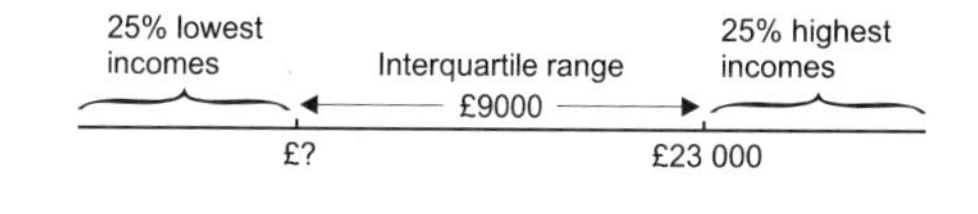

Scatter Graphs and Correlation

1. Scatter Graphs

A **scatter graph** shows the relationship between two quantities.

The heights and weights of 9 children are recorded in the table below.

Height (cm)	121	128	140	150	155	150	160	162	180
Weight (kg)	34	39	42	43	45	48	47	49	56

These values can be plotted as points to make the scatter graph shown below.

NOTE Do not join the points.

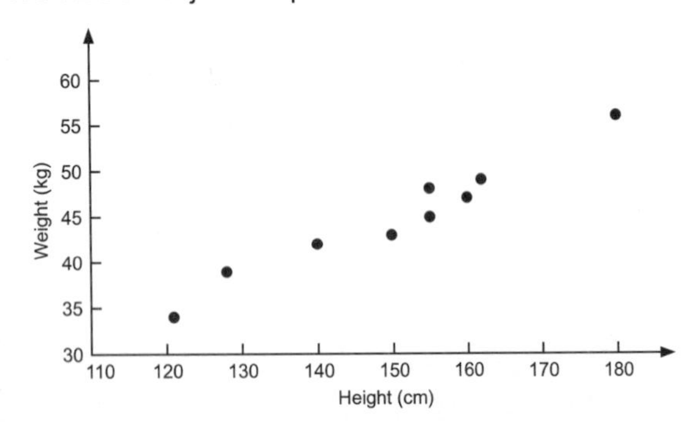

The upward slope of the points shows that, in general, the greater a child's height, the greater their weight.

2. Line of Best Fit

The points in the scatter graph of Box 1 lie roughly along a straight line, called the **line of best fit**.

The line of best fit is drawn so that there are roughly the same number of points on each side of it.

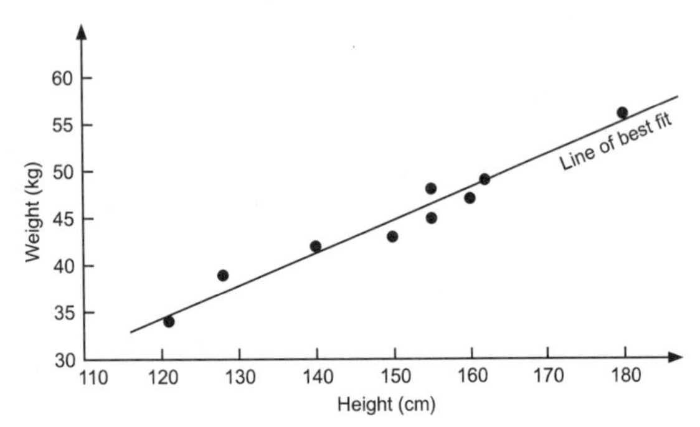

A more accurate line of best fit can be drawn by finding the 'central' point, as follows. Calculate the mean of the x-values (heights) and the mean of the y-values (weights):

Mean height $= \bar{x} = \frac{121+128+....+180}{9} = \frac{1346}{9} = 149.6$ cm

Mean weight $= \bar{y} = \frac{34+39+....+56}{9} = \frac{403}{9} = 44.8$ kg

Now plot the central point $(\bar{x}, \bar{y}) = (149.6, 44.8)$ and draw the line of best fit through it (see top right box).

more

2. Line of Best Fit (Contd)

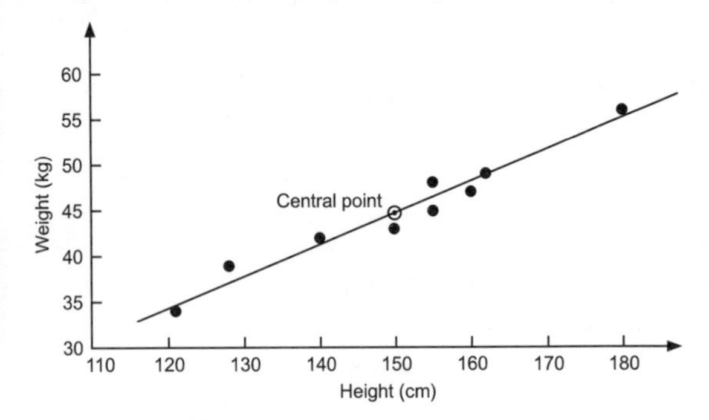

We can use the line of best fit to estimate the heights and weights of children. The graph below shows that a child with height 170 cm is likely to have a weight of about 52 kg. And a child whose weight is 40 kg is likely to be about 136 cm tall.

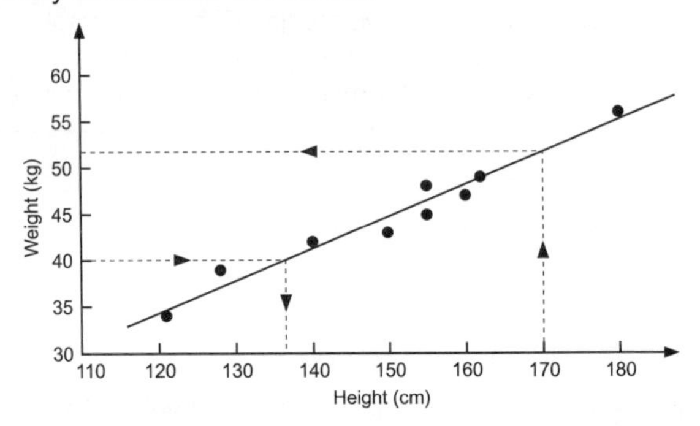

3. Correlation

The word **correlation** means mutual relationship. Two quantities are said to be **correlated** if changes in one are accompanied by changes in the other.

If two quantities are strongly correlated (closely related), the points of their scatter graph will be close to a straight line.

You need to be able to describe the correlation of a scatter graph. The different possibilities are shown below.

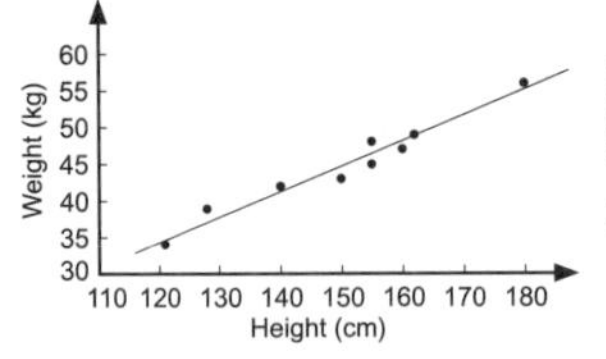

Strong, **positive** correlation because the line of best fit has a positive gradient. As a child's height increases, so does their weight.

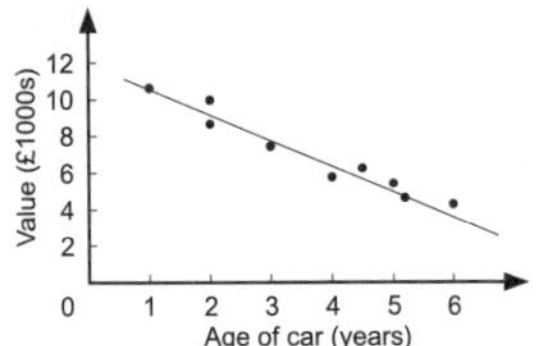

Strong, **negative** correlation because the line of best fit has a negative gradient. The older a car, the less its value.

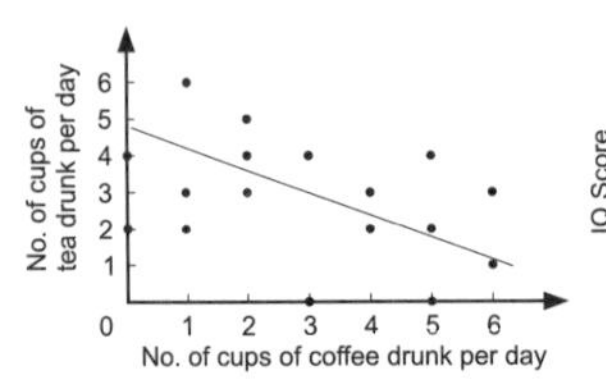

Weak, negative correlation; the points are not very close to the line of best fit but do have a downward slope. There is a weak relationship between tea and coffee drinking habits.

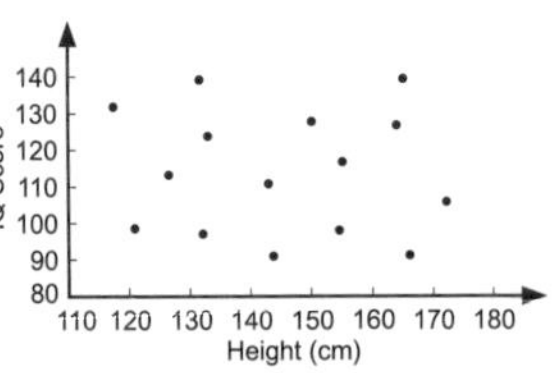

No correlation; because the points have no pattern. There is no relationship between a person's IQ and their height.

Probability

1. Definition of Probability

When a die is thrown, the six **possible outcomes** are 1, 2, 3, 4, 5, 6. If the die is perfectly balanced (**fair**), each of these outcomes is equally likely to occur.

An **event** is something that can happen. For example, when we throw a die an even number may turn up; so, 'an even number' is an event. There are three ways of throwing an even number: 2, 4 or 6; so, there are three ways the event 'an even number' can happen.

The **probability** of an event happening is a measure of how likely it will occur and can be calculated using the formula:

$$\text{Probability} = \frac{\text{Number of ways the event can happen}}{\text{Number of possible outcomes}}$$

NOTE This formula can be used only if all of the outcomes are **equally likely** to occur.

We can use this formula to find the probability of throwing an even number.

$$\text{Probability} = \frac{\text{No. of ways of throwing an even number (2, 4, 6)}}{\text{No. of possible outcomes (1, 2, 3, 4, 5, 6)}} = \frac{3}{6}$$

Probabilities can be written as fractions, decimals or percentages. In the above example:

Probability of throwing an even number $= \frac{3}{6} = 0.5 = 50\%$

Question *10 identical cards are numbered as below.*

2 4 4 4 6 8 8 8 8 8

The cards are shuffled and one chosen at random. Calculate the probability that the number on the card is (a) 2, (b) more than 2, (c) 8, (d) an even number, (e) an odd number.

(a) There are 10 possible outcomes when a card is chosen. The cards are identical and so each outcome is equally likely.

There is only 1 way of choosing a 2 and so:

Probability of choosing a 2 $= \frac{1}{10} = 0.1$

(b) There are 9 cards higher than 2 and so:

Probability of choosing above 2 $= \frac{9}{10} = 0.9$

(c) There are 5 ways of choosing an 8 (because there are 5 cards with an 8) and so:

Probability of choosing an 8 $= \frac{5}{10} = 0.5 = 50\%$

(This is commonly described as a **fifty–fifty** chance, since there is a 50% chance of choosing an 8 and a 50% chance of not choosing an 8.)

(d) All the cards are even and so choosing an even number is an **absolute certainty**. There are 10 ways of choosing an even number and so:

Probability of an even number $= \frac{10}{10} = 1$

(e) There are no cards with odd numbers and so choosing an odd number is **impossible**:

Probability of an odd number $= \frac{0}{10} = 0$

Notice that all the probabilities in this question are numbers between 0 and 1. They are illustrated below:

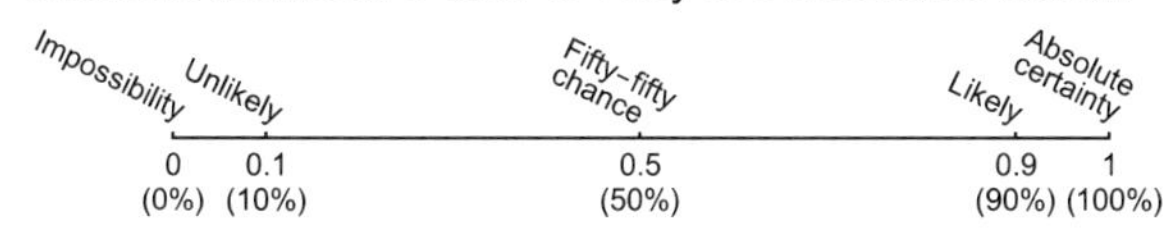

All probabilities lie between 0 and 1.

2. Probability of an Event Not Happening

Question *The numbers 1, 2, 3, 4 and 5 are equally likely when this spinner is used. The spinner is spun once. Calculate the probability of*
(a) obtaining a 3
(b) not obtaining a 3.

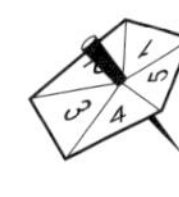

(a) There are 5 possible outcomes: 1, 2, 3, 4, 5.

There is only 1 way of spinning a 3 and so:

Probability of obtaining a 3 $= \frac{1}{5} = 0.2$

(b) There are 4 ways of ***not*** spinning a 3, namely 1, 2, 4 and 5. So:

Probability of ***not*** obtaining a 3 $= \frac{4}{5} = 0.8$

Notice that this probability can also be calculated by subtracting the probability in part (a) from 1: $1 - 0.2 = 0.8$. So:

Probability of ***not*** obtaining a 3 = 1 − Probability of obtaining a 3

Generally, we have the result:

Probability of an event ***not*** happening = 1 − Probability of event happening

Question *The probability of rain on a day in June is 0.3. What is the probability of no rain on 21 June?*

Probability of no rain = 1 − Probability of rain
= 1 − 0.3 = 0.7

3. Total Probability

If we add up the probability of every possible outcome, the answer is always 1. For example, if an ordinary fair die is thrown, the 6 possible outcomes are 1, 2, 3, 4, 5 and 6, each occuring with a probability of $\frac{1}{6}$.

So, total probability $= \frac{1}{6}+\frac{1}{6}+\frac{1}{6}+\frac{1}{6}+\frac{1}{6}+\frac{1}{6} = \frac{6}{6} = 1$

4. Adding Probabilities

Question *A bag contains 2 red, 3 green and 4 white counters. One counter is chosen from the bag at random. Calculate the probability that it is (a) red, (b) green, (c) red or green.*

(a) There are 9 possible outcomes (any one of 9 counters could be chosen).

There are 2 ways of choosing a red counter. So:

Probability of choosing a red counter $= \frac{2}{9}$

We can write this briefly as: P(red) $= \frac{2}{9}$

(b) Similarly, there are 3 ways of choosing a green counter and so:

P(green) $= \frac{3}{9} = \frac{1}{9}$

Probability (Contd)

4. Adding Probabilities (Contd)

(c) There are 5 ways of choosing a red or green counter (2 red + 3 green) and so:

P(red *or* green) = $\frac{5}{9}$

We can also calculate this probability by adding together the probabilities P(red) and P(green) found in parts (a) and (b):

P(red) + P(green) = $\frac{2}{9} + \frac{3}{9} = \frac{5}{9}$

and so we can say

P(red *or* green) = P(red) + P(green)

NOTE It looks as though the word *or* has been replaced by a plus sign

For any two events A and B, we have the general result:

P(A *or* B) = P(A) + P(B) **or means +**

NOTE You can only use this rule if the two events cannot happen together. This is the case in the above example because it is impossible to choose a counter that is both red and green. Here is a question where the rule **cannot** be used.

Question *One of these counters is chosen at random.*

[1] [2] (3) (4) 

The probability of choosing a square counter is $\frac{2}{5}$ *and the probability of choosing an even number is* $\frac{2}{5}$*. Explain why the probability of choosing a square or an even number is not* $\frac{2}{5} + \frac{2}{5}$*.*

One of the counters is both square and even. This means that the events 'choosing a square' and 'choosing an even number' can happen both at once.

The correct answer is $\frac{3}{5}$, because choosing a square or an even number means choosing one of the 3 counters [1] [2] (4) out of a possible 5 counters.

5. Multiplying Probabilities

Question *An ordinary fair die has faces numbered 1, 2, 3, 4, 5, 6. An ordinary fair coin has two sides, head (H) and tail (T).*

(a) The die is thrown. Calculate the probability of obtaining a 3.

(b) The coin is flipped. Calculate the probability of obtaining a head (H).

(c) The die is thrown and the coin is flipped. Complete the list of possible outcomes below.

(1, H) (2, H) ( ) ( ) ( ) ( )

(1, T) ( ) ( ) ( ) ( ) ( )

(d) Use your list to calculate the probability of throwing a 3 and flipping a head.

(a) There are 6 possible outcomes (1, 2, 3, 4, 5, 6) but only 1 way of flipping a 3. So:

P(3) = $\frac{1}{6}$

(b) There two possible outcomes, head (H) or tail (T), but only 1 way of flipping a head. So:

P(H) = $\frac{1}{2}$

more

5. Multiplying Probabilities (Contd)

(c) Here are the possible outcomes:

(1, H) (2, H) (3, H) (4, H) (5, H) (6, H)
(1, T) (2, T) (3, T) (4, T) (5, T) (6, T)

There are 12 possible outcomes:
6 numbers × 2 sides = 12 combinations

(d) There are 12 possible outcomes but only 1 way of throwing a 3 and flipping a head, namely (3, H). So:

P(3 *and* H) = $\frac{1}{12}$

We can also calculate this probability by multiplying the probabilities P(3) and P(H) found in parts (a) and (b): $\frac{1}{6} \times \frac{1}{2} = \frac{1}{12}$ and so we can say

P(3 *and* H) = P(3) × P(H)

NOTE It looks as though the word *and* has been replaced by a multiplication sign

For any two events A and B, we have the general result:

P(A *and* B) = P(A) × P(B) **and means ×**

NOTE You can only use this rule if the two events are independent of each another, i.e. the occurence of one does not affect the occurence of the other. In this example, throwing a die obviously has no effect on flipping a coin, and vice-versa.

6. Tree Diagrams

Tree diagrams can help you to calculate the probability of two or more events happening.

Question *The probability of an archer hitting the centre of this target is 0.2. The archer always hits the target.*

(a) Calculate the probability of the archer hitting the outer ring of the target with one arrow.

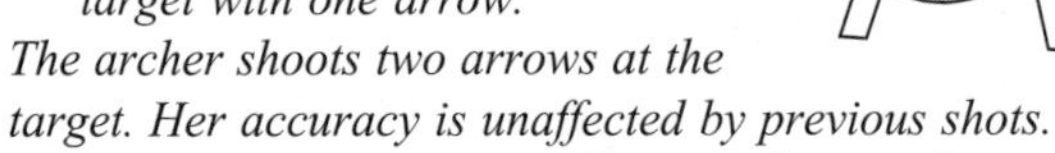

The archer shoots two arrows at the target. Her accuracy is unaffected by previous shots.

(b) Draw a tree diagram to illustrate the two shots.

(c) Use your diagram to calculate the probability of the archer hitting

(i) the centre of the target with both shots

(ii) the centre of the target with only one shot.

(a) P(hitting the outer ring) = P(not hitting the centre)
= 1 − P(hitting the centre)
= 1−0.2
= 0.8

(b) There are two possible outcomes for the first shot: hitting the centre and hitting the outer ring.

Each possible outcome is represented by a straight line labelled with its probability. Notice that the probabilities add up to 1.

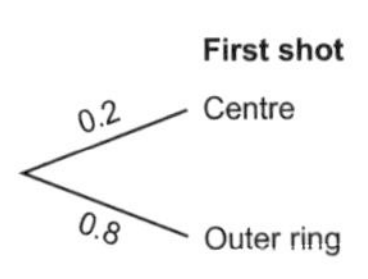

more

6. Tree Diagrams (Contd)

The second shot has the same two outcomes with the same probabilities (because the accuracy of the archer is unaffected by the first shot). The completed tree diagram is shown below:

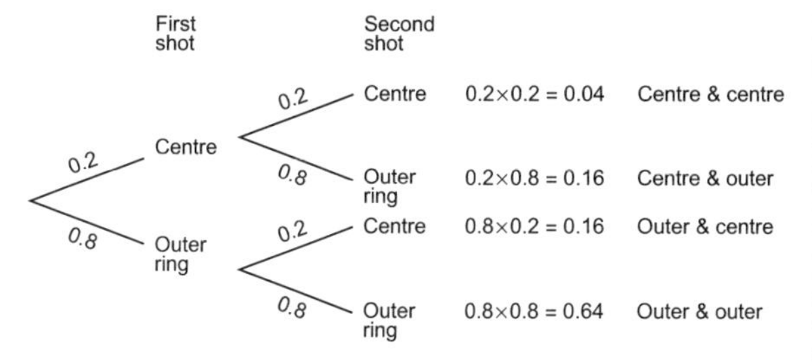

(c) (i) P(hitting centre with both shots)
= P(hitting centre with first shot *and* second shot)
= P(hitting centre with first shot) × P(hitting centre with second shot)
= 0.2×0.2 = 0.04

Remember: **and** means ×

This calculation is shown on the tree diagram above, together with the calculations for the other combinations of outcomes.

(ii) P(hitting centre with only one shot)
= P(hitting centre with first shot *and* then the outer ring with the second shot *or* hitting outer ring with first shot *and* then the centre with the second shot)
= 0.2×0.8 + 0.8×0.2
= 0.16+0.16
= 0.32

Remember: **and** means × and **or** means +

7. Conditional Probability

H

When the occurence of one event affects the probability of another event occuring, use a tree diagram to calculate probabilities.

Question *A bag contains 3 red and 5 blue marbles. Two marbles are taken from the bag. What is the probability that*
(a) they are both red
(b) only one of them is red?

It does not matter whether the two marbles are removed from the bag at the same time or one after the other: the result is the same. It is easier to assume they were removed one after the other, then we can draw a tree diagram.

First marble

There are 8 possible outcomes (3 red and 5 blue marbles) and 3 ways of choosing a red marble.

So, P(red marble first) = $\frac{3}{8}$
and P(blue marble first) = $\frac{5}{8}$

We can now draw the first branches of a tree diagram.

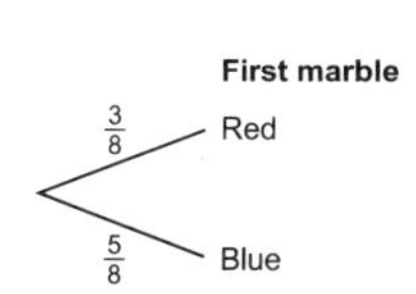

more

7. Conditional Probability (Contd)

Second marble

The choice of the second marble depends on (is conditional on) which one was chosen first.
If the *first marble* was *red*, the bag now contains 2 red and 5 blue marbles (7 marbles altogether) and so:

P(red second) = $\frac{2}{7}$ and P(blue second) = $\frac{5}{7}$

If the *first marble* was *blue*, the bag now contains 3 red and 4 blue marbles (7 marbles altogether) and so:

P(red second) = $\frac{3}{7}$ and P(blue second) = $\frac{4}{7}$

We can now complete the tree diagram:

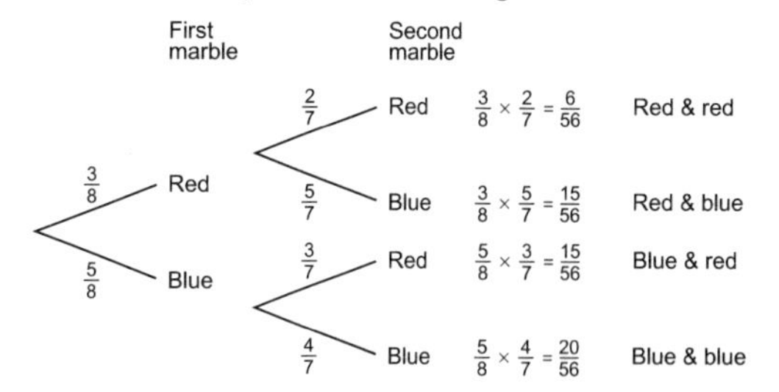

Now that the tree diagram is complete, we can use the same methods as in Box 6 to calculate the combined probabilities:

(a) P(both red) = P(red first *and* red second)
= P(red first) × P(red second)
$= \frac{3}{8} \times \frac{2}{7}$
$= \frac{6}{56}$

(b) P(only one red) = P(red first *and* blue second *or* blue first *and* red second)
$= \frac{3}{8} \times \frac{5}{7} + \frac{5}{8} \times \frac{3}{7}$
$= \frac{15}{56} + \frac{15}{56}$
$= \frac{30}{56}$
$= \frac{15}{28}$

8. Estimating Probability

Chin Lin did an experiment in which she flipped a 2p coin 50 times. She obtained 22 heads and 28 tails.

A **trial** is a repeatable act. In this experiment, each flip of the coin is a trial.

Chin Lin used her results to estimate the probability of obtaining heads or tails in the future:

$$\text{Probability of heads} = \frac{\text{Number of heads}}{\text{Number of flips}} = \frac{22}{50} = 0.44$$

$$\text{Probability of tails} = \frac{\text{Number of tails}}{\text{Number of flips}} = \frac{28}{50} = 0.56$$

These are called **experimental probabilities**.

She knew that, if the coin was perfectly balanced (fair), heads and tails would be equally likely and their probabilities would be:

P(head) = 0.5 and P(tail) = 0.5

Her estimates were fairly close to 0.5 and so she concluded that her 2p coin was probably fair.

more

Probability (Contd)

8. Estimating Probability (Contd)

To be more certain, Chin Lin repeated the experiment, this time flipping the 2p coin 100 times. She obtained 48 heads and 52 tails, giving the experimental probabilities below:

P(head) = $\frac{48}{100}$ = 0.48   and   P(tail) = $\frac{52}{100}$ = 0.52

These estimates are even closer to 0.5 and so she was more certain that the 2p coin was fair.

Her teacher asked her how many heads she would **expect** if the coin were flipped another 200 times.

Chin Lin said that, if the coin were fair, the probability of a head would be 0.5, which is the same as 50%. So, she would expect 50% of flips to be heads:

Expected number of heads = 50% of 200
= 0.5×200 = 100

You can see that the probability 0.5 has been multiplied by the number of flips (trials). So:

Expected number of times an event occurs = Probability of event × Number of trials

Critical Path Analysis H

1. Critical Path Analysis

Many tasks involve several steps before they can be completed. For example, making a loaf of bread involves weighing the ingredients, mixing the dry ingredients (flour, salt and yeast), adding water, kneading the dough, leaving the dough to rise, etc.

The aim of critical path analysis is to arrange the steps of a task in a logical order and find the shortest time in which the task can be completed.

2. Networks

A **network** is a diagram that helps you to organise the steps of a task.

Each step is represented by a straight line labelled with the length of time taken to complete the step. Here is one of the steps in making bread:

Weigh ingredients
5 minutes

The beginning and end of a step are called **nodes** and are indicated by numbered circles:

① Weigh ingredients 5 min ② Make dough 12 min ③

The task begins with the lowest number and ends with highest.

Some steps cannot begin until others are completed. In the bread-making example, the ingredients must be weighed before they can be made into dough (see above diagram).

Steps that do not depend on each other can be performed at the same time. For example, a loaf tin can be greased and the oven can be warmed to the correct temperature whilst the dough is rising, as shown in the diagram below:

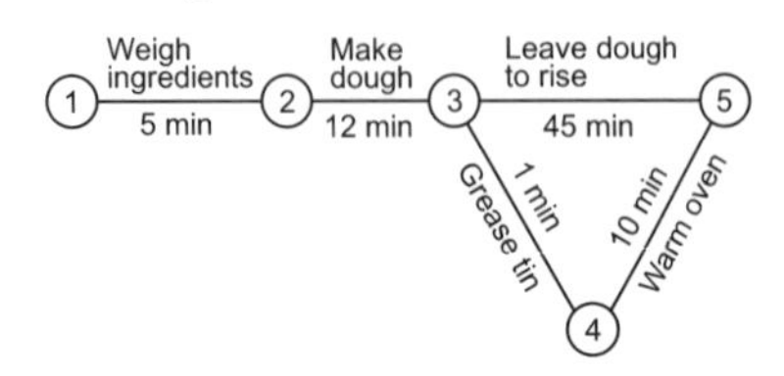

more

2. Networks (Contd)

From this diagram, you can see that greasing the loaf tin and warming the oven only take 11 minutes, compared with the 45 minutes needed for the dough to rise. So, it takes 45 minutes to progress from node 3 to node 5.

The complete network for making a loaf of bread is shown below:

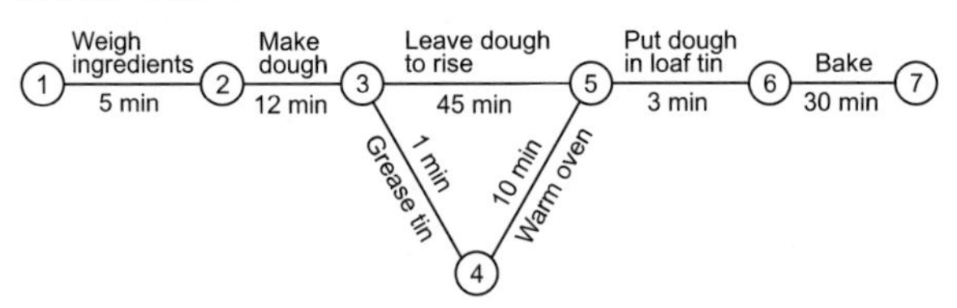

There are two **paths** from node 1 to node 7:

①–②–③–⑤–⑥–⑦

and ①–②–③–④–⑤–⑥–⑦

The total time taken for the steps in the first path is 5+12+45+3+30 = 95 minutes.

The total time taken for the steps in the second path is 5+12+1+10+3+30 = 61 minutes.

So, the shortest time in which to make a loaf of bread is 95 minutes. The path that gives this time is called the **critical path**.

3. More Complicated Example

Question *The steps needed to make an apple tart are listed opposite.*

(a) Given the following information, complete the network below.
When the pastry case has been baked, it can be filled with apples and custard.
Whilst the tart is baking, the glaze can be made.
When the tart has finished baking, it can be glazed.

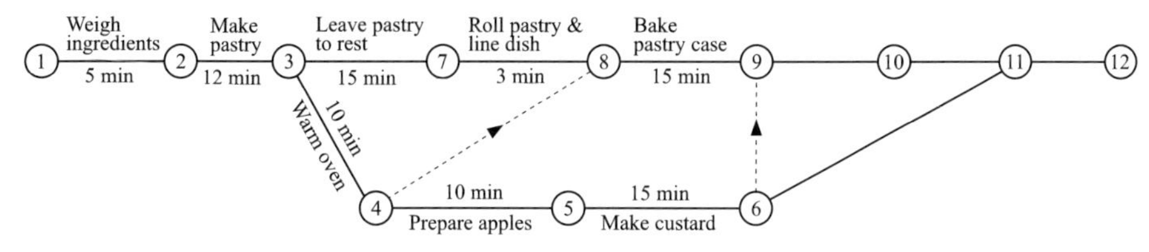

(b) A dashed line shows that one task must be completed before another can begin.
For example, the oven must be warmed before the pastry case can be baked.
Calculate the shortest time needed to make an apple tart.

Step	*Duration*
Weigh ingredients	*5 min*
Make pastry	*12 min*
Leave pastry to rest	*15 min*
Roll pastry and line dish	*3 min*
Warm oven	*10 min*
Bake pastry case	*15 min*
Prepare apples	*10 min*
Make custard	*15 min*
Fill pastry case	*10 min*
Bake tart	*20 min*
Make glaze	*5 min*
Glaze tart	*4 min*

The completed network is shown below

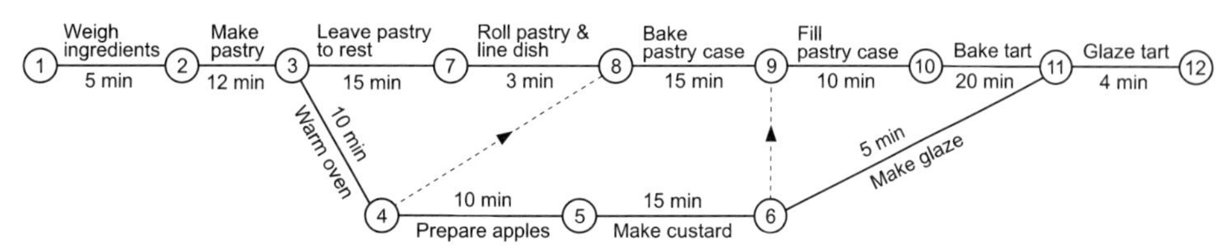

The longest path from node 1 to node 8 is: 1–2–3–7–8

The longest path from node 8 to node 9 is: 8–4–5–6–9

The longest path from node 9 to node 11 is: 9–10–11

So, the longest path from node 1 to node 12 (the critical path) is: 1–2–3–7–8–4–5–6–9–10–11–12

The duration of this path is: 5+12+15+3+10+15+10+20+4 = 94 minutes.

So, the shortest time in which to make an apple tart using this method is 94 minutes.

Examination Questions

The following examination questions have been selected from the 1998 Specimen Papers for the London GCSE. Higher level questions and parts of questions are indicated by **H**. If you have difficulty with a question, turn to the indicated page and box for help. You will find brief solutions on pages 121–123. Edexcel Foundation, London Examinations accepts no responsibility whatsoever for the accuracy or method of working in the answers given.

Number

1. $\frac{3}{5}$ of the cost of a music tape goes to the supplier. A music tape costs £6. How much goes to the supplier? (Box 9, p17)

2. $\frac{3}{8}$ of the Highlands of Scotland is covered in forest.

   (a) (i) Change $\frac{3}{8}$ to a decimal. (Box 11, p20)

   (ii) Write down your answer to part (i) correct to 2 decimal places. (Box 3, p21)

   (b) Work out the percentage of the Highlands of Scotland NOT covered in forest.

   Here is a list of fractions, decimals and percentages:

   67% $\frac{1}{2}$ 0.6 25% 0.3 $\frac{3}{8}$

   (c) Rewrite the list in order of size, starting with the smallest first. (Box 1, p25)

3. The distance from the Earth to the Moon is 250 000 miles.

   (a) Express this number in standard form. (Box 4, p31)

   The distance from the Earth to the Sun is 9.3×10^7 miles.

   (b) Calculate the value of the expression

   $$\frac{\text{Distance from the Earth to the Moon}}{\text{Distance from the Earth to the Sun}}$$

   giving your answer in standard form. (Box 8, p32)

4. Jake buys a television. He pays £125 deposit and 12 monthly instalments of £29.62.

   (a) Work out the total amount that Jake pays. (Box 8, p19)

   In Cooper's store, BRITE colour televisions are priced at £390 each in 1996. Lyn pays cash and is given a discount of 12%.

   (b) Calculate the amount that Lyn pays. (Box 6, p26)

   The price of a BRITE colour television has risen by 4% since 1995 to £390.

   (c) Calculate the price of the television in 1995. (Box 7, p26)

5. **H**

   length
   width
   3.7 cm
   6.3 cm
   Diagram NOT accurately drawn

   The dimensions of the rectangle are given correct to 1 decimal place.

   (a) Calculate the lower bound of the area of the rectangle. (Box 7, p22)

   Rectangles with the same dimensions as the one in part (a) are to be cut from a large piece of card of length 1 metre, correct to the nearest centimetre and width exactly 4 cm.

   Diagram NOT accurately drawn

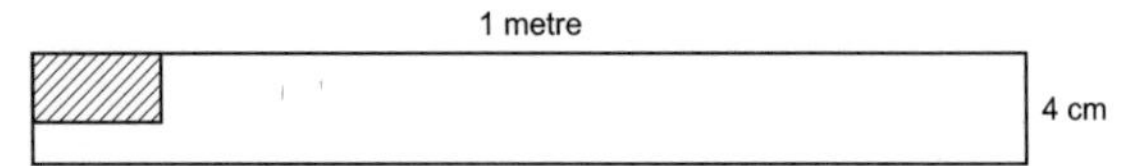

5. (b) Calculate the maximum number of rectangles that could be cut from the large piece of card. (Box 7, p22)

6. Ivan builds fences in different lengths using pieces of wood.

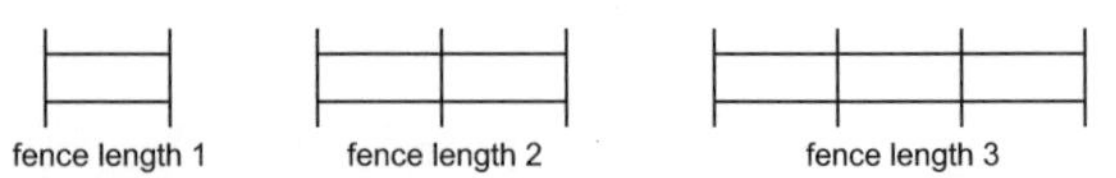

   (a) Sketch fence length 5. (Box 1, p13)

   Ivan counted how many pieces he needed to make each fence length. He then drew the table below:

Fence length	1	2	3	4	5	6
Number of pieces	4	7	10			

   (b) Complete the table to show how many pieces of wood he would use for fence lengths 4, 5 and 6. (Box 4, p14)

   (c) Explain how you would work out the number of pieces needed for fence length 25. (Box 4, p13)

   (d) Write down, in terms of n, an expression for the number of pieces of wood needed for fence length n. (Box 5, p14)

Algebra

7. Sarah uses the formula:

   $$t = \frac{2s}{u+v}$$

   She has to calculate the value of t when $s = 623.25$, $u = 11.37$ and $v = 87.22$. Sarah estimates the value of t **without using her calculator**.

   (a) (i) Write down the numbers Sarah could use in the formula to estimate the value of t. (Box 5, p21)

   (ii) Work out the estimate for the value of t that these numbers would give. (Box 5, p21)

   (b) Use your calculator to work out the actual value of t. Give your answer to an appropriate degree of accuracy. (Box 13, p24)

8. The heat setting of a gas oven is called its Gas Mark. A Gas Mark, G, may be converted to a temperature, F, in degrees Fahrenheit, using the formula:

   $$F = 25G+250$$

   (a) Factorise completely $25G+250$. (Box 6, p41)

   A Gas Mark, G, may be converted to a temperature, C, in degrees Celsius, using the formula:

   $$C = 14G+121$$

   (b) Make G the subject of the formula $C = 14G+121$. (Box 4, p39)

9. The air temperature, T °C, outside an aircraft at a height of h feet is given by the formula:

   $$T = 26 - \frac{h}{500}$$

The air temperature outside an aircraft is −52 °C. Calculate the height of the aircraft. (Box 3, p38)

10. The two circles have radii of R cm and r cm, where $R > r$. The shaded area, A cm^2, between the circles is given by the formula:

    $A = \pi(R+r)(R-r)$

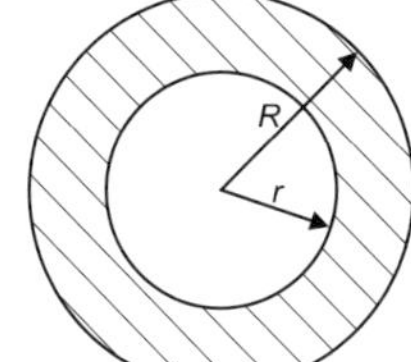

    (a) Expand $(R+r)(R-r)$. Express your answer as simply as possible. (Box 3, p41)

    (b) Calculate the value of r when $A = 147$ and $R = 21$. (Box 5, p39)

11. A shop sells chests of drawers in two different widths, 'standard' and 'wide'. The cost, S pounds, of a 'standard' chest of drawers with d drawers may be calculated using the formula:

    $S = 29+15d$

    A 'standard' chest of drawers costs £119.

    (a) Calculate the number of drawers this chest has. (Box 7, p37)

    The cost, W pounds, of a 'wide' chest of drawers may be calculated using the formula:

    $W = k+md$

    k and m are constants and d is the number of drawers. The cost of a "wide" chest of drawers with 4 drawers is £117. The cost of a "wide" chest of drawers with 6 drawers is £149.

    (b) (i) Use the information to write down two equations in k and m. (Box 6, p48)

    (ii) Solve the equations to find the value of m. (Box 2, p47)

12. The graph represents part of Mrs Hinton's journey from Manchester to London. Mrs Hinton stopped for a rest at a service station.

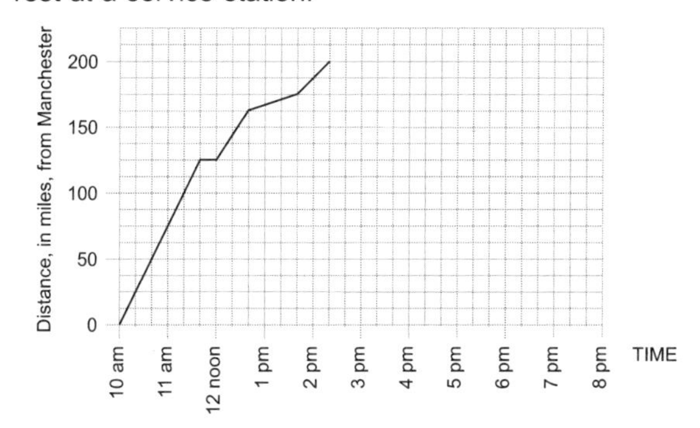

    (a) (i) Write down the time at which she stopped. (Box 4, p61)

    (ii) For how long did she stop? (Box 4, p61)

    For part of the journey Mrs Hinton had to slow down because of a traffic queue.

    (b) For how many miles did she travel at this slower speed? (Box 4, p61)

    Mrs Hinton spent an hour at a meeting in London. She then returned home to Manchester, travelling at a steady speed of 50 miles per hour.

    (c) Use this information to complete the graph of her journey. (Box 2, p60)

13. $y = x^3-4x-1$

    (a) Complete the table of values. (Box 1, p55)

x	−2	−1	0	1	2	3
y		1				

    (b) On the grid below, draw the graph of $y = x^3-4x-1$. (Box 5, p54)

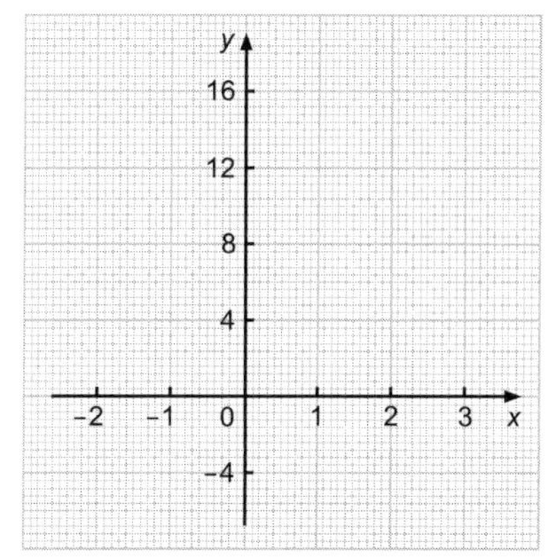

    (c) By drawing a suitable straight line on the grid, solve the equation:

    $x^3-4x-1 = -2$ (Box 1, p63)

    (d) Using the method of trial and improvement, or otherwise, solve the equation $x^3-4x-1 = 30$ correct to 1 decimal place. (Box 1, p45)

14. **H** This is a sketch of the graph of $y = f(x)$, where

    $f(x) = (x+3)(x-2)(x-4)$

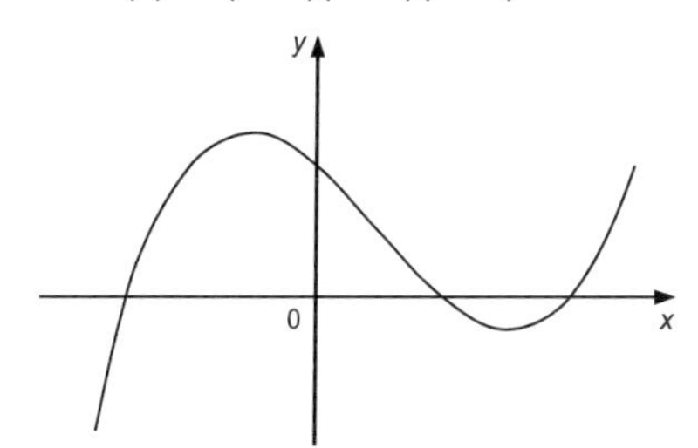

    (a) Calculate the value of $f(0)$. (Box 1, p68)

    (b) On the axes above sketch the graph of $y = f(-x)$. (Box 3, p68 and Box 4, p69)

    (c) Describe fully the single geometric transformation which maps the graph of $y = f(x)$ onto the graph of $y = f(-x)$. (Box 4, p69)

    The equation $f(x) = f(-x)$ has a solution $x = 0$. It also has a positive solution x such that

    $n < x < n+1$

    where n is a positive integer.

    (d) Write down the value of n. (Box 3, p64)

Shape and Space

15. The diagram represents an L-shaped room whose corners are all right angles.

    (a) Work out the area of the room. (Box 2, p70)

    The height of the room is 2.7 m.

    (b) Calculate the volume of the room. (Box 2, p74)

16. The diagram represents a tea packet in the shape of a cuboid.

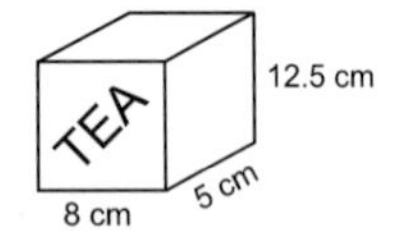

    (a) Calculate the volume of the packet. (Box 2, p74)

    There are 125 g in a full packet. Jason has to design a new packet that will contain 100 g of tea when full.

    (b) (i) Work out the volume of the new packet. (Box 3, p27)

    (ii) Express the weight of tea in the new packet as a percentage of the weight in the packet shown. (Box 3, p25)

17. The diagram represents a metal cone of height 90 cm made in two parts, labelled T and S. The top part, T, has a height of 45 cm.

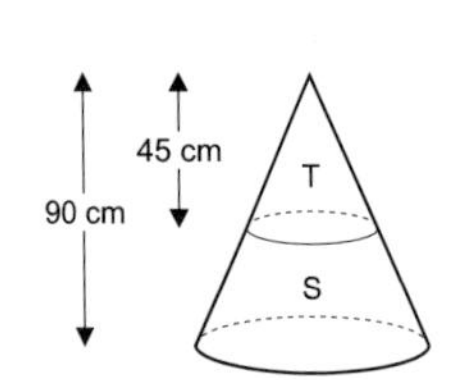

    Given that the volume of S and T together is 10 500π cm^3,

    (a) calculate the volume of S. (Box 7, p76)

    A second cone is also made up of two parts, A and B. The radius of the top part, A, is 20 cm and the radius of the base of B is 30 cm. The height of the bottom part is 120 cm.

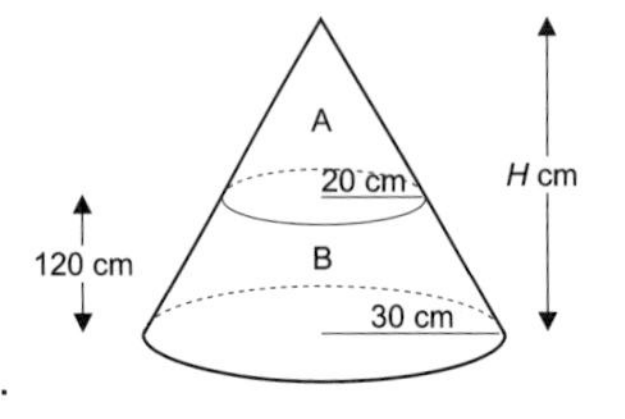

    (b) Calculate the height H cm. (Box 6, p81)

18. The diagram shows Nelson's voyage from Great Yarmouth to position B. Nelson's boat sails due East from Great Yarmouth for 14 km to a position A. The boat then changes course and sails for 20 km due South to a position B. On a map, the distance between G and A is 56 cm.

    (a) Work out the scale of the map. Give your answer in the form 1:n, where n is an integer. (Box 4, p27)

    (b) Calculate the distance, in km, of B from Great Yarmouth. (Box 5, p81)

    (c) Calculate the bearing of Great Yarmouth from B. (Box 2, p87 and Box 8, p95)

19. ABCDE is a regular pentagon. O is the centre of the pentagon.

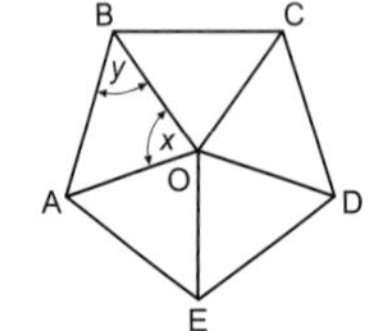

    (a) Work out the value of (i) x, (ii) y. (Box 2, p83 and Box 4, p80)

    (b) On the grid below, show how regular hexagons tessellate. (Box 4, p92)

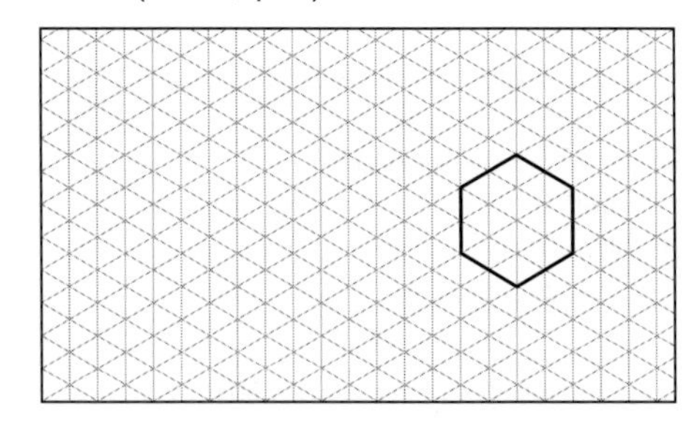

    (c) Explain why regular pentagons will not tessellate. (Box 2, p92)

    (d) Write down the order of rotational symmetry of a regular pentagon. (Box 2, p92)

20. (a) Reflect the triangle A in the x-axis. Label the reflection B. (Box 3, p89)

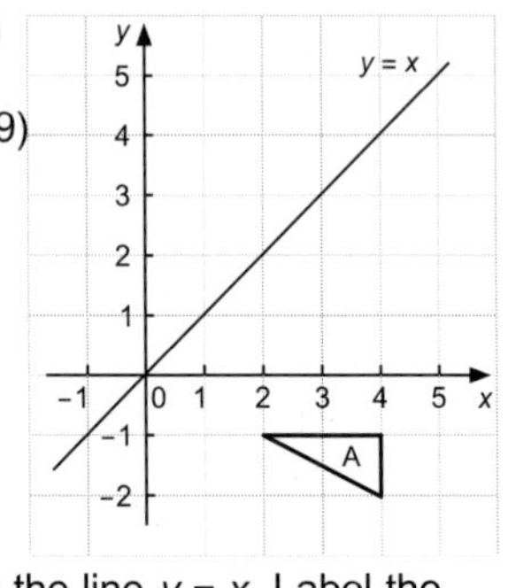

    (b) Reflect the triangle B in the line $y = x$. Label the reflection C. (Box 6, p90)

    (c) Describe fully the single transformation which maps triangle A onto triangle C. (Box 7, p90)

    (d) Write down the equation of the line which is parallel to $y = x$ and which passes through the point (0, 8). (Box 2, p57)

    This line crosses the x-axis at point P.

    (e) Calculate the coordinates of P. (Box 5, p58)

Handling Data

21. 720 students were asked how they travelled to school. The pie chart shows the results of this survey. Work out how many of the students travelled to school by bus. (Box 4, p103)

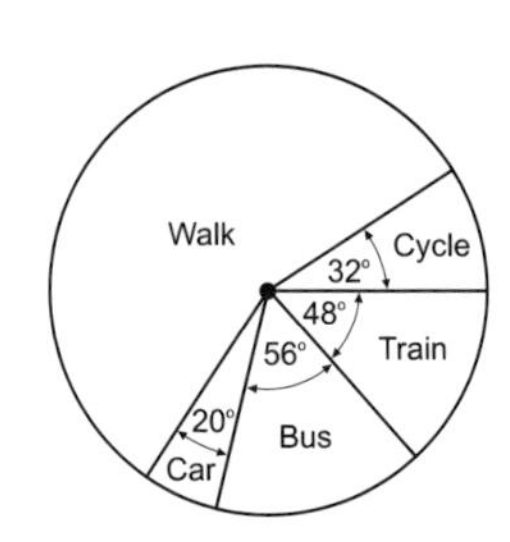

22. Ian looked at a passage from a book. He recorded the number of words in each sentence in a frequency table using class intervals 1–5, 6–10, 11–15, etc.

Class interval	Frequency f
1–5	16
6–10	28
11–15	26
16–20	14
21–25	10
26–30	3
31–35	1
36–40	0
41–45	2

    (a) Write down

    (i) the modal class interval (Box 2, p105)

    (ii) the class interval in which the median lies. (Box 4, p105)

    (b) Work out an estimate for the mean number of words per sentence. (Box 7, p106)

23. This table gives you the marks scored by pupils in a French test and in a German test.

French	15	35	34	23	35	27	36	34	23	24	30	40	25	35	20
German	20	37	35	25	33	30	39	36	27	20	33	35	27	32	28

(a) Work out the range of the pupils' marks in French. (Box 2, p107)

(b) Draw a scatter graph of the marks scored in the French and German tests. (Box 1, p112)

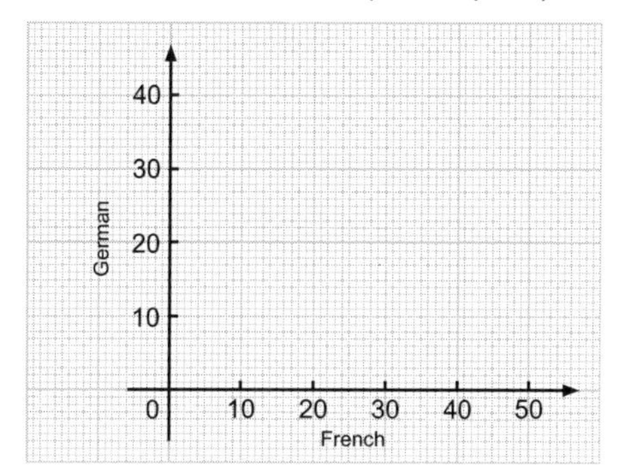

(c) Draw the line of best fit. (Box 2, p112)

(d) Use your line of best fit to estimate the mark of a pupil's test in French when their mark in German was 23. (Box 2, p112)

(e) Describe the relationship between the marks scored in the two tests. (Box 3, p112)

24. The speeds, in miles per hour (mph), of 200 cars travelling on the A320 road were measured. The results are shown in the table.

Speed (mph)	Cumulative frequency
Not exceeding 20	2
Not exceeding 25	6
Not exceeding 30	14
Not exceeding 35	28
Not exceeding 40	66
Not exceeding 45	112
Not exceeding 50	164
Not exceeding 55	196
Not exceeding 60	200

(a) On the grid below, draw a cumulative frequency graph to show these figures. (Box 2, p110)

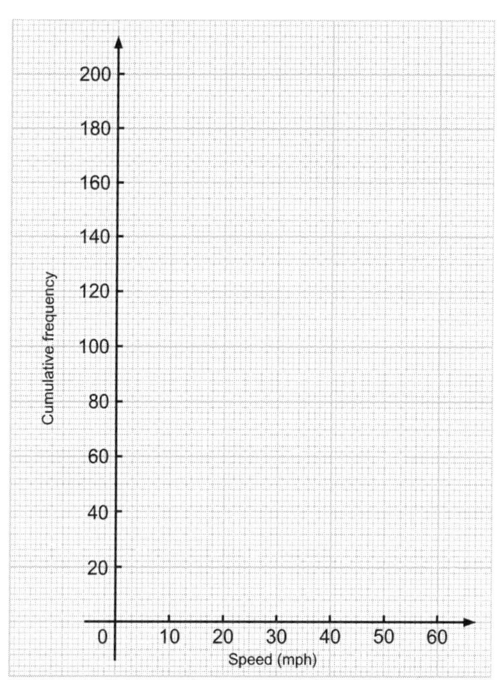

(b) Use your graph to find an estimate for
   (i) the median speed (in mph) (Box 3, p110)
   (ii) the interquartile range (in mph) (Box 4, p111)
   (iii) the percentage of cars travelling at less than 32 miles per hour. (Box 2, p110)

25. **H** This set of marks was obtained by 10 pupils in an English GCSE examination:

73, 70, 62, 67, 69, 76, 55, 65, 61, 82

The mean of this set of marks is 68.

(a) Calculate the standard deviation of these marks. (Box 3, p107)

All ten pupils had their marks increased by 3 for good spelling.

(b) Write down for the **new** set of marks
   (i) the mean (Box 6, p109)
   (ii) the standard deviation. (Box 6, p109)

26.

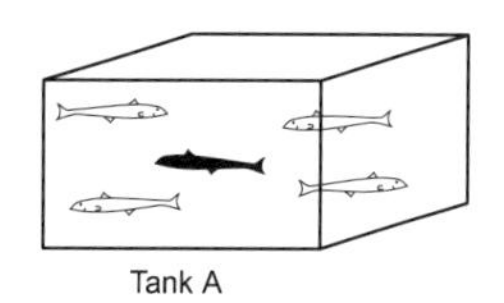

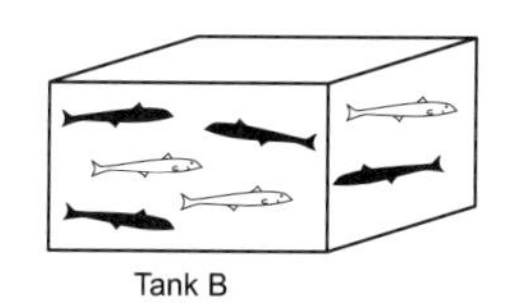

There are two fish tanks in a pet shop. In tank A there are four white fish and one black fish. In tank B there are three white fish and four black fish. One fish is to be taken out of tank A at random. One fish is to be taken out of tank B at random. Using a tree diagram, or otherwise, calculate the probability that

(a) the two fish will both be white (Box 6, p114)

(b) the two fish will both be of different colours. (Box 6, p114)

Solutions

1. $\frac{3}{5}$ of £6 = 3÷5×£6 = £3.60

2. (a) (i) $\frac{3}{8}$ = 3÷8 = 0.375 (ii) 0.375 ≈ 0.38 (2 dp)

   (b) $\frac{3}{8}$ = 0.375 = 0.375×100% = 37.5% is forest.
   So, 100−37.5 = 62.5% is not forest

   (c) Convert percentages and fractions to decimals:

25%	0.3	$\frac{3}{8}$	$\frac{1}{2}$	0.6	67%
0.25	0.3	0.375	0.5	0.6	0.67

3. (a) 250 000 = 2.5×10^5

   (b) $2.5\times10^5 \div 9.3\times10^7 \approx 2.69\times10^{-3}$

4. (a) Jake pays £125+12×£29.62 = £480.44

   (b) Discount = 12% of £390 = 12÷100×£390 = £46.80
   Cost = Price−Discount = £390−£46.80 = £343.20

   (c) 1995 Price + Price rise = 1996 Price
   100% + 4% = 104%
   £? + £? = £390

   104% is £390 and so 1% is £390÷104 = £3.75
   1995 price = 100% = 100×£3.75 = £375

5. (a) Lower bound of width = 6.25 cm
   Lower bound of length = 3.65 cm
   Lower bound of area = 6.25×3.65 = 22.8125 cm^2

   (b) Upper bound of large piece of card = 100.5 cm
   Max. no. of rectangles = 100.5÷6.25 = 16.08 ≈ 16

6. (a) & (b)

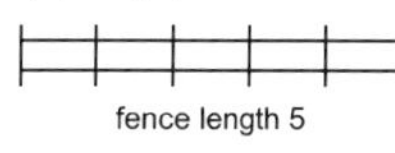

Fence length	1	2	3	4	5	6
Number of pieces	4	7	10	13	16	19

   (c) No. of pieces = 3×Fence length+1 = 3×25+1 = 76

   (d) No. of pieces = $3\times n+1 = 3n+1$

7. (a) (i) $s = 623.5 \approx 600$, $u = 11.37 \approx 10$,
$v = 87.22 \approx 90$ (so that $u+v \approx 10+90 = 100$)

(ii) $t = \dfrac{2s}{u+v} \approx \dfrac{2\times600}{10+90} = \dfrac{1200}{100} = 12$

(b) 2 × 6 2 3 . 2 5 = ÷ (1 1 . 3 7 +
8 7 . 2 2) = 12.64327

Answer $\approx$ 12.64 (2 dp)

8. (a) $25G+250 = 25(G+10)$

(b) $C = 14G+121$ $\therefore C-121 = 14G$ $\therefore 14G = C-121$
$\therefore G = \dfrac{C-121}{14}$

9. $T = 26 - \dfrac{h}{500}$ $\therefore -52 = 26 - \dfrac{h}{500}$ $\therefore -78 = -\dfrac{h}{500}$
$\therefore -78\times500 = -h$ $\therefore -39\,000 = -h$ $\therefore h = 39\,000$

10. (a) $(R+r)(R-r) = R(R-r)+r(R-r) = R^2-Rr+rR-r^2$
$= R^2-Rr+Rr-r^2 = R^2-r^2$

(b) $A = \pi(R+r)(R-r) = \pi(R^2-r^2)$ From part (a)
$\therefore 147 = \pi(21^2-r^2)$ $\therefore 147\div\pi = 21^2-r^2$
$\therefore 46.79 = 441-r^2$ $\therefore 46.79-441 = -r^2$
$\therefore -394.21 = -r^2$ $\therefore r = \sqrt{394.21} \approx 19.9$ (1 dp)

11. (a) $119 = 29+15d$ $\therefore 119-29 = 15d$ $\therefore 90 = 15d$
$d = 90\div15 = 6$. This chest has 6 drawers

(b) (i) $117 = k+m4$ $\therefore k+4m = 117$ .... (A)
$149 = k+m6$ $\therefore k+6m = 149$ .... (B)

(ii) (B)−(A) gives: $2m = 32$ $\therefore m = 32\div2 = 16$

12. (a) (i) 11.40 am (ii) 20 min (b) 12.5 miles

(c) Manchester to London = 200 miles. Time taken on return = 200÷50 = 4 hours, arriving at 7.20 pm

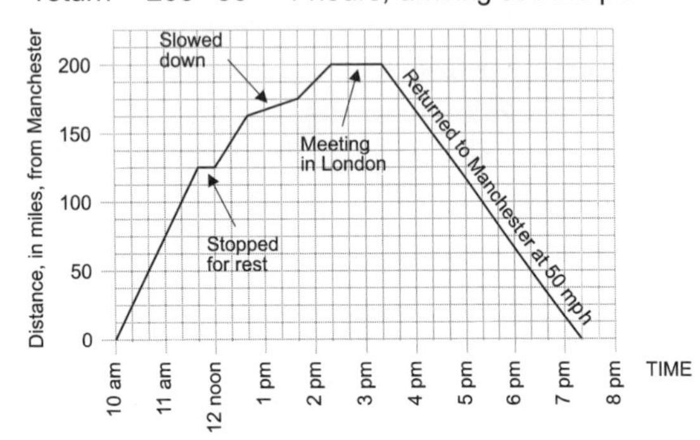

13. (a)

x	-2	-1	0	1	2	3
y	-1	1	-1	-4	-1	14

(b)

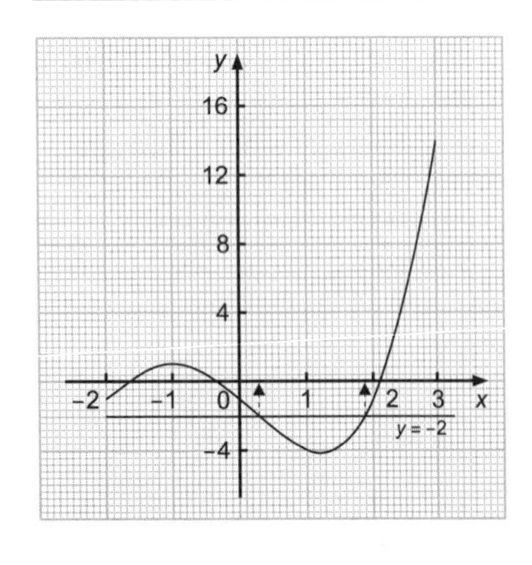

(c) Draw line $y = -2$. Gives: $x \approx 0.3, 1.9$

(d) Try $x = 4$:
$4^3-4\times4-1 = 47$ (too high)
Try $x = 3.5$, etc.
Table shows $x \approx 3.6$, correct to 1 decimal place

Guess	x^3-4x-1	Comment
4	47	Too high
3.5	27.875	Too low
3.7	34.853	Too high
3.6	31.256	Too high
3.55	29.5389	Too low
3.58	30.56271	Too high

14. (a) $f(0) = (0+3)(0-2)(0-4) = 3\times-2\times-4 = 24$

(b) & (c) Reflection in y-axis

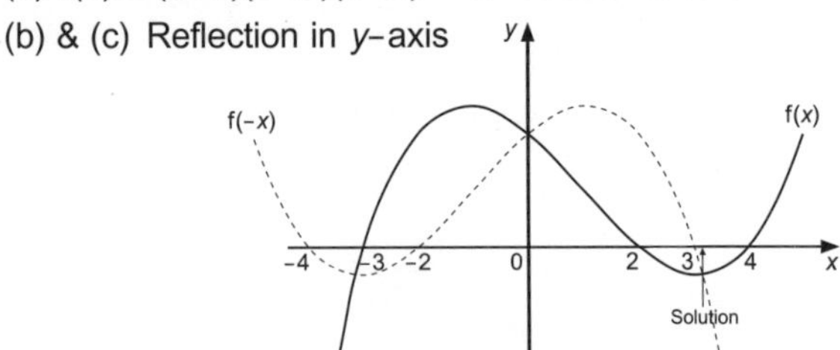

(d) $f(x)$ crosses x-axis when $f(x) = 0$, i.e. when $x = -3$, $x = 2$ and $x = 4$ (see graph). Since $f(-x)$ is a reflection in the y-axis, it crosses the x-axis at $x = -4$, $x = -2$ and $x = 3$. Graphs cross where $f(x) = f(-x)$, in between $x = 3$ and $x = 4$. So, $n = 3$

15. (a) Area = $4\times3+5\times2 = 22$ m^2

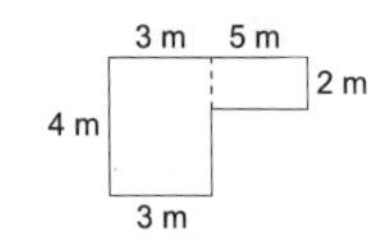

(b) Volume of room = 22×2.7
$= 59.4$ m^3

16. (a) Volume = $8\times5\times12.5 = 500$ cm^3

(b) (i) $100:125 = 1:1.25$ $\therefore$ Vol. = $500\div1.25 = 400$ cm^3
(ii) $100\div125\times100 = 80\%$

17. (a) Cones are similar.
Height of small cone : Big cone = 45 : 90 = 1 : 2
So, volume of small cone : Big cone = $1^3:2^3 = 1:8$
$\therefore$ Volume of T = $10\,500\pi\div8 = 4123.3$ m^3
$\therefore$ Volume of S = $10\,500\pi-4123.3 = 28\,863.4$ m^3

(b) Large triangle is an enlargement of small triangle.
Scale factor = 30÷20 = 1.5.

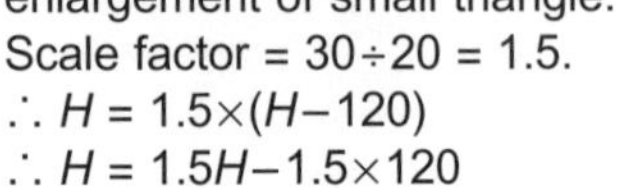

$\therefore H = 1.5\times(H-120)$
$\therefore H = 1.5H-1.5\times120$
$\therefore H = 1.5H-180$
$\therefore 180 = 1.5H-H$
$\therefore 0.5H = 180$ $\therefore H = 180\div0.5 = 360$ cm

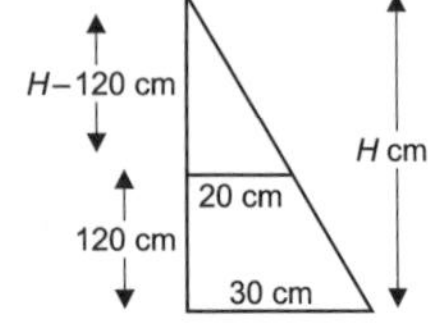

18. (a) 56 cm : 14 km = 56 : 1 400 000 = 1 : 1 400 000÷56
= 1 : 25 000

(b) Pythagoras. $BG^2 = 14^2+20^2 = 596$
$\therefore BG = \sqrt{596} = 24.4$ km

(c) $\tan B = 14\div20 = 0.7$ $\therefore B = \tan^{-1} 0.7 \approx 35°$
Bearing of G from B $\approx 360°-35° = 325°$

19. (a) (i) $x = 360°\div5 = 72°$ (ii) Isosceles triangle.
$180°-72° = 108$ $\therefore y = 108°\div2 = 54°$

(b)

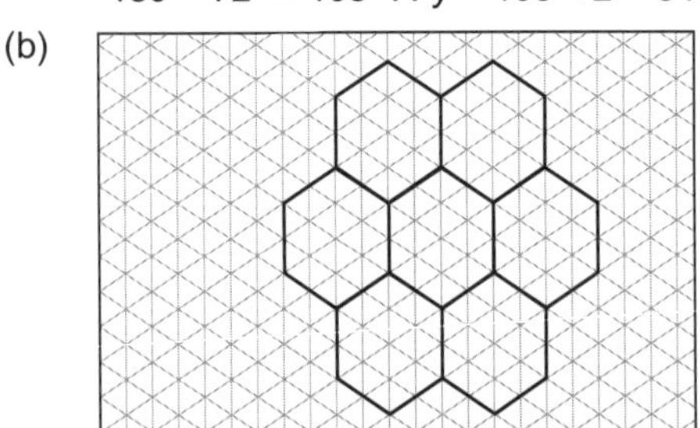

(c) Interior angle is 108°, which does not divide into 360°

(d) 5 (same as number of sides)

20. (a) & (b)

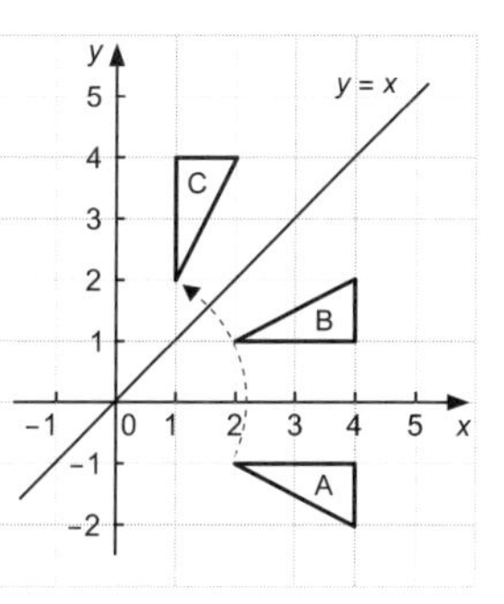

(c) 90° anticlockwise rotation about (0, 0)

(d) Gradient is 1 and y-intercept is 8, giving $y = x+8$

(e) Crosses x-axis when $y = 0$. $\therefore 0 = x+8$
$\therefore x = -8$
giving P (−8, 0)

21. 360° represents 720 students.
So, 1° represents 720÷360 = 2 students.
No. of bus students = 56° = 56×1° = 56×2 = 112

22. (a) (i) 6–10 words (highest frequency)
(ii) Total frequency = 16+28+....+2 = 100. Median lies between 50th and 51st largest values. Cumulative frequencies: 16, 16+28 = 44, 16+28+26 = 70. Median lies in class 11–15

(b) Calculate mid-class values.

$$\text{Mean} = \frac{16\times3+....+2\times43}{100}$$
$= 12.95$ words/sentence

Mid-class value	Frequency f
3	16
8	28
13	26
18	14
23	10
28	3
33	1
38	0
43	2

23. (a) Range for French = 40−15 = 25

(b) & (c)

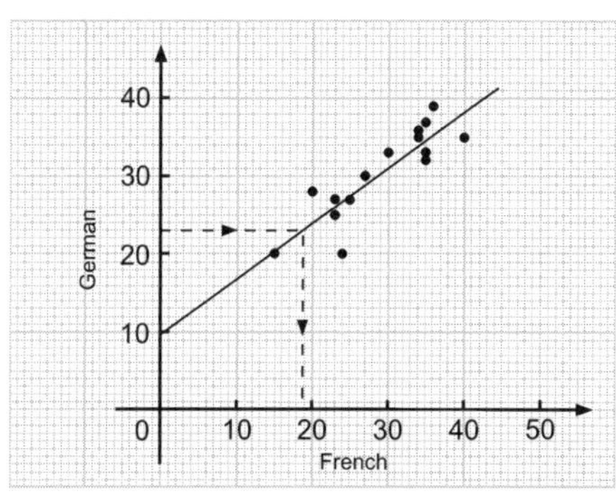

(d) From graph, French mark is approximately 19

(e) Fairly strong, positive correlation (the line of best fit has a positive gradient and the points are fairly close to this line)

24. (a)

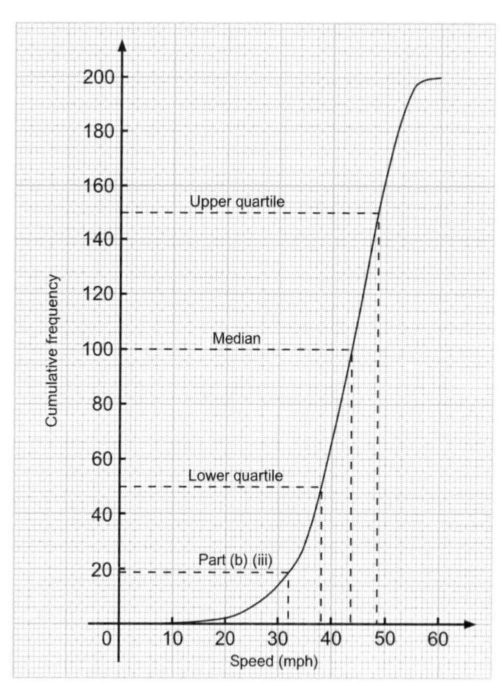

(b) (i) Median ≈ 43.5 mph
(ii) Lower quartile ≈ 38 mph
Upper quartile ≈ 48.5 mph
Interquartile range ≈ 48.5 − 38 = 10.5 mph
(iii) ≈ 19 cars out of 200 = 9.5%

25. (a) $\bar{x} = 68$ (given). Square values

Value, x	73	70	62	67	69	76	55	65	61	82
Square, x^2	5329	4900	3844	4489	4761	5776	3025	4225	3721	6724

$\sum x^2 = 5329+4900+....+6724 = 46\,794$

$$\text{Variance} = \frac{\sum x^2}{n} - \bar{x}^2 = \frac{46\,794}{10} - 68^2$$
$= 4679.4 - 4624 = 55.4$

Standard deviation = $\sqrt{55.4} = 7.4$

(b) (i) New mean = 68+3 = 71
(ii) Standard deviation is unchanged at 7.4

26. (a)

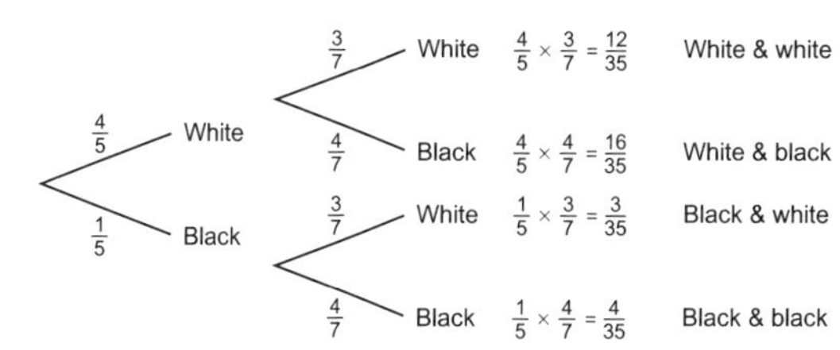

P(both white) = P(white & white)
$= \text{P(white)}\times\text{P(white)} = \frac{4}{5}\times\frac{3}{7} = \frac{12}{35}$

(b) P(different colours)
= P(white & black or black & white)
= P(white)×P(black) + P(black)×P(white)
$= \frac{4}{5}\times\frac{4}{7}+\frac{1}{5}\times\frac{3}{7}$
$= \frac{19}{35}$

INDEX

Box numbers are indicated in brackets

FORMULA SHEET

Area of a triangle $= \frac{1}{2} \times \text{Base} \times \text{Height}$

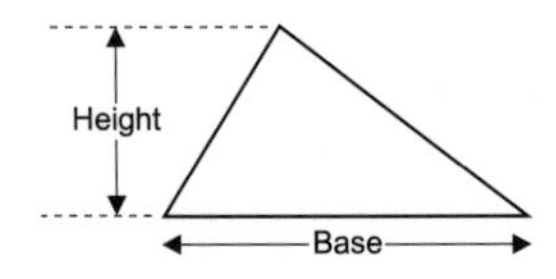

Area of a trapezium $= \frac{1}{2}(a+b)h$

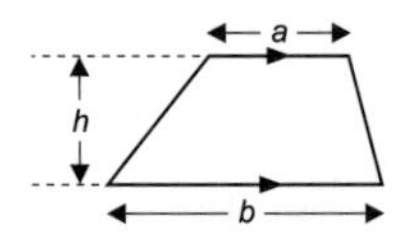

Area of a parallelogram
$= \frac{1}{2} \times \text{Base} \times \text{Height}$

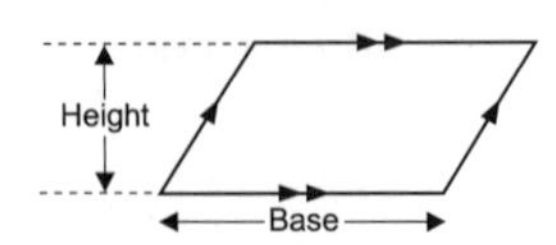

Area of a circle $= \pi \times (\text{Radius})^2 = \pi r^2$
Circumference $= 2 \times \pi \times \text{Radius} = 2\pi r$
$= \pi \times \text{Diameter} = \pi d$

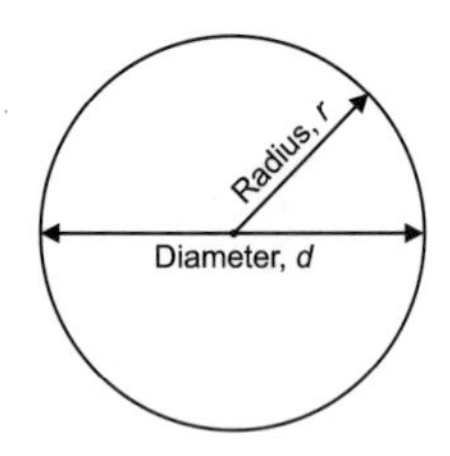

Area of a sector $= \frac{\theta}{360} \times \pi r^2$
Length of arc $= \frac{\theta}{360} \times 2\pi r$

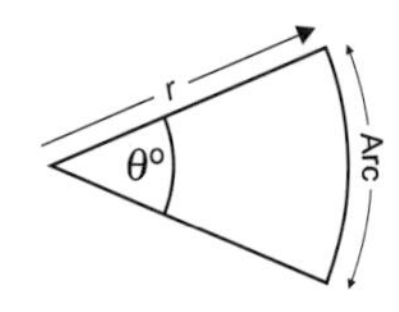

Volume of a cuboid
$= \text{Length} \times \text{Breadth} \times \text{Height}$

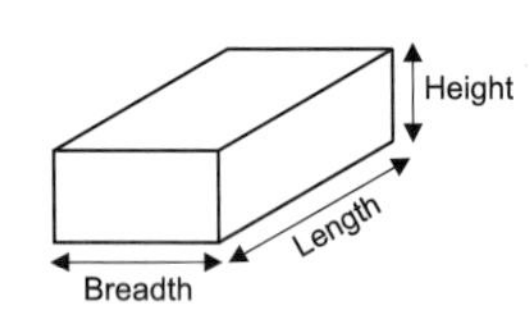

Volume of a cylinder $= \pi r^2 h$
Curved surface area $= 2\pi rh$

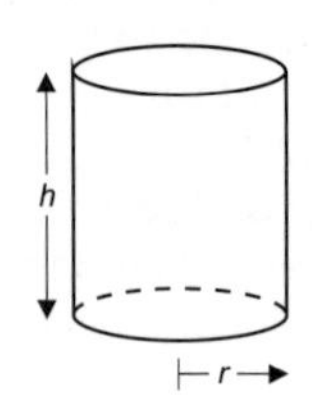

Volume of a cone $= \frac{1}{3}\pi r^2 h$
Curved surface area $= \pi rl$

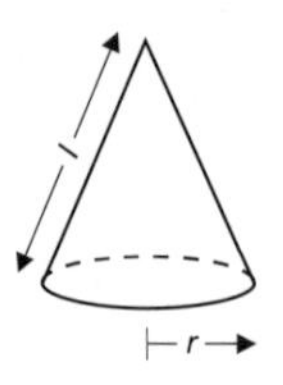

Volume of a sphere $= \frac{4}{3}\pi r^3$
Surface area $= 4\pi r^2$

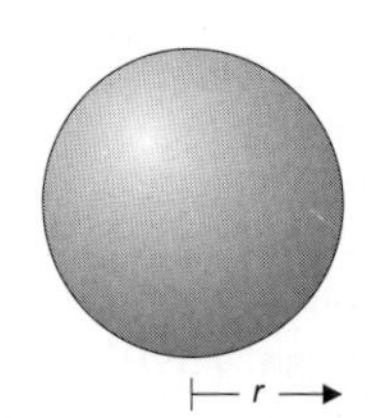

Volume of a prism
$= \text{Area of cross-section} \times \text{Length}$

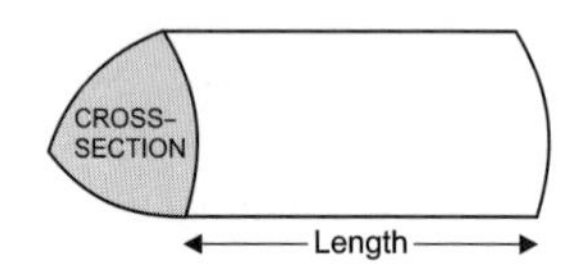

Volume of a pyramid
$= \frac{1}{3} \times \text{Area of base} \times \text{Height}$

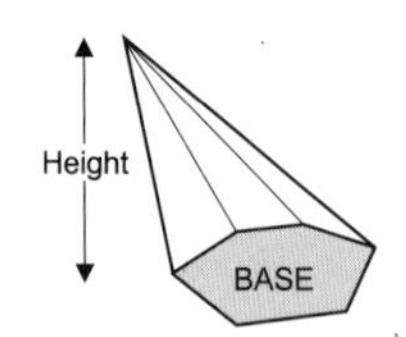

Pythagoras' theorem

$a^2 = b^2 + c^2$

Trigonometry

$\sin\theta = \dfrac{\text{Opp}}{\text{Hyp}}$

$\cos\theta = \dfrac{\text{Adj}}{\text{Hyp}}$

$\tan\theta = \dfrac{\text{Opp}}{\text{Adj}}$

For any triangle ABC

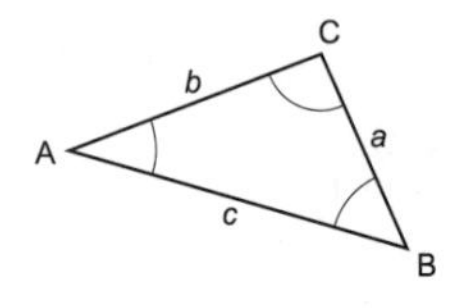

Sine rule $\dfrac{a}{\sin A} = \dfrac{b}{\sin B} = \dfrac{c}{\sin C}$

Cosine rule $a^2 = b^2 + c^2 - 2bc\cos A$

$\cos A = \dfrac{b^2 + c^2 - a^2}{2bc}$

Area of triangle $= \frac{1}{2}ab\sin C$

Quadratic equations

The solutions of $ax^2+bx+c=0$ where $a \neq 0$ are given by:

$$x = \frac{-b \pm \sqrt{b^2-4ac}}{2a}$$

Mean

$\bar{x} = \dfrac{\sum x}{n}$ or $\bar{x} = \dfrac{\sum fx}{n}$

Standard deviation

$s = \sqrt{\dfrac{\sum(x-\bar{x})^2}{n}}$ or $s = \sqrt{\dfrac{\sum x^2}{n} - \left(\dfrac{\sum x}{n}\right)^2}$